TEXAS
INSTRUMENTS

TI-85
ADVANCED SCIENTIFIC CALCULATOR
GUIDEBOOK

Guidebook developed by: The staff of Texas Instruments Instructional Communications

With contributions by:

Brad Christensen
Franklin Demana
Doug Feltz
Linda Ferrio
Pat Hatcher
Dave Hertling

Don La Torre
Pat Milheron
John Powers
Dave Stone
Bert K. Waits
C. B. Wilson

Texas Instruments gratefully acknowledges the contributions of Bert K. Waits and Franklin Demana, who provided ideas for some of the applications and examples in this manual.

Important

Texas Instruments makes no warranty, either expressed or implied, including but not limited to any implied warranties of merchantability and fitness for a particular purpose, regarding any programs or book materials and makes such materials available solely on an "as-is" basis.

In no event shall Texas Instruments be liable to anyone for special, collateral, incidental, or consequential damages in connection with or arising out of the purchase or use of these materials, and the sole and exclusive liability of Texas Instruments, regardless of the form of action, shall not exceed the purchase price of this equipment. Moreover, Texas Instruments shall not be liable for any claim of any kind whatsoever against the use of these materials by any other party.

FCC Information Concerning Radio Frequency Interference

This device complies with Part 15 of the FCC rules. Operation is subject to the following two conditions:
(1) This device may not cause harmful interference, and
(2) This device must accept any interference received, including interference that may cause undesired operation.

This equipment has been tested and found to comply with the limits for a Class B digital device, pursuant to Part 15 of the FCC rules. These limits are designed to provide reasonable protection against harmful interference in a residential installation. This equipment generates, uses, and can radiate radio frequency energy and, if not installed and used in accordance with the instructions, may cause harmful interference with radio communications. However, there is no guarantee that interference will not occur in a particular installation.

If this equipment does cause harmful interference to radio or television reception, which can be determined by turning the equipment off and on, you can try to correct the interference by one or more of the following measures:

- Reorient or relocate the receiving antenna.
- Increase the separation between the equipment and receiver.
- Connect the equipment into an outlet on a circuit different from that to which the receiver is connected.
- Consult the dealer or an experienced radio/television technician for help.

Caution: Any changes or modifications to this equipment not expressly approved by Texas Instruments may void your authority to operate the equipment.

> This digital apparatus does not exceed the Class B limits for radio noise emissions from digital apparatus set out in the Radio Interference Regulations of the Canadian Department of Communications.

Table of Contents

This guidebook describes how to use the TI-85 Graphics Calculator. Getting Started gives a quick overview of its features. The first two chapters give general instructions on operating the TI-85. Chapters 3 through 16 describe its interactive features. Chapter 17 provides applications showing how to use these features together.

Table of Contents (Continued)

Table of Contents (Continued)

Table of Contents (Continued)

Using this Guidebook Effectively

The structure of the TI–85 guidebook and the design of its pages can help you find the information you need quickly. Consistent presentation techniques are used throughout to make the guidebook easy to use.

Structure of the Guidebook

The guidebook contains sections that teach you how to use the calculator.

- Getting Started is a fast-paced introduction to several important features of the TI–85.

- Chapters 1 and 2 describe general operation and lay the foundation for Chapters 3 through 16, which describe specific functional areas of the TI–85 and include short examples.

- Chapter 17 contains application examples that incorporate features from different functional areas of the calculator. These examples can help you see how commands, functions, and instructions work together to accomplish meaningful tasks.

- Chapter 18 describes memory management and Chapter 19 describes the communications link.

Page-Design Conventions

When possible, units of information are presented on a single page or on two facing pages. Several page-design elements help you find information quickly.

- **Page headings**—The descriptive heading at the top of the page or two-page unit identifies the subject of the unit.

- **General text**—Just below the page heading, a short section of bold text provides general information about the subject covered in the unit.

- **Left-column subheadings**—Each subheading identifies a specific topic or task related to the page or unit subject.

- **Specific text**—The text to the right of a subheading presents detailed information about that specific topic or task. The information may be presented as paragraphs, numbered procedures, bulleted lists, or illustrations.

- **Page "footers"**—The bottom of each page shows the chapter name, chapter number, and page number.

**Information-
Mapping
Conventions**

Several conventions are used to present information
concisely and in an easily referenced format.

- **Numbered procedures**—A procedure is a sequence
  of steps that performs a task. In this guidebook, each
  step is numbered in the order in which it is performed.
  No other text in the guidebook is numbered;
  therefore, when you see numbered text, you know
  you must perform the steps sequentially.

- **"Bulleted" lists**—If several items have equal
  importance, or if you may choose one of several
  alternative actions, this guidebook precedes each
  item with a "bullet" (•) to highlight it—like this list
  you are reading now.

- **Tables and charts**—Sets of related information are
  presented in tables or charts for quick reference.

Reference Aids

Several techniques have been used to help you look up
specific information when you need it. These include:

- A chapter table of contents on the first page of each
  chapter, as well as the full table of contents at the
  front of the guidebook.

- A glossary at the end of this section, defining
  important terms used throughout the guidebook.

- An alphabetical table of commands in Appendix A,
  showing their correct formats, the keys and menus
  that access them, and page references for more
  information.

- Tables of system variables and built-in constants in
  Appendix A.

- A table of error codes in Appendix B, showing the
  codes and their meanings, with problem-handling
  information.

- An alphabetical index at the back of the guidebook,
  listing tasks and topics you may need to look up.

Glossary

This glossary provides definitions for important terms that are used throughout this guidebook.

Command	A command is either an instruction or an expression used to calculate a result.
Equation Variable	An equation variable may contain an equation or an expression. An equation is two expressions that are equal or a variable equal to an expression.
Expression	An expression is a complete sequence of numbers, variables, functions, and their arguments that can be evaluated to a single result. An expression can include an = sign (a mathematical equation).
Function	A function, which may have arguments, returns a value and can be used in an expression.
Home Screen	The Home Screen is the primary screen of the TI–85, where expressions can be entered and evaluated and instructions can be entered and executed.
Instruction	An instruction, which may have arguments, initiates an action. Instructions are not valid in expressions.
List	A list is a set of values that the TI–85 can use for activities such as graphing a family of curves or evaluating a function at multiple values.
Matrix	A matrix is a two-dimensional array on which the TI–85 can perform operations.
Menu Items	Menu items are shown on the seventh and eighth lines of the display and are associated with the menu keys below them.
Menu Keys	Menu keys are the keys [F1] through [F5] below the display. They are used to select menu items.
Variable	A variable is the name given to a location in memory in which a value, an expression, a list, a matrix, a vector, or a string is stored.
Vector	A vector is a one-dimensional array on which the TI–85 can perform operations.

Getting Started

This section takes you through several examples to introduce you to some of the principal operating and graphing features of the TI-85. You can learn to use the TI-85 more quickly by completing these examples first. Operating details are provided in the remaining chapters of the guidebook.

The Menu Keys

The TI–85 uses display menus to give you access to more operations than you can access from the keyboard alone.

The Menus and Menu Keys

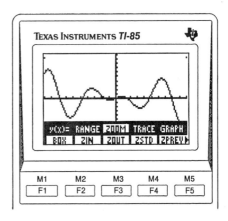

On the TI–85 keyboard, the menu keys are F1, F2, F3, F4, and F5. The 2nd functions of the menu keys are [M1], [M2], [M3], [M4], and [M5]. Menu items are shown on the bottom line(s) of the display, above the five menu keys.

Selecting Menu Items

- To select a menu item from the eighth (bottom) line of the display, press the menu key below the item.

- To select a menu item from the seventh (next-to-the-bottom) line of the display, press and release 2nd and then press the menu key below the item.

In this guidebook, the menu items are indicated by < > brackets. For example, press F2 to select ⟨ZIN⟩ or press 2nd [M5] to select ⟨GRAPH⟩.

The First Steps

Before beginning these sample problems, follow the steps on this page to ensure that the TI-85 is reset to its factory settings. (Resetting the TI-85 erases all previously entered data types.)

1. Press ⟨ON⟩ to turn the calculator on.

2. Press and release ⟨2nd⟩ and then press ⟨+⟩. (Pressing ⟨2nd⟩ accesses the operation printed to the left above the next key that you press. MEM is the 2nd operation of ⟨+⟩.)

   The bottom line of the display shows the MEM (memory) menu.

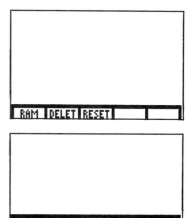

3. Press the ⟨F3⟩ menu key to select ⟨RESET⟩, the third item in the MEM menu.

   The bottom line is relabeled with the RESET menu and the MEM menu moves up a line.

4. Press ⟨F1⟩ to select ⟨ALL⟩. The display shows the message **Are you sure?**

   Press ⟨F4⟩ to select ⟨YES⟩. The display shows the messages **Mem cleared** and **Defaults set.**

   The display contrast was reset to the default. To adjust the display contrast, press and release ⟨2nd⟩ and then press ⟨▲⟩ (to make the display darker) or ⟨▼⟩ (to make the display lighter).

   Press ⟨CLEAR⟩ to clear the display.

Entering Expressions: Savings Account Example

The TI-85 display can show up to eight lines of 21 characters per line. This lets you see each expression or instruction in its entirety as it is entered. Variable names can be up to eight characters. You can enter more than one command on a line; separate them with a : (colon).

If you invest $25 at the beginning of each month at 6% annual interest, compounded monthly, how much money will you have at the end of three years? The formula is shown on the right.

$$PMT \frac{(1+I)^{N+1} - (1+I)}{I}$$

1. To store the payment amount ($25) in the variable **PMT**, press **25** [STO▶]. When you press [STO▶], the symbol → is copied to the cursor location, and the keyboard is set in ALPHA-lock. This makes each subsequent keystroke an uppercase alpha character. Alpha characters are printed to the right above the keys.

```
25→M
```

2. Type **P M T**. Press [ALPHA] to take the keyboard out of ALPHA-lock.

```
25→PMT
```

3. Press [2nd] [:] (the 2nd function of [.]) to begin another command on the same line.

4. Press **3** [×] **12** [STO▶] **N** [ALPHA] to store the number of periods (years *12) in the variable **N**. The TI-85 evaluates the expression before storing the value.

5. Press [2nd] [:] **.06** [÷] **12** [STO▶] **I** [ALPHA] to begin a new command and store the interest per period (rate/12) in the variable **I**.

The entry is more than 21 characters, so it "wraps" to the next line.

```
25→PMT:3*12→N:.06/12→
I
```

On the TI–85, you enter expressions as you would write them, as shown on the right.

$$PMT*((1+I)^\wedge(N+1)-(1+I))/I$$

6. To enter the expression for the future value formula, press [2nd] [:] to begin the next command, press [ALPHA] [ALPHA] to set the keyboard in ALPHA-lock, and then type **PMT** [ALPHA].

7. Press [×] [(] [(] **1** [+] [ALPHA] **I** [)] [∧] [(] [ALPHA] **N** [+] **1** [)] [−] [(] **1** [+] [ALPHA] **I** [)] [)] [÷] [ALPHA] **I**.

8. Press [ENTER] to store the values in the variables and evaluate the expression. The 12-digit result is shown on the right side of the next line of the display.

```
25→PMT:3*12→N:.06/12→
I:PMT*((1+I)^(N+1)-(1
+I))/I
            988.319637236
```

9. Press [2nd] [MODE] (the 2nd function of [MORE]) to display the MODE screen. Press [▼] [▶] [▶] [▶] to position the cursor over the **2**.

10. Press [ENTER]. This changes the display format to two fixed decimal places.

```
Normal Sci Eng
Float 01▌345678901
Radian Degree
RectC PolarC
Func Pol Param DifEq
Dec Bin Oct Hex
RectV CylV SphereV
dxDer1 dxNDer
```

11. Press [2nd] [QUIT] (the 2nd function of [EXIT]), which always returns you to the Home screen. Press [ENTER]. The last expression is reevaluated and the result displayed with two fixed decimal places.

If you save $25 at the beginning of each month for 36 months, invested at 6%, you will have $988.32.

```
25→PMT:3*12→N:.06/12→
I:PMT*((1+I)^(N+1)-(1
+I))/I
            988.319637236
                   988.32
```

Recalling and Editing a Calculation

On the TI-85, the Last Entry feature lets you recall the command that was executed when you last pressed [ENTER]. If more than one command is entered on a line and separated with a colon, the commands are stored together in Last Entry. The last result is stored in Last Answer.

If you continue to invest $25 a month for another year, how much will you have?

1. Press [2nd] [ENTRY]. This recalls the last executed command into the display. The cursor is positioned following the command.

2. Use [▲] and [▶] to position the cursor over the **3** in the instruction **3∗12→N**. Type **4**.

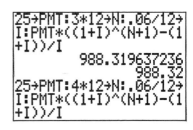

```
25→PMT:3∗12→N:.06/12→
I:PMT∗((1+I)^(N+1)-(1
+I))/I
                988.319637236
                       988.32
25→PMT:4∗12→N:.06/12→
I:PMT∗((1+I)^(N+1)-(1
+I))/I
```

3. You do not need to be at the end of a command to execute it, so press [ENTER] now. The solution is displayed on the next line.

   If you save $25 at the beginning of each month for 48 months, invested at 6%, you will have $1359.21.

```
+I))/I
                988.319637236
                       988.32
25→PMT:4∗12→N:.06/12→
I:PMT∗((1+I)^(N+1)-(1
+I))/I
                      1359.21
```

4. If you were able to save $50 per month, the amount would double because **PMT** is directly proportional to the total.

   Press **2** [×]. Press [2nd] [ANS]. The variable name **Ans** is copied to the cursor location.

   Press [ENTER]. You will have $2718.42 if you save $50 per month.

```
                       988.32
25→PMT:4∗12→N:.06/12→
I:PMT∗((1+I)^(N+1)-(1
+I))/I
                      1359.21
2∗Ans
                      2718.42
```

Graphing on the TI-85

Users familiar with the TI-81 will find that all of the popular TI-81 graphing features are also on the TI-85. When you press [GRAPH], the menu keys are labeled with the same graphing options (in the same order) that are on the top row of keys on the TI-81.

Graph $y = x^3 - 2x$ and $y = 2\cos x$.
Determine the solution to
$x^3 - 2x = 2\cos x$.

1. Press [GRAPH]. The menu keys are labeled on the eighth line of the display with the TI-81 graphing commands.

   The Home screen and cursor are still displayed. You do not leave the Home screen and enter the graphing application until you select a menu key.

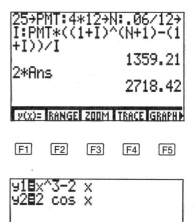

2. Press [F1] to select ⟨y(x)=⟩, which accesses the y(x) editor, where you enter and select functions to graph. Press [x-VAR] (you may press [F1] to select ⟨x⟩ instead) [^] 3 [−] 2 [x-VAR] [ENTER] to enter the equation **y1 = x^3 − 2x**. Press 2 [COS] [x-VAR] to enter **y2 = 2 cos x**. The highlighted **=** shows **y1** and **y2** are "selected" to be graphed.

   Notice, however, that the TI-85 uses lowercase **x** and **y** as its graphing variables, rather than the uppercase **X** and **Y** used by the TI-81.

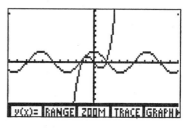

3. Press [2nd] [M3] to select ⟨ZOOM⟩. With the ZOOM instructions, you can easily display the current graph in a different viewing rectangle.

   Press [F4] to select ⟨ZSTD⟩. This is the same as the ZOOM **Standard** option on the TI-81.

Graphing on the TI-85 (Continued)

4. Press F4 to select <TRACE>. Press
▶ to trace along function **y1**, then
press ▲ to move to function **y2**.
Notice the **1** or **2** in the upper right
of the display, which indicates
which function you are tracing.

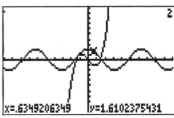

5. Press EXIT to leave TRACE and
display the GRAPH menu.

Press F3 to select <ZOOM>. Press
F2 to select <ZIN>. Move the cursor
over the apparent intersection in
the first quadrant. Press ENTER.

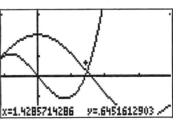

6. Press EXIT to leave ZIN and display
the ZOOM menu.

Press F4 to select <ZSTD> to display
the original graph.

(The coordinate values may
vary depending on the cursor
location.)

7. To explore the apparent solution in
the second quadrant, press F1 to
select <BOX>. Move the cursor to the
upper right corner of the area you
want to examine more closely. Press
ENTER. Move the cursor to the lower
left corner (the box defining the
area is shown as you move the
cursor). Press ENTER.

8. If necessary, repeat the procedure
for ZIN or BOX to see if the two
functions intersect in the second
quadrant (they do not).

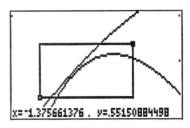

Entering an Equation: Illumination Example

On the TI-85, you can explore problems in several different ways. For example, you can solve many problems either by using the SOLVER feature or graphically. The remaining pages in Getting Started present an illumination example to show how to enter equations and explore them both by using the SOLVER and by graphing.

The illumination on a surface is:

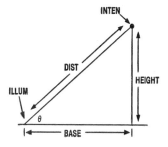

- Proportional to the intensity of the source.

- Inversely proportional to the square of the distance.

- Proportional to the sine of the angle between the source and the surface.

The formula for illumination of a point on a surface is shown on the right. A substitution from trigonometry allows us to define illumination in terms of INTEN (intensity), HEIGHT (height of the pole), and DIST (distance).

$$\text{ILLUM} = \frac{\text{INTEN} * \sin \theta}{\text{DIST}^2}$$

$$\sin \theta = \frac{\text{HEIGHT}}{\text{DIST}}$$

Appropriate units are ft-c (foot-candles) for illumination, CP (candlepower) for intensity, and ft (feet) for distances.

$$\text{ILLUM} = \frac{\text{INTEN} * \text{HEIGHT}}{\text{DIST}^3}$$

Assume the height of a light on a pole in a parking lot is 50 ft and the intensity is 1000 CP. Determine the illumination on the surface 25 ft from the pole.

1. Press [2nd] [MEM] ⟨RESET⟩ ⟨ALL⟩ ⟨YES⟩ [CLEAR] to reset the calculator.

   On the TI-85, you can store an unevaluated expression as an equation variable. From geometry, DIST=$\sqrt{(\text{BASE}^2 + \text{HEIGHT}^2)}$.

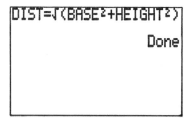

2. Press [ALPHA] [ALPHA] to set ALPHA-lock, type **DIST =**, and then press [ALPHA] to take the keyboard out of ALPHA-lock. Press [2nd] [√] [(] [ALPHA] [ALPHA] **BASE** [ALPHA] [x²] [+] [ALPHA] [ALPHA] **HEIGHT** [ALPHA] [x²] [)] [ENTER].

Entering an Equation in the SOLVER

With the SOLVER feature of the TI-85, you can solve an equation for any variable in the equation. In the SOLVER, you can observe the effect that changing the value of one variable has on another and apply "what if" scenarios. This page shows how to enter the illumination equation in the SOLVER.

1. Press [2nd] [SOLVER] to display the SOLVER equation entry screen.

2. Press [ALPHA] [ALPHA] **ILLUM = INTEN** [ALPHA] [×] [ALPHA] [ALPHA] **HEIGHT** [ALPHA] [÷]. Press [F1] to select ⟨DIST⟩ from the menu; the characters **DIST** are copied to the cursor location.

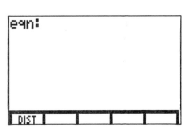

3. Press [∧] **3** to complete the equation that defines illumination in terms of intensity and height:
ILLUM = INTEN * HEIGHT/DIST ∧ 3.

   As you enter the equation beyond 17 characters, it scrolls. Ellipsis marks (...) indicate that not all of the equation is displayed on the line. You can use [▶] and [◀] to scroll the equation.

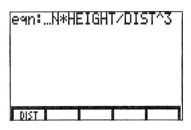

4. Press [ENTER]. The SOLVER edit screen is displayed.

   The equation is displayed on the top line. The variables are listed in the order in which they appear in the equation. The variables **HEIGHT** and **BASE**, which define the equation variable **DIST**, are shown. The cursor is positioned after the **=** following the first variable. If the variables have current values, the value is shown.

   bound defines the interval in which the SOLVER searches for a solution. The default values are -1E99 to 1E99.

Solving for a Variable

The TI-85 solves the equation for the variable on which the cursor is placed when you select <SOLVE>. Enter values for all known variables, and then solve for the unknown variable.

1. Use [ENTER], [▼], or [▲] to move the cursor between the variables. Enter **1000** as the value for **INTEN**. Enter **50** as the value for **HEIGHT**. Enter **25** as the value for **BASE**. The values of **INTEN, HEIGHT**, and **BASE** in memory are updated.

```
ILLUM=INTEN*HEIGHT/D…
ILLUM=█
INTEN=1000
HEIGHT=50
BASE=25
bound={-1E99,1E99}
GRAPH│RANGE│ZOOM│TRACE│SOLVE
```

2. Press [▲] to move the cursor to **ILLUM**, the unknown variable.

3. Press [F5] to select <SOLVE> from the menu. A moving bar is shown in the upper right of the display to indicate that the TI-85 is busy calculating or graphing.

The solution is displayed. The square dots to the left of **ILLUM** and **left-rt** indicate that these are calculated results. The value of **ILLUM** in memory is updated.

```
ILLUM=INTEN*HEIGHT/D…
■ILLUM=.286216701119…
INTEN=1000
HEIGHT=50
BASE=25
bound={-1E99,1E99}
■left-rt=0
GRAPH│RANGE│ZOOM│TRACE│SOLVE
```

left-rt is the difference between the left side and the right side of the equation, evaluated at the current value of the independent variable.

If the height is 50 ft and the intensity is 1000 CP, the illumination on the surface 25 ft from the pole is .28621670111999 ft-c.

Additional Solutions with the SOLVER

You can continue to explore solutions to equations with the SOLVER. You can solve for any variable within the equation to explore "what if" questions.

If the desired illumination is exactly 0.2 ft-c, and the intensity is still 1000 CP, at what height on the pole should the light be placed?

1. To change the value of **ILLUM** to .2, press the [CLEAR] key to clear the value on the line quickly and then type **.2**. The square dots disappear to show that the solution is not current.

```
ILLUM=INTEN*HEIGHT/D...
 ILLUM=.2
 INTEN=1000
 HEIGHT=50
 BASE=25
 bound={-1E99,1E99}
 left-rt=0
GRAPH RANGE ZOOM TRACE SOLVE
```

2. Move the cursor to **HEIGHT**. Press [F5] to select <SOLVE>. It is not necessary to clear the value of the variable for which you are solving. If the variable is not cleared, the value is used as the initial guess by the SOLVER. The equation is solved for **HEIGHT** and the value displayed.

```
ILLUM=INTEN*HEIGHT/D...
 ILLUM=.2
 INTEN=1000
■HEIGHT=63.458763246...
 BASE=25
 bound={-1E99,1E99}
■left-rt=0
GRAPH RANGE ZOOM TRACE SOLVE
```

The illumination on the surface is .2 ft-c and the intensity is 1000 CP, if the height of the light source is 63.45876324653 ft.

The solution is dependent on the initial guess and bound.

Changing the Viewing Rectangle

You can graphically examine equations entered in the SOLVER. The viewing rectangle defines the portion of the graphing coordinate plane that is shown in the display. The values of the RANGE variables determine the size of the viewing rectangle. You can display and edit the values of the RANGE variables.

1. Press [F2] to display the RANGE editor.

   You display and edit the values of the RANGE variables on this screen. The values shown are the standard default values.

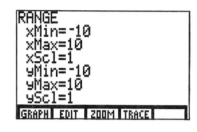

The RANGE variables define the viewing rectangle as shown. **xMin**, **xMax**, **yMin**, and **yMax** define the boundaries of the display. **xScl** and **yScl** define the tick marks on the **x** and **y** axes.

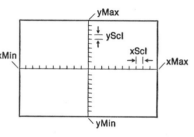

2. Graph the illumination example using new values for the RANGE variables, as shown.

   Use [▼] or [ENTER] to move the cursor to each value and then type over the existing values to enter the new value. To enter - 1, press [(-)], not [−], and then press 1.

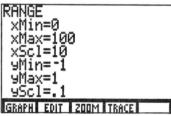

Finding a Solution from a SOLVER Graph

The graph plots the variable on which the cursor is placed as the independent variable on the x axis and left-rt as the dependent variable on the y axis. Solutions exist for the equation where the function intersects the x axis.

1. Press [F1] to select ⟨GRAPH⟩. The graph plots **HEIGHT** on the **x** axis and **left-rt** on the **y** axis in the chosen viewing rectangle. The calculation for left-rt in this case is shown on the right.

    $$\text{left-rt} = \text{ILLUM} - \frac{\text{INTEN} * \text{HEIGHT}}{\sqrt{(\text{BASE}^2 + \text{HEIGHT}^2)^3}}$$

    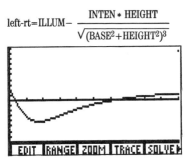

    Notice from the graph that this problem has at least two solutions; we found the solution for **HEIGHT** at the larger value, 63.45876324653.

2. To solve for the other value of **HEIGHT**, we must supply a new initial guess or alter the **bound**. You can select a new initial guess with the graph cursor.

    Use ◄ and ► to position the cursor near where the function crosses the axis at the smaller value. As you move the cursor, the coordinate values are displayed.

    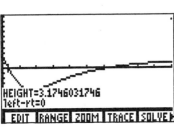

3. Press [F5] to select ⟨SOLVE⟩. The value of **HEIGHT** identified by the cursor is used as the new initial guess. The busy indicator is displayed during the calculation. The solution screen is displayed again, with another solution for **HEIGHT**, 3.2022212466711.

    ```
    ILLUM=INTEN*HEIGHT/D...
     ILLUM=.2
     INTEN=1000
    ■HEIGHT=3.2022212466...
     BASE=25
     bound={0,100}
    ■left-rt=1E-14
    GRAPH RANGE ZOOM TRACE SOLVE
    ```

    The illumination on the surface is .2 ft-c and the intensity is 1000 CP, if the height of the light source is either 3.2022212466711 ft or 63.458763246530 ft.

Defining Functions to Graph

On the TI-85, functions are graphed for x and y when x is the independent variable and y=y(x). You can store unevaluated expressions with the = symbol (ALPHA function of the [STO▶] key). This page shows how to enter the illumination problem for a graphic solution.

Graph the illumination equation and find the height that provides the maximum illumination for a base of 25 feet and an intensity of 1000 CP.

1. Press [2nd] [QUIT] to return to the Home screen.

2. Press [ALPHA] [ALPHA] **HEIGHT =** [ALPHA] [x-VAR] [ENTER] to store the unevaluated expression **x** in an equation variable, **HEIGHT**. Use [x-VAR] to enter **x** quickly. **INTEN** and **BASE** still contain **1000** and **25**.

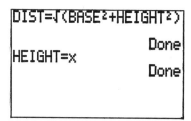

3. Press [GRAPH] to display the GRAPH menu. Press [F1] to select ⟨y(x)=⟩.

The display shows the name of the first function, **y1**.

4. Press [2nd] [RCL]. The cursor is positioned after **Rcl** on the sixth line. The RCL feature lets you recall the expression stored in an equation variable to the cursor location. In the SOLVER, the illumination equation was stored in the equation variable **eqn**.

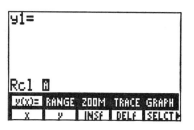

5. Press [2nd] [alpha] to change to lowercase alpha-lock and type **e q n** [ENTER]. The equation is copied to the cursor location.

6. Press [2nd] [◄] to move the cursor to the beginning of the expression quickly. Press [DEL] six times to delete **ILLUM =**.

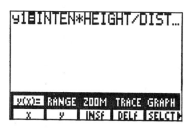

Displaying the Graph

After you have created and selected the function to graph and entered the appropriate viewing rectangle, you can display the graph.

1. Press [2nd] [M5] to select ⟨GRAPH⟩ to graph the selected functions in the viewing rectangle. ([2nd] accesses the menu items on the seventh line.)

   Because **HEIGHT** is replaced by **x**, the current value of **x** is used each time a point is plotted. The graph of the function for $0 \leq x \leq 100$ is plotted.

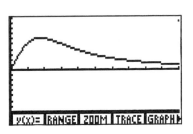

2. The graph shows that there is likely one maximum value of **ILLUM** for a height between 0 and 100.

   Press [▶] once to display the graphics cursor just to the right of the center of the display. The line above the menu shows the **x** and **y** display coordinate values for the cursor position (**x**,**y**).

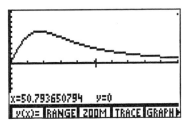

3. Using the cursor-movement keys ([◀], [▶], [▲], and [▼]), move the cursor until it is positioned at the apparent maximum of the function. As you move the cursor, the **x** and **y** display coordinate values are updated continually with the cursor position.

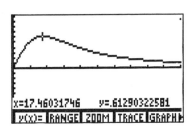

   The free-moving cursor shows maximum illumination of .61290322581 CP for heights from 14.285714286 ft to 21.428571429 ft, within an accuracy of one display point width. In this example, accuracy$_x$ is .793650793651 and accuracy$_y$ is .032258064516, calculated as shown on right.

$$\text{Accuracy}_x = \frac{(\text{xMax} - \text{xMin})}{126}$$

$$\text{Accuracy}_y = \frac{(\text{yMax} - \text{yMin})}{62}$$

Tracing along a Function

Using the TRACE feature of the TI–85, you can move the cursor along a function, showing the x and y display coordinate values of the cursor location on the function.

1. Press F4 to select ⟨TRACE⟩. The TRACE cursor appears near the middle of the display on the function.

   The coordinate values of the cursor location (**x**,**y1**(**x**)) are displayed on the bottom line of the display. No menu items are shown. The **y** value shown is the calculated value of the function for the displayed value of **x**. That is, if **y1** = f(**x**), then the value of **y** shown is f(**x**).

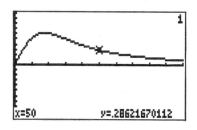

x=50   y=.28621670112

2. Use ▶ and ◀ to move along the function until you have traced to the largest y value.

   The maximum illumination is .61577762623 CP if the height is 17.46031746 ft.

   This value of **y** is the function value f(**x**) at the **x** display coordinate value. It is different from the value found with the free-moving cursor, which is based on the RANGE settings.

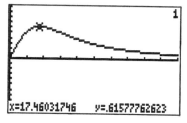

x=17.46031746   y=.61577762623

Finding a Maximum Graphically

With the operations on the GRAPH MATH menu, you can analyze a displayed graph to determine where minimum and maximum values, inflection points, and intercepts occur.

1. Press [EXIT] to display the GRAPH menu. Press [MORE] to display additional items on the GRAPH menu.

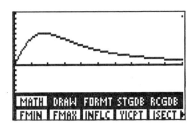

2. Press [F1] to select ⟨MATH⟩. Press [MORE] to display additional items on the GRAPH MATH menu.

3. Press [F2] to select ⟨FMAX⟩. The TRACE cursor appears near the middle of the display on the function at the point (**x**,**y1**(**x**)).

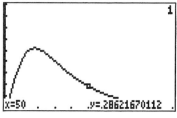

4. Press [ENTER]. The calculated maximum is displayed in the cursor coordinates at the bottom of the display, **.61584028714** at an **x** value of **17.677668581**.

This value of **y**, which is the mathematically calculated maximum, is larger than the value found with the TRACE cursor. This calculated maximum is the most accurate of the three graphical solutions we have tried.

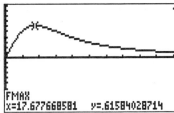

Graphing the Derivative

The maxima and minima of a continuous differentiable function, if they exist, occur where the first derivative is equal to 0. On the TI-85, you can graph the derivative of a function.

1. Press (GRAPH). Press (F1) to display the y(x) editor.

   Press (ENTER) to move to **y2**.

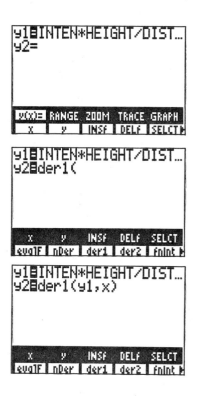

2. The calculus functions are grouped on the CALC menu. Press (2nd) [CALC] to display the calculus menu on the bottom line.

3. Press (F3). The function name for the exact first derivative, **der1(**, is copied to the cursor location.

4. Press (2nd) [M2] to copy **y** from the menu on the seventh line to the cursor location, then type **1** to enter the name of the first equation, **y1**. Press (,).

5. On the TI-85, you can evaluate the calculus functions with respect to any variable, but to be meaningful in graphing, the variable of differentiation or integration must be **x**.

   Press (x-VAR) or (2nd) [M1] to copy **x** to the cursor location. Press ()).

   der1(y1,x) is the exact derivative, evaluated at the current value of **x**. When this equation is graphed, the derivative is calculated for each value of **x** on the graph.

Zooming In on the Graph

You can magnify the viewing rectangle around a specific cursor location by selecting the Zoom In instruction from the ZOOM menu.

1. Press [EXIT] [2nd] [M5] to select ⟨GRAPH⟩ and graph both functions. The busy indicator displays while the graph is plotted.

   The viewing rectangle is the same as you defined in the SOLVER, $0 \le x \le 100$ and $-1 \le y \le 1$. In this viewing rectangle, the graph of the derivative function is very close to the x axis.

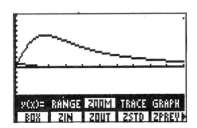

2. Press [F3] to select ⟨ZOOM⟩.

3. To zoom in, press [F2] to select ⟨ZIN⟩ from the menu.

   The cursor appears at the middle of the display.

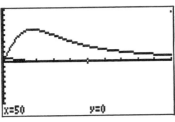

4. Use the cursor-movement keys to position the cursor near where the derivative function appears to cross the x axis. Press [ENTER]. The position of the cursor becomes the center of the new viewing rectangle. The busy indicator displays while the graph is plotted.

   The new viewing rectangle has been adjusted in both the x and y directions by factors of **4**, which are the default values for the zoom factors.

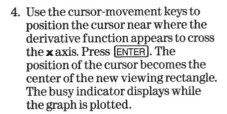

(The coordinate values may vary depending on the cursor location.)

Finding a Root Graphically

The TI–85 can find the root (zero) of a graphed function and can calculate the value of the function for any value of x. Find the x value where the root of the derivative function der1(y1,x) occurs, and use it to calculate the maximum of the function.

1. Press [EXIT] [EXIT] to display the GRAPH menu on the bottom line and press [MORE] to display additional menu items. Press [F1] to select ⟨MATH⟩ to display the GRAPH MATH operations.

2. Press [F3] to select ⟨ROOT⟩. The TRACE cursor is near the middle **y** value "on" the **y1** function, indicated by the **1** in the upper right corner of the display. The **y1** function is "above" the display.

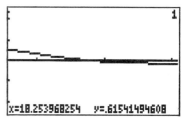

x=18.253968254   y=.61541494608

3. Press [▼] to move the cursor to the derivative function, **y2**, as indicated by the **2** in the upper right corner of the display. You can use [▶] and [◀] to move the cursor to a point near the root.

4. Press [ENTER]. The busy indicator displays while the root is calculated. The calculated root is displayed in the cursor coordinates at the bottom of the display: **y** = -1.21363E-15 at an **x** value of 17.67766953.

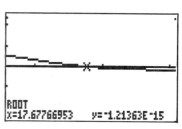

ROOT
x=17.67766953   y=-1.21363E-15

5. Press [EXIT] [EXIT] [MORE] [F1] to select ⟨EVAL⟩. Press [2nd] [ANS] [ENTER] to enter the solution to ROOT as the value for **x**. The results cursor is displayed on the **y1** function at the specified **x**.

On page 18, FMAX found a function maximum of **y** = .61584028714 at **x** =17.677668581. Corresponding to that maximum, ROOT found a root of the derivative at **x** =17.67766953, which evaluated to a maximum, **y1** = .61584028714.

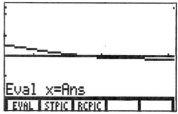

Eval x=Ans
EVAL | STPIC | RCPIC |

Other Features

This Getting Started section introduced you to operating the calculator, the function graphing features, and one equation-solving feature. The remainder of this guidebook describes these features in more detail and also covers the other capabilities of the TI-85.

Other Capabilities of the TI-85

- Store, graph, and analyze up to 99 functions in function graphing (Chapter 4), up to 99 polar equations in polar graphing (Chapter 5), up to 99 parametric equations in parametric graphing (Chapter 6), and a system of up to nine first-order differential equations (Chapter 7).

- Use DRAW and **Shade** features to emphasize or analyze on function, polar, parametric, and differential equation graphs (Chapter 4).

- Solve an equation for any variable, solve a system of up to 30 simultaneous linear equations, and find the real and complex roots of up to a 30th order polynomial equation (Chapter 14).

- Enter and store any number of matrices and vectors with dimension up to 255. Has standard matrix operations, including elementary row operations, and standard vector operations (Chapter 13).

- Perform one-variable and two-variable statistical analyses. Enter and store any number of data points. Seven regression models are available: linear, logarithmic, exponential, power, and second-, third-, and fourth-order polynomial models. You can analyze data graphically with histograms, scatter plots, and line drawings and plot regression equation graphs (Chapter 15).

- Enter programs that include extensive control and input/output instructions. Enter and store any number of programs (Chapter 16).

- Share variables and programs with another TI-85. Print graphs and programs, enter programs, and store data on a disk through an IBM®-compatible or Macintosh® computer (Chapter 19).

- The TI-85 has 32K of RAM.

Chapter 1: Operating the TI-85

This chapter describes the TI-85 and provides general information about its operation.

Turning the TI-85 On and Off

To turn the TI-85 on, press the ON key. To turn it off, press and release 2nd and then press [OFF]. After about five minutes without any activity, the APD™ Automatic Power Down feature turns the TI-85 off automatically.

Turning the Calculator On

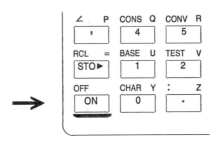

Press ON to turn the TI-85 on.

- If you pressed 2nd [OFF] to turn the calculator off, the display shows the Home screen as it was when you last used it.

- If the APD feature turned the calculator off, the TI-85, including the display, cursor, and any error conditions, will be exactly as you left it.

Turning the Calculator Off

Press and release 2nd and then press [OFF] to turn the TI-85 off.

- Any error condition is cleared.

- All settings and memory contents are retained in memory by the Constant Memory™ feature.

The APD™ Automatic Power Down Feature

To prolong the life of the batteries, the APD feature turns the TI-85 off automatically after about five minutes without any activity. When you press ON , the TI-85 will be exactly as you left it.

- The display, cursor, and any error conditions are exactly as you left them.

- All settings and memory contents are retained in memory by the Constant Memory feature.

Batteries

The TI-85 uses four AAA alkaline batteries and has a user-replaceable back-up lithium battery. You can change the batteries (Appendix B) without losing any information in memory.

Setting the Display Contrast

The brightness and contrast of the display depend on room lighting, battery freshness, viewing angle, and adjustment of the display contrast. The contrast setting is retained in memory when the TI-85 is turned off.

Adjusting the Display Contrast

You can adjust the display contrast to suit your viewing angle and lighting conditions at any time. As you change the contrast setting, the display contrast changes, and a number in the upper right corner indicates the current contrast setting between 0 (lightest) and 9 (darkest).

Note that there are 32 different contrast levels, so each number 0 through 9 represents more than one setting.

To adjust the contrast:

1. Press and release the 2nd key.

2. Use one of two keys:

   • To increase the contrast, press and hold ▲.

   • To decrease the contrast, press and hold ▼.

Note: If you adjust the contrast setting to zero, the display may become completely blank. If this happens, press and release 2nd and then press and hold ▲ until the display reappears.

When to Replace Batteries

When the batteries are low, the display begins to dim (especially during calculations), and you must adjust the contrast to a higher setting. If you find it necessary to set the contrast to a setting of 8 or 9, you should replace the four AAA batteries soon.

Note: To replace batteries without losing information stored in memory, follow the directions on page B-2.

The 2nd and ALPHA Keys

Most keys on the TI-85 access more than one operation. The additional operations are printed above the keys. To access them, press [2nd] or [ALPHA] before you press the key.

Key Labels

2nd operation ——— $\sqrt{}$ K ——— Alpha operation

$\boxed{x^2}$ ——— Primary operation

2nd Operations

To access a 2nd operation, first press and release [2nd] and then press the appropriate key.

When you press [2nd], the cursor changes to ↑ to indicate that the next keystroke is a 2nd operation.

To cancel 2nd, press [2nd] again.

In this guidebook, 2nd operations are shown in brackets and preceded by [2nd]; for example, [2nd] [√].

ALPHA Characters

To access the letter or character printed to the right above a key, first press [ALPHA] or [2nd] [alpha] and then press the appropriate key.

- To make the next keystroke an uppercase alphabetic character, press [ALPHA]. The cursor changes to **A**. To cancel ALPHA, press [ALPHA] until the normal cursor appears.

- To make the next keystroke a lowercase alphabetic character, press and release [2nd] and then press [alpha]. The cursor changes to **a**. To cancel alpha, press [ALPHA] until the normal cursor appears.

Alpha-Lock

ALPHA-lock (uppercase) and alpha-lock (lowercase) make each subsequent keystroke an alphabetic character. You do not need to press [ALPHA] or [2nd] [alpha] before every character to enter display text or the names of variables, functions, or instructions.

Action	Keystrokes
Set uppercase ALPHA-lock	[ALPHA] [ALPHA]
Set lowercase alpha-lock	[2nd] [alpha] [ALPHA] or [2nd] [alpha] [2nd] [alpha] or [ALPHA] [2nd] [alpha]
Cancel ALPHA-lock	[ALPHA]
Cancel alpha-lock	[2nd] [alpha] or [ALPHA] [ALPHA]
Change from uppercase ALPHA-lock to lowercase alpha-lock	[2nd] [alpha]
Change from lowercase alpha-lock to uppercase ALPHA-lock	[ALPHA]

Note: [STO▶] and name prompts automatically set the keyboard in ALPHA-lock. [2nd] does not take the keyboard out of ALPHA-lock or alpha-lock.

The Display

The TI-85 displays text, graphs, and menus. Graphs are described in Chapter 4. Menus are described on pages 1-16 through 1-19.

The Home Screen

The Home screen is the primary screen of the TI-85, where you enter expressions to be evaluated and see the results.

```
17*3+ln 3
            52.0986122887
```
Expression
Result

If text is displayed, the screen can have up to eight lines of 21 characters per line. If all text lines of the display are filled, text "scrolls" off the top of the display.

The MODE settings control the way expressions are interpreted and results are displayed (pages 1-24 through 1-27).

Displaying Expressions

On the Home screen and in the program editor (Chapter 16), if an expression is longer than one line, it wraps to the beginning of the next line.

Displaying Results

When an expression is evaluated on the Home screen, the result is displayed on the right side of the next line. If a result is too long to display in its entirety, ellipsis marks (...) are shown at the left or right. Use ▶ and ◀ to scroll the result. If the result is a matrix with more rows than the screen can display, use ▲ and ▼ to scroll the result vertically. For example:

```
[[1/3,π][4,5]]
[[.333333333333  3.14...
[4              5    ...
```
Expression
Result

Returning to the Home Screen

To return to the Home screen from any other screen, press 2nd [QUIT].

Display Cursors In most cases, the appearance of the cursor indicates what will happen when you press the next key.

Cursor	Appearance	Meaning
Entry cursor	Solid blinking rectangle	The next keystroke is entered at the cursor; it types over any character.
INS (insert) cursor	Blinking underline	The next keystroke is inserted at the cursor.
2nd cursor	Blinking ↑	The next keystroke is a 2nd operation.
ALPHA cursor	Blinking **A**	The next keystroke is an uppercase alphabetic character.
alpha cursor	Blinking **a**	The next keystroke is a lowercase alphabetic character.
"full" cursor	Checkerboard rectangle	You have entered the maximum characters in a name, or memory is full.

If you press ALPHA, 2nd [alpha], or 2nd during an insertion, the underline cursor changes to an underlined **A**, **a**, or ↑ cursor.

Busy Indicator When the TI–85 is calculating or graphing, a moving vertical bar shows in the upper right of the display as a busy indicator. (When you pause a graph or a program, the busy indicator is a dotted bar.)

The Equation Operating System

With the TI-85's Equation Operating System (EOS™), you enter numbers and functions in a simple, straightforward sequence. EOS evaluates expressions according to the standard priorities of mathematical functions and uses parentheses for grouping.

Order of Evaluation

A function returns a value. EOS evaluates functions in an expression in this order:

- Functions that are entered after the argument, such as x^2, x^{-1}, ı, °, ʳ, %, ᵀ, and conversions.

- Powers and roots, such as **2^5** or **5^x√32**.

- Implied multiplication where the second argument is a number, variable name, constant, list, matrix, or vector or begins with an open parenthesis, such as **4A**, **A B**, **(A + B)4**, or **4(A + B)**.

- Single-argument functions that precede the argument, such as negation, √, **sin**, or **ln**.

- Implied multiplication where the second argument is a multiargument function or a single-argument function that precedes the argument, such as **2 gcd(144,64)** or **A sin 2**.

- Permutations (**nPr**) and combinations (**nCr**).

- Multiplication and division.

- Addition and subtraction. An **=** in an expression, rather than an equation, is evaluated as **−(**. For example, **A + B = C + 1** is evaluated as **A + B − (C + 1)**.

- Relational functions, such as > or ≤.

- Boolean operator **and**.

- Boolean operators **or** and **xor**.

Within a priority group, EOS evaluates functions from left to right. However, two or more single-argument functions that precede the same argument are evaluated from right to left. For example, **sin fPart ln 8** is evaluated as **sin(fPart(ln 8))**.

Calculations within a pair of parentheses are evaluated first. Multiargument functions, such as **gcd(144,64)** or **der1(sin ANG,ANG,π)**, are evaluated as they are encountered.

Implied Multiplication

The TI–85 recognizes implied multiplication. For example, it understands 2π, **4 sin 45**, **5(1 + 2)**, and **(2 ∗ 5)7** as implied multiplication. Except between two numbers, a space indicates implied multiplication, as in **A B** or **B 3**.

Variable names can be more than one character; the TI–85 recognizes **AB** and **b2** as variable names. Variable names cannot start with a number; **3AB** and **3b2** are interpreted as implied multiplication (**3 ∗ AB** and **3 ∗ b2**).

Parentheses

All calculations inside a pair of parentheses are completed first. For example, in the expression **4(1 + 2)**, EOS first evaluates the portion of the expression inside the parentheses, 1+2, and then multiplies the result, 3, by 4.

You can omit any right (close) parenthesis at the end of an expression. All "open" parenthetical elements are closed automatically at the end of an expression and preceding the → (store) or display conversion instructions.

Note: If the name of a list, matrix, or vector is followed by an open parenthesis, it does not indicate implied multiplication. It is used to access specific elements in the list, matrix, or vector.

Negation

To enter a negative number, use the negation function. Press $\boxed{(\text{-})}$ and then enter the number. On the TI–85, negation is in the fourth group in the EOS hierarchy. Functions in the first group, such as squaring, are evaluated before negation. For example, the result of **-X²** is a negative number; the result of **-9²** is **-81**. Use parentheses to square a negative number: **(-9)²**.

Note: Use the $\boxed{-}$ key for subtraction and the $\boxed{(\text{-})}$ key for negation. If you press $\boxed{-}$ to enter a negative number, as in **9** $\boxed{\times}$ $\boxed{-}$ **7**, it is an error. If you press **9** $\boxed{(\text{-})}$ **7** or $\boxed{\text{ALPHA}}$ **A** $\boxed{(\text{-})}$ $\boxed{\text{ALPHA}}$ **B**, it is interpreted as implied multiplication (**9 ∗ -7** or **A ∗ -B**).

Entering and Editing

The arrow keys in the upper right of the keyboard control the movement of the cursor. In normal entry, a keystroke types over the character or characters at the position of the cursor. The [DEL] and [2nd] [INS] keys delete or insert characters.

The Cursor-Movement Keys

[◄] and [►] move the cursor within an expression. The cursor stops when it reaches the beginning or end of the expression, except in the program editor.

[2nd] [◄] or [2nd] [►] moves the cursor to the beginning or end of the expression.

[▼] and [▲] move the cursor between lines in the current expression on the Home screen. [▲] on the top line of an expression on the Home screen moves the cursor to the beginning of the expression. [▼] on the bottom line moves the cursor to the end.

If you press and hold a cursor-movement key, the cursor movement repeats until you release the key.

The Edit Keys

Key	Action
[2nd] [INS]	Inserts characters at the underline cursor.
[DEL]	Deletes the character at the cursor.
[ENTER]	Executes the expression or instruction.
[CLEAR]	• On a line with text on the Home screen, clears (blanks) that line.
	• In an editor, clears (blanks) the expression or value where the cursor is located; it does not store a zero.
	• On a blank line on the Home screen, clears everything on the Home screen.

To end insertion, press [2nd] [INS], a cursor-movement key, [DEL], or (except in the program editor) [ENTER].

You can press and hold [DEL] to delete a long sequence of characters.

Entering a Name   You can enter the names of functions, instructions, variables, and constants in one of several ways:

- Type the characters of the name.

- Press the key or select from a menu to copy the name to the cursor location.

- Select the name from the CATALOG.

If you type the name, you must enter each character, including a space (the alpha character above $\boxed{(-)}$) preceding the name and the space or open parenthesis, if required, after the name. If you select the name from the keyboard or a menu, all required characters are copied.

The TI-85 ignores uppercase and lowercase when it interprets names of functions and instructions (but not the names of variables and constants). For example, to calculate a log, you can press $\boxed{\text{LOG}}$, type the letters **l o g** (followed by a space), or type the letters **L O G** (followed by a space).

Character Entry   The TI-85 treats an expression as individual characters, regardless of whether a name was entered by typing each character or by copying the name from a key, menu, or selection screen. Names copied from a key, menu, or selection screen are copied as if the individual letters were typed. You can type over any character in the name. For example, if you press $\boxed{\text{SIN}}$, the characters **sin** followed by a space are displayed. If you then press $\boxed{\triangleleft}$ $\boxed{\triangleleft}$ $\boxed{\text{ALPHA}}$ $\boxed{\text{ALPHA}}$ **G N**, the function is changed to **siGN**.

Expressions and Instructions

On the TI-85, you can enter expressions, which return a value, in most places where a value is required. You enter instructions, which initiate an action, on the Home screen or in the program editor (Chapter 16).

Expressions

An expression is a complete sequence of numbers, variables, functions, and their arguments that evaluate to a single result. On the TI-85, you enter an expression in the same order that it normally is written. For example, $\pi*$**radius**^{2} is an expression.

Expressions can be used as commands on the Home screen to calculate a result. Expressions may be used in instructions to enter a value. In editors, expressions may be used to enter a value.

Instructions

An instruction is a command that initiates an action. For example, **ClDrw** is an instruction that clears any drawn elements from a graph. Instructions cannot be used in expressions.

Entering an Expression

To create an expression, you enter numbers, variables, and functions from the keyboard and from display menus. An expression is completed when you press [ENTER], regardless of the cursor location. The entire expression is evaluated according to EOS (page 1–8), and the result is displayed.

Example of Entering an Expression

Calculate $3.76 \div (-7.9 + \sqrt{5}) + 2 \log 45$.

3.76 ÷ ((-) **7.9** +
[2nd] [√] **5**) + **2** [LOG]   3.76/(-7.9+√5)+2 log
45   45
[ENTER]   2.64257525233

Entering More than One Command on a Line

To enter more than one instruction or expression on a line, separate them with a colon (:). For example, **5→A:2→B:A/B** [ENTER] displays **2.5**. All the commands are stored together in Last Entry (page 1–14).

Interrupting a Calculation

While the busy indicator is displayed, indicating that a calculation or a graph is in progress, you can press [ON] to stop the calculation. (There may be a delay.) Except in graphing, the break ERROR screen is shown.

- To go to where the interrupt occurred, select ⟨GOTO⟩.

- To return to the Home screen, select ⟨QUIT⟩.

Last Answer

When an expression is evaluated successfully from the Home screen or from a program, the TI–85 stores the result to a special variable, Ans (Last Answer). When you turn the TI–85 off, the value in Ans is retained in memory.

Using Last Answer in an Expression

You can use the variable **Ans** in most places where its data type is valid. Press [2nd] [ANS] and the variable name **Ans** is copied to the cursor location. When the expression is evaluated, the TI–85 uses the value of **Ans** in the calculation.

Calculate the volume of a cube 1.5 feet on each side, and then calculate the volume in cubic inches.

1.5 [∧] **3**	1.5∧3	
[ENTER]		3.375
12 [∧] **3** [2nd] [ANS]	12∧3 Ans	
[ENTER]		5832

Continuing an Expression

You can use the value **Ans** as the first entry in the next expression without entering the value again. On the blank line on the Home screen, enter the function; the TI–85 "types" the variable name **Ans** followed by the function.

Calculate the area of a circle of radius 5 inches. Then calculate the volume of a cylinder of height 3 inches and radius 5 inches.

[2nd] [π] **5** [x²]	π5²	
[ENTER]		78.5398163397
[×] **3**	Ans∗3	
[ENTER]		235.619449019

Storing Results

To store a result, store **Ans** to a variable before you evaluate another expression.

[STO▶] **VOLUME**	Ans→VOLUME	
[ENTER]		235.619449019

Last Entry

When you press ENTER on the Home screen to evaluate an expression or execute an instruction, the expression or instruction is stored in a special storage area called Last Entry, which you can recall. When you turn the TI–85 off, Last Entry is retained in memory.

Using Last Entry

To recall Last Entry and edit it, press 2nd [ENTRY]. The cursor is positioned at the end of the entry. Because the TI–85 updates the Last Entry storage area only when ENTER is pressed, you can recall the previous entry even if you have begun entering the next expression. However, when you recall Last Entry, it replaces what you have typed.

5 + **7**	5+7	
ENTER		12
2nd [ENTRY]	5+7	

Entries Containing More than One Command

If the previous entry contained more than one command separated with a colon (page 1–12), all the commands are recalled. You can recall all commands, edit any command, and then execute all commands.

Using the equation $A = \pi r^2$, find by trial and error the radius of a circle that covers 200 square inches. Use 8 as your first guess.

8 STO▶ **R** ALPHA 2nd [:]		
2nd [π] ALPHA **R** x^2	8→R:πR^2	
ENTER		201.06192983
2nd [ENTRY]	8→R:πR^2	
2nd ◀ **7** 2nd [INS] **.95**	7.95→R:πR^2	
ENTER		198.556509689

Continue until the result is as accurate as you want.

Reexecuting the Previous Entry

Press ENTER on a blank line on the Home screen to execute Last Entry; the entry does not display again.

0 STO▶ **N**	0→N	
ENTER		0
ALPHA **N** + **1** STO▶ **N**		
2nd [:] **N** ALPHA x^2 − **1**	N+1→N:N^2−1	
ENTER		0
ENTER		3
ENTER		8

Example: Convergence of a Series

Show that when A<1, the series A^N converges to $A/(1-A)$ as N gets large. You can use the TI-85 functions sum and seq (Chapter 3) to calculate a series.

Procedure

Calculate the series A^N for **A** = 1/2 at **N** = 1, 5, and 100. **sum** returns the sum of all elements in a list. **seq** generates a list; the form for **seq** is:

seq(*expression,variablename,begin,end,increment*)

Enter all expressions and instructions on the same command line so that you can recall, edit, and execute them. Store **1** to the variable **NTH** (for the *nth* element) and **1/2** to the variable **A**.

Remember that function names are not case-sensitive, but variable names are. The keyboard remains in ALPHA-lock after STO▶ , even when you press 2nd .

```
1 STO▶  N T H 2nd [:] ALPHA
1 ÷ 2 STO▶  A 2nd [:]
S E Q ALPHA ( ( ALPHA A       1→NTH:1/2→A:SEQ(A^N,N
^ ALPHA N , ALPHA N
, 1 , ALPHA ALPHA
N T H ALPHA , 1 ) STO▶          ,1,NTH,1)→LIST:SUM LI
L I S T 2nd [:] S U M [↩] L I    ST
S T
ENTER                                        .5
```

Recall Last Entry. Change **NTH** to **5** and evaluate. Repeat for **NTH = 100**.

2nd [ENTRY]	1→NTH:1/2→A:seq(A^N,N ,1,NTH,1)→LIST:sum LI ST
2nd ◀ 5	5→NTH:1/2→A:seq(A^N,N ,1,NTH,1)→LIST:sum LI ST
ENTER	.96875
2nd [ENTRY] 2nd ◀ 1 2nd [INS] 00	100→NTH:1/2→A:seq(A^N ,N,1,NTH,1)→LIST:sum LIST
ENTER	1

The TI-85 Menus

To leave the keyboard uncluttered, the TI-85 uses display menus to access many additional operations. The five keys immediately below the display are used to select items from menus. Specific menus are described in the appropriate chapters.

The Menu Keys

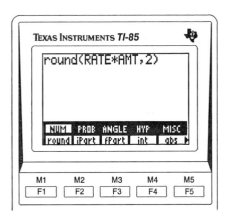

On the TI-85 keyboard, the menu keys are [F1], [F2], [F3], [F4], and [F5]. The 2nd operations of the menu keys are [M1], [M2], [M3], [M4], and [M5]. Menu items are shown above the five menu keys.

The Menu Items

Menu items can display on the bottom two lines (seventh and eighth lines) of the display. If any text is displayed on a line where a menu is to be displayed, the text in the display scrolls up a line.

The appearance of a menu item generally helps to identify what the menu item is.

● The names of functions, which return a value and are valid within an expression, generally begin with a lowercase letter; for example, **fPart** or **imag**.

● The names of instructions, which initiate an action from a command line, generally begin with a capital letter; for example, **Shade** or **ClDrw**.

● Menu items that access a lower-level menu or that perform immediate actions, generally are in all uppercase letters; for example, NUM or ZOUT.

Displaying Menus

If you select a menu item that displays another menu, the first menu may move to the seventh line; the new menu displays on the eighth line.

Displaying a Menu

Many of the 2nd operations, such as MATRX, VECTR, CPLX, MATH, and LIST, access menus of characters or names of variables, functions, and instructions to copy to the cursor location. When you press one of these keys, the eighth line of the display shows the menu items. For example, 2nd [CPLX] labels the menu keys with complex number functions:

conj   real   imag   abs   angle

The menu items may access lower-level menus. For example, if you press 2nd [MATH], the menu keys are labeled with the names of menus, each of which accesses a menu of math functions:

NUM   PROB   ANGLE   HYP   MISC

Displaying Additional Items in a Menu

A menu may have up to fifteen menu items, but only five are displayed at one time. ▶ at the right of the menu items indicates that there are more items in the menu. Press MORE to label the menu keys with the next group of menu items. If you are on the final group, MORE displays the first group. For example, on the MATH NUM menu:

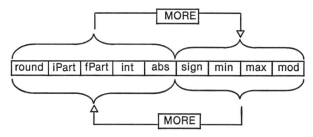

In this guidebook, all items in a menu usually are shown at once, stacked vertically; for example:

round	**iPart**	**fPart**	**int**	**abs**
sign	**min**	**max**	**mod**	

Selecting from Menus

You can select an item from the menu on the eighth line or from the menu on the seventh line. In this guidebook, menu items shown surrounded by brackets (for example, ⟨HYP⟩) indicate that you are to select that menu item.

Selecting an Item from the Menu on the Eighth Line

To select a menu item from the eighth line, press the corresponding menu key, F1, . . . , F5.

- If the item is a character or a name, it is copied to the cursor location, typing over existing characters (except in insert mode). If not all characters in a name can display, the name is truncated in the menu item, but the full name is copied to the cursor location. The menus do not change.

- If the item is an editing operation, such as INSr (insert row), the display changes as soon as you select the operation. The menus do not change.

- If the item is an action, such as SOLVE, the action occurs immediately. The menus change if appropriate.

- If the item accesses another menu, the menu keys are labeled immediately with the new menu.

The Menu on the Seventh Line

If you select a menu item that accesses another menu, the menu from the eighth-line may move to the seventh line, and the name of the selected menu is highlighted.

For example, selecting ⟨NUM⟩ from the MATH menu on the Home screen moves the MATH menu to the seventh line and displays the MATH NUM menu items in the eighth line. On the seventh line, NUM is highlighted.

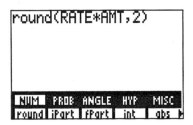

**Accessing Menus
from an Editor**

An exception occurs if you are in a full-screen editor, such as the program or matrix editor. In this case, the editor menu remains on the seventh line for convenience.

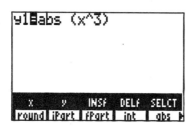

**Selecting
an Item from
the Menu on
the Seventh Line**

If a menu is displayed on the seventh line, you can select an item from it in one of the following ways:

- Press [2nd] and then press the menu key, [M1], ..., [M5], that corresponds to the item that you want. For example, [2nd] [M2] on the screen above would copy **y** to the cursor location.

- Press [EXIT], which causes the menu on the seventh line to "move down" to the eighth line. Then press the menu key ([F1], ..., [F5]) that corresponds to the item that you want. For example, [EXIT] [F4] on the screen above would delete function **y1**.

"Exiting" a Menu

When you press [EXIT]:

- If a menu is displayed on the seventh line, that menu "moves down" to the eighth line. The display does not change.

- If a menu is displayed only on the eighth line, you are returned to the Home screen.

Moving around the TI-85

In addition to changes in the menu lines, the display may change when you press a key or select from a menu.

Moving to a Full-Screen Editor

Many of the keys on the TI-85 access applications with full-screen editors where you enter expressions as you do on the Home screen. The full-screen editors are:

CONS EDIT	POLY	GRAPH y(x)=
LIST EDIT	SOLVER	GRAPH r(θ)=
MATRX EDIT	SIMULT	GRAPH E(t)=
VECTR EDIT	MATH INTER	GRAPH Q'(t)=
STAT EDIT	STAT FCST	GRAPH RANGE
PRGM EDIT		GRAPH ZOOM ZFACT

When you select one of these:

- You "leave" the Home screen or the application in which you are working, and the appropriate editor displays.

- Any existing menu lines are cleared. The editor menu, if any, displays on the eighth line.

Working on a Full-Screen Editor

When you are working on a full-screen editor and press a key that displays a menu:

- The editor remains unchanged.

- The editor menu moves to the seventh line (if it is not already there), and the selected menu displays on the eighth line. You still can access editing operations (such as INSr) or instructions (such as SOLVE) with the [2nd] key.

Leaving an Editor

To leave an editor:

- Press [2nd] [QUIT] to return to the Home screen.

- Press [EXIT] one or more times to return to the previous menu, display, or the Home screen.

- Press the appropriate keys to move to another application, such as [2nd] [SOLVER].

Pull-Down Screens

The VARS and CATALOG selection screens temporarily replace the current display.

- The current display is replaced, but you have not "left" the application in which you are working.

- The VARS or CATALOG menu is displayed.

When you press EXIT or make a selection, the current display and menus are shown again.

The Prompt Line

Sometimes you will be prompted for a value or variable name on the prompt line, the line above the menu(s).

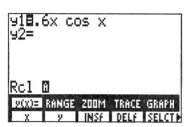

Clearing a Prompt

Press CLEAR to clear anything on the prompt line. Press CLEAR on a blank prompt line to clear the prompt and return the cursor to the editor or graph.

Correcting an Error on the Prompt Line

When an error occurs on the prompt line, ERR *nn* is displayed at the right of the line. It is not necessary to clear the error message to edit the entry. To clear the error and the entry, press CLEAR.

Returning to the Home Screen

To return to the Home screen from any other screen, press 2nd [QUIT].

You also can press EXIT one or more times until the Home screen is displayed.

The CATALOG

You can use the CATALOG to copy the name of an instruction
or a function to the cursor location in an expression that you
are editing. These include the functions and instructions
from the keyboard and from menus.

**The CATALOG
Selection Screen**

When you press [2nd] [CATALOG], the CATALOG screen
temporarily replaces the screen on which you are
working.

```
CATALOG
 abs
 and
▶angle
 Ans
 arc(
 aug(
 PAGE↓ PAGE↑ CUSTM BLANK
```

The names of functions and instructions are displayed in
alphabetical order. Names that do not begin with an
alphabetic character (such as **+** or ▶**Bin**) follow **Z**. An
arrow at the left of the name indicates the selection
cursor. To move around the list:

• Press a letter to move quickly to names beginning
  with that letter. (The keyboard is set in ALPHA-lock.)
  Uppercase and lowercase names are intermixed.

• Press [▲] on the first item in the CATALOG to move
  quickly to names beginning with special characters at
  the end of the list.

• Use ⟨PAGE↓⟩ and ⟨PAGE↑⟩ to move to the next page of
  names.

• Use [▼] and [▲] to move down and up the list.

**Copying a Name
to an Expression**

Press [ENTER] to select the name to copy. The CATALOG
selection screen disappears and the name is copied to the
cursor location.

**Leaving the
CATALOG**

To leave the CATALOG without making a selection:

• Press [EXIT] or [CLEAR] to return to the application in
  which you are working.

• Press [2nd] [QUIT] to return to the Home Screen.

The CUSTOM Menu

The CUSTOM menu has fifteen items. You can copy the names of up to fifteen functions or instructions from the CATALOG to the CUSTOM menu. This provides easy access to those you use most frequently.

Entering the Name of a Function or Instruction in the CUSTOM Menu

The names of functions and instructions are copied from the CATALOG to the CUSTOM menu.

1. Display the CATALOG selection screen. Move the cursor to the name you want to copy to the CUSTOM menu.

2. Select ⟨CUSTM⟩ from the CATALOG. The menu keys are labeled with the first five items of the CUSTOM menu (which may be blank). To display the other menu items, press MORE.

3. When the CUSTOM menu item to which you want to copy the name from the CATALOG is displayed, press that menu key. The name is copied to the CUSTOM menu, replacing any name that might be there. The CUSTOM menu remains.

Blanking a CUSTOM Menu Entry

1. Press 2nd [CATALOG].

2. Select ⟨BLANK⟩. The menu keys are labeled with the first five items of the CUSTOM menu. Press MORE to move around the menu.

3. When the menu item that you want to clear is displayed, press that menu key. The item is cleared. The CUSTOM menu remains.

Using a CUSTOM Menu Entry in an Expression

To copy a function or instruction from the CUSTOM menu to the expression you are entering or editing, press CUSTOM and select the appropriate menu key.

Setting Modes

Modes control how numbers and graphs are displayed and interpreted. MODE settings are retained by the Constant Memory™ feature when the TI-85 is turned off. All numbers, including elements of matrices, vectors, and lists, are displayed according to the current MODE settings.

Checking MODE Settings

Press [2nd] [MODE] to display the MODE settings. The current settings are highlighted. The specific MODE settings are described on the following pages.

Setting	Meaning
Normal Sci Eng	Numeric display format
Float 012345678901	Number of decimal places
Radian Degree	Unit of angle measure
RectC PolarC	Complex number display
Func Pol Param DifEq	Type of graphing
Dec Bin Oct Hex	Number base
RectV CylV SphereV	Vector display format
dxDer1 dxNDer	Type of differentiation

Changing MODE Settings

1. Use [▼] or [▲] to move the cursor to the line of the setting that you want to change. The setting that the cursor is on blinks.

2. Use [►] or [◄] to move the cursor to the setting that you want.

3. Press [ENTER].

Leaving the MODE Selection Screen

When the MODE settings are as you want them, leave the MODE selection screen in one of the following ways:

• Press the appropriate keys to go to an application.

• Press [2nd] [QUIT], [EXIT], or [CLEAR] to return to the Home screen.

Normal, Scientific, or Engineering Notation Display Format

Notation formats affect only how a numeric result is displayed on the Home screen. Numeric results can display with up to 12 digits and a three-digit exponent. You can enter a number in any format.

Normal display format is the way in which we usually express numbers, with digits to the left and right of the decimal, as in 12345.67.

Sci (scientific) notation expresses numbers in two parts. The significant digits display with one digit to the left of the decimal. The appropriate power of 10 displays to the right of ε, as in 1.234567ε4.

Eng (engineering) notation is similar to scientific notation. However, the number may have one, two, or three digits before the decimal, and the power-of-10 exponent is a multiple of three, as in 12.34567ε3.

Note: If you select normal display format, but the result cannot display in 12 digits or the absolute value is less than .001, the TI–85 changes to scientific notation for that result only.

Floating or Fixed Decimal Display Setting

Decimal settings affect only how a result is displayed on the Home screen. They apply to all three notation display formats. You can enter a number in any format.

Float (floating) decimal setting displays up to 12 digits, plus the sign and decimal.

The fixed decimal setting displays the selected number of digits (0 to 11) to the right of the decimal. Place the cursor on the number of decimal digits you want and press [ENTER].

Radians or Degrees Angle Setting

Angle settings control how the TI–85 interprets angle arguments in trig functions, polar/rectangular conversions, complex polar numbers, and 2-element and 3-element cylindrical or spherical vectors.

Radian setting interprets the arguments as radians. Results display in radians. **Degree** setting interprets the arguments as degrees. Results display in degrees.

Setting Modes (Continued)

Rectangular or Polar Complex Number Display Format

Complex number format affects only how a complex result is displayed. You can enter a complex number in either format.

RectC (rectangular complex) number format displays the result in the format (*real,imag*).

PolarC (polar complex) number format displays the result in the format (*magnitude ∠ angle*).

Function, Polar, Parametric, or Differential Equation Graphing MODE

Func (function) graphing plots functions where **y** is expressed in terms of **x** (Chapter 4).

Pol (polar) graphing plots functions where **r** is expressed in terms of θ (Chapter 5).

Param (parametric) graphing plots relations where **x** and **y** are each expressed in terms of **t** (Chapter 6).

DifEq (differential equation) graphing plots differential equations in terms of **t** (Chapter 7).

Decimal, Binary, Octal, or Hexadecimal Number Base

Number base format controls how an entered number is interpreted, unless another base is specified (Chapter 10), and how results are displayed. Nondecimal modes are valid only on the Home screen and in programs. Nondecimal modes are not valid for some functions.

In **Dec** (decimal) number base, numbers are interpreted and displayed as decimal (base 10).

In **Bin** (binary) number base, numbers are interpreted as binary (base 2). Results display with the **b** suffix.

In **Oct** (octal) number base, numbers are interpreted as octal (base 8). Results display with the **o** suffix.

In **Hex** (hexadecimal) number base, numbers are interpreted as hexadecimal (base 16). Results display with the **h** suffix.

Vector Coordinate Display Format

Vector coordinate format affects only how a 2-element or 3-element vector result is displayed. You can enter a vector in any format. Both cylindrical and spherical vector formats display 2-element vectors in polar format.

RectV (rectangular vector) coordinate format displays results in the format [**x y**] for 2-element or [**x y z**] for 3-element vectors.

CylV (cylindrical vector) coordinate format displays results in the format [**r** ∠ θ] for 2-element or [**r** ∠ θ **z**] for 3-element vectors.

SphereV (spherical vector) coordinate format displays results in the format [**r** ∠ θ] for 2-element or [**r** ∠ θ ∠ φ] for 3-element vectors.

For example, if the MODE is **CylV** and **Radian**, [**1,2,3**] returns [**2.2360679775** ∠ **1.10714871779 3**]

Differentiation Type

Differentiation is used in the instruction **TanLn**, function **arc**, and interactive graphing activities dy/dx, dr/dθ, dy/dt, dx/dt, ARC, TANLN, and INFLC. You can select the type of differentiation to use.

dxDer1 (exact differentiation) uses **der1** (Chapter 3) to differentiate exactly and calculate the value for each function in an expression. It is more accurate than **dxNDer**, but more restrictive, in that only certain functions are valid in the expression.

dxNDer (numeric differentiation) uses **nDer** to differentiate numerically and calculate the value for an expression. It is less accurate than **dxDer1**, but less restrictive in the functions that are valid in the expression. The variable δ applies (Chapter 3).

Setting Modes from a Command Line

To set a MODE on the Home screen or in a program, enter the name of the MODE as an instruction. For example, **Func** or **Float**. The form for fixed decimal setting is **Fix** n. You can select the name in the program editor from an interactive selection screen (Chapter 16).

Error Conditions

The TI–85 detects any errors at the time it evaluates an expression, executes an instruction, plots a graph, or stores a value. Calculations stop and an error message with a menu displays immediately. Error codes and conditions are described in detail in Appendix B.

Diagnosing an Error

If the TI–85 detects an error, it displays the ERROR screen. An example is shown below.

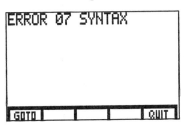

The error message on the top line indicates a two-digit error number and the type of error. The menu keys are labeled with appropriate actions.

- If you select ⟨GOTO⟩, the cursor is at the location where the error was detected.

  Note: If the error was detected in the contents of an equation variable, this option creates the appropriate assignment statement on the Home screen (page 2–9). Enter the correction and press [ENTER]. (Errors arising from program commands must be corrected in the program.)

- If you select ⟨QUIT⟩ or press [2nd] [QUIT], [EXIT], or [CLEAR], you return to the Home screen.

Correcting an Error

1. Note the number and type of the error.

2. Select ⟨GOTO⟩, if that option is available, and look at the expression, especially at the location of the cursor, for syntax errors.

3. If the error in the expression is not readily apparent, turn to Appendix B and read the information about the error message.

4. Correct the expression.

Chapter 2: Entering and Using Data

This chapter describes the types of data used by the TI-85
and how to enter and use them. More detailed descriptions of
the data types and particular operations relating to them are
in the appropriate chapters.

**Chapter
Contents**

Data Types

On the TI-85, you can enter and use several types of data, including real and complex numbers, matrices, vectors, and lists; strings; equations; constants; graph databases; pictures; and programs. User-assigned variable names reference them in memory.

Data Types

Data Type	Entry/Display Format

Numbers
Real or complex
	7.135E1
	        71.35
	(-2,0)
	        (-2,0)

Matrices
Real or complex
	[[1,2][3,4]]
	    [[1 2]
	     [3 4]]

Vectors Real or complex	[1,2,3] [1 2 3]
Lists Real or complex	{1,2,3,4} {1 2 3 4}
Strings Characters	"HELLO" HELLO
Equations Expressions	AREA=π*RADIUS^2 Done
Constants Real or complex	Na 6.0221367E23

Notes about Data Types

Any of these data types can be stored to and recalled from memory with a user-assigned variable name.

The MODE settings may control the entry and/or display format of a particular type of data (pages 1–24 through 1–27).

You can enter numbers, matrices, vectors, lists, and strings in an expression directly, or you can enter the name of a variable or constant to refer to values in memory.

You also can use editors to define or edit matrices, vectors, lists, equations, and constants.

Other Named Items

Programs are defined and edited using an editor (Chapter 16). Graph databases and pictures are stored and recalled using specific instructions (Chapter 4).

Entering and Using Numbers

Numbers on the TI–85 can be real or complex. You can enter a number in normal or scientific notation or in decimal, binary, octal, or hexadecimal base (Chapter 10). The MODE settings may control the entry and/or display format.

Real Numbers

Real numbers are displayed using the notation format, decimal setting, and number base setting specified by the MODE settings. You can enter a real number in any of these formats, with up to 14 digits and a three-digit decimal exponent.

Entering a Number in Scientific or Engineering Notation

Use the EE key to enter the exponent (power of 10) in scientific or engineering notation.

1. If the number is negative, press (-), and then type the portion of the number that precedes the exponent.

2. Press EE. E in the expression indicates the exponent.

3. If the exponent is negative, press (-), and then type the exponent, which can be up to three decimal digits.

Complex Numbers

On the TI–85, the complex number $a + bi$ is entered as (a,b) in rectangular format or $(a ∠ b)$ in polar format.

For example, **(1,2) + (-3,1)** returns **(-2,3)** and **(1 ∠ 2) ⋆3** returns **(-1.24844050964,2.72789228048)** in **Radian** MODE.

Variables

Values can be stored to and recalled from memory with variable names. A variable is a name that refers to a location in memory where the value is stored. In an expression, the variable name represents the value.

Variables Names A variable can represent a number, a matrix, a vector, a list, a string, an equation, a program, a graph database, or a picture.

Variable names in the TI–85 can be up to eight characters long. They must begin with a letter (including Greek and international letters, and special characters Ç, ç, Ñ, and ñ). You can use letters, numbers, hex numbers, Greek letters, international characters, and special characters Ç, ç, Ñ, and ñ in variable names. The symbols ^{2} and $'$ are used in the names of system variables, such as Σx^2 and **Q'1**.

The following are not valid as variable names:

• Names of constants

• Names of functions

• Names of instructions

Note: All variable and data type names are case-sensitive; the names **AREA** and **area** refer to different variables. The names of functions and instructions are not case-sensitive; the function names **SIN** and **sin** both refer to the same function and are not valid as variable names.

System Variables In addition to user-assigned variable names, there are some system variables that are used by the TI–85. Most of these variables are related to specific applications and are described in the appropriate chapters. These names are case-sensitive; the variable names **xMin** and **XMIN** refer to different variables.

You can use system variables in expressions. You can store to some, but not all of them. Restrictions on the use of system variables are described in Appendix A.

Storing Values to Variables

Values and strings are stored to variables using the [STO▶] key. You can enter the value as an expression. It is evaluated when you press [ENTER], and the result is stored in the variable. For information about storing unevaluated expressions in variables, see page 2-9.

Storing a Value to a Variable with STO▶

1. On a blank line on the Home screen or in the program editor, enter the value to store. This value can be a real or complex number, matrix, vector, list, or string, or an expression that evaluates to one of these types.

2. Press the [STO▶] key. The instruction → is copied to the cursor location.

3. Enter the name of the variable to which to store the value.

   Note: After you press [STO▶], the TI–85 keyboard is set in ALPHA-lock (uppercase alphabetical entry). To enter digits in the name, press [ALPHA] to cancel ALPHA-lock. To enter lowercase letters, press [2nd] [alpha].

4. Press [ENTER] to complete the instruction. If you entered an expression, it is evaluated before the value is stored to the variable.

Example

Add 10 to 25 and store the result in the variable **TEMP**. Then divide 75 by the result (**TEMP**).

Procedure	Keystrokes	Display	
Enter expression	**10** [+] **25**	10+25	
Store value in **TEMP**	[STO▶] **TEMP** [ENTER]	10+25→TEMP	35
Begin expression	**75** [÷]	75/	
Set ALPHA-lock	[ALPHA] [ALPHA]	75/	
Divide by **TEMP**	**TEMP**	75/TEMP	
Evaluate expression	[ENTER]	75/TEMP	2.14285714286

Using Variable Values

Once you have stored a value to a variable, you can use the variable name to recall the value. Simply enter the name of the variable in an expression.

Using a Variable in an Expression

Generally, you can use a variable as any element in an expression where its data type is valid. When the expression is evaluated, the current value of that variable is used. There are three ways to enter the name of a variable in an expression:

- Type the characters of the name. Variable names are case-sensitive.

- Use a VARS selection screen to copy the variable name to the cursor location (pages 2–7 and 2–8).

- Use the LIST NAME, MATRX NAME, VECTR NAME, CONS USER, or CONS BLTIN menu to copy the name of a matrix, vector, or constant to the cursor location.

  Note: If not all characters in a name can display in the menu item, the name is truncated in the menu, but the entire name is copied to the cursor location.

Displaying the Value of a Variable

You can display variable contents in three ways.

- Enter the variable name on a blank line on the Home screen. Press ENTER. The value is displayed in the current display format.

- Use the RCL (recall) feature (page 2–10) to display the unevaluated contents of the variable on a blank line on the Home screen. If the contents are an expression or equation, you can press ENTER to evaluate the expression.

- View the contents in an editor (for lists, see Chapter 12; for matrices and vectors, see Chapter 13).

Copying a Variable

To copy the contents of any variable to another variable, use the STO▶ key. For example, **VAR1▶VAR2** copies **VAR1** to **VAR2**.

Deleting a Variable

Variables are deleted from memory through the memory management menu (Chapter 18).

The VARS (Variables) Menu

[2nd] [VARS] accesses the names of variables for use in expressions. Variables are classified by the contents stored to the variable name. Press [MORE] to move around the menu.

The VARS Menu   When you press [2nd] [VARS], the menu keys are labeled with the first five items of the variables menu.

ALL	REAL	CPLX	LIST	VECTR
MATRX	STRNG	EQU	CONS	PRGM
GDB	PIC	STAT	RANGE	

When you select an item from the VARS menu, the VARIABLES selection screen is displayed.

Item	Accesses
ALL	Names of all variables and named items.
REAL	Names of real number variables.
CPLX	Names of complex number variables.
LIST	Names of list variables.
VECTR	Names of vector variables.
MATRX	Names of matrix variables.
STRNG	Names of string variables.
EQU	Names of equation variables, including current yn, rn, xtn, ytn, and $Q'n$ equations.
CONS	Names of user-defined constants.
PRGM	Names of programs.
GDB	Names of graph databases.
PIC	Names of picture images.
STAT	Names of statistics variables.
RANGE	Names of RANGE variables.

Accessing Variable Names

You can copy the name of a variable from the VARIABLES selection screen to the cursor location in an expression.

Copying a Variable Name to an Expression

1. Press [2nd] [VARS] to display the VARS menu. The VARIABLES screen temporarily replaces the screen on which you are working.

2. Select the data type. ⟨ALL⟩ displays variable names of all data types.

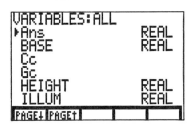

3. The names are displayed in alphabetical order (uppercase, then lowercase, then special characters). An arrow at the left indicates the selection cursor. The data type is shown at the right. (Constants and some system variables with no current value do not show a type.) To move around the list:

   - Press a letter to move quickly to names beginning with that letter. (The keyboard is set in ALPHA-lock; press [2nd] [alpha] to change to alpha-lock.)

   - Use ⟨PAGE↓⟩ and ⟨PAGE↑⟩ to move to the next page of names.

   - Use [▼] and [▲] to move down and up the list.

4. Press [ENTER] to select the name the cursor is on. The VARIABLES selection screen disappears and the name is copied to the cursor location.

Leaving the VARIABLES Screen

To leave this screen without making a selection:

- Press [EXIT] or [CLEAR] to return to the application in which you are working.

- Press [2nd] [QUIT] to display the Home Screen.

Equation Variables

You can store an unevaluated expression or a series of
characters from the Home screen or a program to the
equation data type. You can recall the unevaluated expression
or characters to the cursor location at a later time.

Equations

An equation is a variable data type that contains an
unevaluated expression or series of characters. In
addition to user-defined equation variables, several
editors store to equation variables; for example, the
graphing equations (**y1**, **y2**, **r1**, etc.), the SOLVER **eqn**, and
the STAT **RegEq**. The expression in an equation variable
can include an equal sign; therefore, it can be a
mathematical equation. For example, an equation data
type may contain **A+B**, **A=B+C**, or **ClDrw**.

If an equation variable contains an instruction (for
example, **ClDrw**), you can recall the contents to the
cursor location and then execute the instruction, but you
cannot enter the name of the equation variable on a line
by itself as a command to execute.

**Storing an
Expression to
an Equation
Variable**

The assignment instruction, entered with the $\boxed{\text{ALPHA}}$ [=]
key, stores an unevaluated expression to an equation
variable. (The store instruction, entered with the $\boxed{\text{STO▶}}$
key, evaluates the expression when the instruction is
executed and stores the value.)

The form for a completed assignment instruction is:

variable = *expression*

When the assignment instruction is executed, the
expression is not evaluated. The TI–85 stores the
unevaluated expression to the variable.

For example, **EQ1=A+B−7**, stores the expression
A+B−7 in the variable **EQ1** and **EQ2=A+B=C + sin D**
stores **A+B=C + sin D** in the variable **EQ2**.

Errors

Expressions stored using an assignment instruction are
not evaluated. Therefore, any errors in the expression
are not detected when the assignment is performed.

When an error, such as a syntax error, is encountered
within an equation or equation variable and you select
⟨GOTO⟩, the Home screen is displayed with the
appropriate assignment instruction for you to edit.

Recalling Variable Contents

The RCL (recall) feature copies the contents of a variable to the cursor location. It is useful for equation variables that have had expressions stored to them with assignment instructions and to display the values of variables before evaluation.

Recalling the Contents of a Variable

1. Press [2nd] [RCL]. The cursor is positioned after **Rcl** on the prompt line and the keyboard is set in ALPHA-lock.

2. Enter the name of the variable by typing it or by selecting it from a menu (but not the VARS selection screen).

3. Press [ENTER]. The contents of the variable are inserted at the cursor location, whether the calculator is in insert mode or not.

   - If the contents were stored with the [ALPHA] [=] key, the contents are recalled exactly as entered.

   - If the contents were stored with [STO►] , the contents are a value. The elements of the value are recalled according to the current modes, but in an entry format. For example, the keystrokes [2nd] [π] [STO►] **A** [ENTER] [2nd] [RCL] **A** [ENTER] recalls the characters **3.14** if the MODE is **Fix 2**.

After you use RCL to copy the contents of a variable to the cursor location, you can edit the characters in the display.

You cannot recall a program, graph database, or picture onto the Home screen.

Clearing Recall

If there are characters in the prompt following **Rcl**, [CLEAR] clears (blanks) the prompt entry.

If the prompt entry is blank, [CLEAR] cancels RCL and returns the cursor to the Home screen or the editor.

Recalling a Program

You can recall the contents of another program to the cursor location in the program editor. This copies (inserts) all of the commands, which you then can edit (Chapter 16). You cannot recall a program onto the Home screen.

Variable Examples

The following examples show the relationship between how information is stored to a variable, how it is retrieved, and the result. These examples use Fix 2 display MODE.

Procedure	Keystrokes	Result
Store instruction	**20** ⎡+⎦ **3** ⎡STO►⎦ **A** ⎡ENTER⎦	20+3→A 23.00 in memory, **A** contains 23
Assignment instruction	⎡ALPHA⎦ **B** ⎡ALPHA⎦ [=] **7** ⎡ENTER⎦	B=7 Done in memory, **B** contains **7**
Assignment instruction	⎡ALPHA⎦ **C** ⎡ALPHA⎦ [=] **4** ⎡+⎦ ⎡ALPHA⎦ **A** ⎡ENTER⎦	C=4+A Done in memory, **C** contains **4+A**
Use value of contents of **A** (23)	**3** ⎡÷⎦ ⎡ALPHA⎦ **A** ⎡ENTER⎦	3/A .13
Recall contents of **A** (23) into expression according to MODE settings	**3** ⎡÷⎦ ⎡2nd⎦ [RCL] **A** ⎡ENTER⎦ ⎡ENTER⎦	3/23.00 .13
Use value of contents of **B** (7)	**3** ⎡÷⎦ ⎡ALPHA⎦ **B** ⎡ENTER⎦	3/B .43
Recall contents of **B** (7) into expression	**3** ⎡÷⎦ ⎡2nd⎦ [RCL] **B** ⎡ENTER⎦ ⎡ENTER⎦	3/7 .43
Use value of contents of **C** (4+23)	**3** ⎡÷⎦ ⎡ALPHA⎦ **C** ⎡ENTER⎦	3/C .11
Recall contents of **C** (4+A) into expression	**3** ⎡÷⎦ ⎡2nd⎦ [RCL] **C** ⎡ENTER⎦ ⎡ENTER⎦	3/4+A 23.75

Constants, Programs, Graphs, and Pictures

You can store named items (constants, programs, graph databases, and pictures) and recall them from memory by name. See the appropriate chapter for further information.

Constants

The TI–85 has several built-in constants. In addition, you can create user-defined constants (Chapter 8).

You create and edit user-defined constants only through the CONSTANT editor. Constant names are case-sensitive; **CONST1** and **const1** refer to different constants. They can be used in expressions.

Programs

A program is a series of commands that can be executed. Programs are described in Chapter 16.

You store and recall programs by name in the program editor. Program names are not valid in expressions. The names are case-sensitive; **PROG1** and **prog1** refer to different programs.

Graph Databases

A graph database is all of the elements that define a particular graph. The graph can be recreated from these elements (Chapter 4).

You can store and recall a graph database by name. Graph database names are not valid in expressions. The names are case-sensitive; **GRAPH1** and **graph1** refer to different graphs.

Pictures

A picture is an image of the current graph display at a particular time (Chapter 4).

You can store and recall a picture by name. Picture names are not valid in expressions. The names are case-sensitive; **PIC1** and **pic1** refer to different pictures.

Storing to Named Items

You cannot store to a variable name if that name is currently used for a named item, such as a constant, program, graph database, or picture. This prevents one of these data types from being overwritten. Before you can use the name as a variable, you must delete the named item through the memory management menu (Chapter 18).

Chapter 3: Math, Calculus, and Test Operations

This chapter describes the math, calculus, and relational functions and instructions that are available on the TI-85 from the keyboard, MATH menu, CALC menu, and TEST menu.

Keyboard Math Functions

The most commonly used math functions are on the keyboard. The placement of the arguments of each function is described in Appendix A. These examples assume that the default MODE settings are in effect.

Functions	Example	Keystrokes	Display
$+, -, \times, \div$	$75 - 12 \times 2$	**75** [−] **12** [×] **2** [ENTER]	$75-12*2$ 51
Powers	$6^2 + 2^5$	**6** [x^2] [+] **2** [∧] **5** [ENTER]	$6^2+2^\wedge 5$ 68
$\sqrt{x}$	$\sqrt{16}$	[2nd] [√] **16** [ENTER]	$\sqrt{16}$ 4
x^{-1}	$1/4$	**4** [2nd] [x^{-1}] [ENTER]	4^{-1} $.25$
Negation	$-2 + -5$	[(−)] **2** [+] [(−)] **5** [ENTER]	$-2+-5$ -7
sin, cos, tan $\sin^{-1}, \cos^{-1}, \tan^{-1}$	$\sin \pi$	[SIN] [2nd] [π] [ENTER]	$\sin \pi$ 0
log, ln	$\ln 1$	[LN] **1** [ENTER]	$\ln 1$ 0
$10^x, e^x$	e^0	[2nd] [e^x] **0** [ENTER]	$e^\wedge 0$ 1

Notes about Keyboard Math Functions

Arguments may be real or complex values. These functions are valid also for lists. They return a list of results calculated on an element-by-element basis. If two lists are used in the same expression, they must be the same length.

sin⁻¹, **cos⁻¹**, and **tan⁻¹** are the inverse trig functions, arcsin, arccos, and arctan.

x⁻¹, the multiplicative inverse, is the equivalent of the reciprocal, 1/**x**.

Pi

Pi is stored as a constant in the TI–85. Press [2nd] [π] and the symbol π is copied to the cursor location; the number 3.1415926535898 is used internally in calculations.

The MATH Menu

The MATH menu accesses additional mathematical functions and features that are not on the keyboard. Press [MORE] to move around the menu.

The MATH Menu

When you press [2nd] [MATH], the menu keys are labeled with the MATH menu.

NUM INTER	PROB	ANGLE	HYP	MISC

Item	Accesses
NUM	Menu of number functions (page 3–4).

round	iPart	fPart	int	abs
sign	min	max	mod	

	Accesses
PROB	Menu of probability functions (page 3–6).

!	nPr	nCr	rand

	Accesses
ANGLE	Menu of angle functions (page 3–7).

°	r	'	►DMS

	Accesses
HYP	Menu of hyperbolic functions (page 3–8).

sinh	cosh	tanh	sinh^{-1}	cosh^{-1}
tanh^{-1}				

	Accesses
MISC	Menu of miscellaneous mathematical functions and instructions (page 3–9).

sum	prod	seq	lcm	gcd
►Frac	%	pEval	$^x\sqrt{}$	

	Accesses
INTER	Interpolation editor (page 3–11).

The NUM (Number) Menu

The MATH NUM menu displays number functions. When you select an item from the menu, the name is copied to the cursor location. Press [MORE] to move around the menu. These examples assume that the default MODE settings are in effect.

The MATH NUM Menu

When you select ⟨NUM⟩ from the MATH menu, the menu keys are labeled with the first five items of the number menu.

round	iPart	fPart	int	abs
sign	min	max	mod	

The functions that are valid for lists return a list of results calculated on an element-by-element basis.

The round Function

round returns a number or numbers rounded to a specified number of decimal places or digits. The first argument is the real or complex number, list, matrix, or vector to round. The second argument (optional) is the number of decimal places (0 to 11) to round to. If there is no second argument, the number is rounded to twelve digits. The parentheses are required.

round(*value,#decimals*) or **round**(*value*)

The iPart Function

iPart (integer part) returns the integer part or parts of a real or complex number, or of each element of a list, matrix, or vector.

For example, **iPart** -23.45 returns -23.

The fPart Function

fPart (fractional part) returns the fractional part or parts of a real or complex number, or of each element of a list, matrix, or vector.

For example, **fPart** -23.45 returns -.45.

The int Function

int (greatest integer) returns the largest integer less than or equal to a real number, each element of a complex number, or each element of a list, matrix, or vector. The result is the same as **iPart** for nonnegative numbers and negative integers, but one integer less than **iPart** for negative noninteger numbers.

For example, **int** -23.45 returns -24.

The abs
Function

abs (absolute value) returns the absolute value of a real number or the magnitude (modulus), $\sqrt{(real^2 + imag^2)}$, of a complex number or of each element of a list, matrix, or vector.

For example, **abs -23.45** returns **23.45**.

The sign
Function

sign returns 1 for a positive real number, 0 for 0, or -1 for a negative real number or for each element of a real list.

For example, **sign -23.45** returns **-1**.

The min
Function

min (minimum value) returns the smaller of two real numbers or two complex numbers or the smallest element in a real or complex list. If two lists are compared, the result is a list of the smaller of each pair of elements. If the argument is complex, the comparison is based on magnitude (modulus). The parentheses are required.

min(*list***)**, **min(***value,value***)**, or **min(***list,list***)**

For example, **min(3,-5)** returns **-5**, **min({1,3,-5})** returns **-5**, and **min({1,2,3},{3,2,1})** returns **{1 2 1}**.

The max
Function

max (maximum value) returns the larger of two real numbers or two complex numbers or the largest element in a real or complex list. If two lists are compared, the result is a list of the larger of each pair of elements. If the argument is complex, the comparison is based on magnitude (modulus). The parentheses are required.

max(*list***)**, **max(***value,value***)**, or **max(***list,list***)**

The mod
Function

mod (modulus) returns the modulo value of the first (real) argument with respect to the second (real) argument (the modulus). The parentheses are required.

mod(*value,modulus***)**

For example, **mod(23.45,10)** returns **3.45**.

The PROB (Probability) Menu

The MATH PROB menu displays probability functions. When you select an item from the menu, the name is copied to the cursor location. These examples assume that the default MODE settings are in effect.

The MATH PROB Menu

When you select ⟨PROB⟩ from the MATH menu, the menu keys are labeled with the probability menu.

| ! | nPr | nCr | rand |

The Factorial Function

! (factorial) returns the factorial of a positive integer between 0 and 449.

For example, **6!** returns **720**.

The nPr Function

nPr (number of permutations) returns the number of permutations of n items taken r at a time. The arguments must be nonnegative integers.

items **nPr** *number*

For example, **5 nPr 2** returns **20**.

The nCr Function

nCr (number of combinations) returns the number of combinations of n items taken r at a time. The arguments must be nonnegative integers.

items **nCr** *number*

For example, **5 nCr 2** returns **10**.

The rand Function

rand (random number) generates and returns a random number greater than 0 and less than 1. To control a random number sequence, first store an integer seed value in **rand**; for example, **0→rand**. If you store 0 to **rand**, the TI–85 uses the factory-set seed value. When you reset the TI–85, **rand** is set to the factory seed.

For example, **0→rand:rand∗3** always returns **2.83079220748**.

The ANGLE Menu

The MATH ANGLE menu displays angle indicators and instructions. When you select an item from the menu, the name is copied to the cursor location.

The MATH ANGLE Menu

When you select ⟨ANGLE⟩ from the MATH menu, the menu keys are labeled with the angle menu.

°	ʳ	'	►DMS

The ° Function

° (degree) lets you designate the real number argument as degree, regardless of the current angle MODE setting. The argument may be a real list.

angle°

The ʳ Function

ʳ (radian) lets you designate the real number argument as radian, regardless of the current angle MODE setting. The argument may be a real list.

*angle*ʳ

The ' Notation

The ' (minute) entry notation is used to enter numbers in DMS format. Degrees (≤ 999,999), minutes (< 60), and seconds (< 60, may have decimal places) must be entered as numbers, not as variable names or expressions.

degrees'minutes'seconds'

For example, enter **54'32'30'** for 54 degrees, 32 minutes, 30 seconds. The MODE setting must be **Degree** for the TI–85 to interpret this entry as degrees, minutes, and seconds (in **Radian** MODE, enter **54'32'30'°**).

(Note that **5°59'** is interpreted as implied multiplication of 5° and 59' according to the current MODE setting.)

The ►DMS Instruction

►**DMS** (display as degree/minute/second) displays the (real) result in degree, minute, second format. The MODE setting must be **Degree** for the TI–85 to interpret the result as degrees, minutes, and seconds. It is valid only at the end of a command.

result►**DMS**

The HYP (Hyperbolic) Menu

The MATH HYP menu displays hyperbolic functions. When you select an item from the menu, the name is copied to the cursor location. Press (MORE) to move around the menu.

The MATH HYP Menu

When you select ⟨HYP⟩ from the MATH menu, the menu keys are labeled with the first five items of the hyperbolic menu.

**sinh   cosh   tanh   sinh⁻¹   cosh⁻¹
tanh⁻¹**

The sinh, cosh, and tanh Functions

sinh, **cosh**, and **tanh** are the hyperbolic functions. The arguments may be real or complex numbers.

sinh *value*

These functions are valid for lists. They return a list of results calculated on an element-by-element basis.

The sinh⁻¹, cosh⁻¹, and tanh⁻¹ Functions

sinh⁻¹, **cosh⁻¹**, and **tanh⁻¹** are the hyperbolic arcsin, hyperbolic arccos, and hyperbolic arctan, respectively. The arguments may be real or complex numbers.

sinh⁻¹ *value*

These functions are valid for lists, returning a list of results calculated on an element-by-element basis.

The MISC (Miscellaneous) Menu

The MATH MISC menu displays miscellaneous mathematical functions. When you select an item from the menu, the name is copied to the cursor location. Press $\boxed{\text{MORE}}$ to move around the menu. These examples assume that the default MODE settings are in effect.

The MATH MISC Menu

When you select ⟨MISC⟩ from the MATH menu, the menu keys are labeled with the first five items of the mathematical menu.

sum	prod	seq	lcm	gcd
►Frac	%	pEval	×√	eval

The sum Function

sum (summation) returns the sum of the elements of a real or complex list.

sum *list*

For example, **sum** {**1,2,4,8**} returns **15**.

The prod Function

prod (product) returns the product of the elements of a real or complex list.

prod *list*

For example, **prod** {**1,2,4,8**} returns **64**.

The seq Function

seq (sequence) returns a real list, in which each element is the value of the expression, evaluated at increments for the specified variable from the beginning value to the ending value. The increment can be negative. **seq** is not valid in the expression.

seq(*expression,variablename,begin,end,increment*)

For example, **seq(N²,N,1,11,3)** returns {**1 16 49 100**}.

Sums and Products of Numeric Sequences

You can combine **sum** or **prod** with **seq** to obtain:

$$\sum_{x=lower}^{upper} expression(x) \qquad \prod_{x=lower}^{upper} expression(x)$$

For example, to evaluate $\sum 2^{(N-1)}$ from N=1 to 4, enter **sum seq(2^(N−1),N,1,4,1)**, which returns **15**.

The lcm Function

lcm (least common multiple) returns the least common multiple of two nonnegative integers.

lcm(*value,value*)

The MISC (Miscellaneous) Menu (Continued)

The gcd Function **gcd** (greatest common divisor) returns the greatest common divisor of two nonnegative integers.

gcd(*value,value***)**

The ►Frac Instruction **►Frac** (display as fraction) displays a result as the rational equivalent. The argument can be a real or complex number, list, matrix, or vector. If it cannot be simplified or the denominator is more than four digits, the decimal equivalent is returned. **►Frac** is valid only at the end of a command.

*result***►Frac**

For example, **1/3 + 2/7►Frac** returns **13/21**.

The % Function **%** (percent) returns the percent (divides the argument by 100) of a real number.

*value***%**

For example, **5%∗200** returns **10**.

The pEval Function **pEval** (polynomial evaluation) returns the value of a polynomial for a given **x**. The first argument is a real or complex list of the coefficients. The second argument is the real or complex value of **x**.

pEval(*list,value***)**

For example, **pEval({2,2,3},5)** returns **63**, the value of $2x^2 + 2x + 3$ at **x**=5.

The ˣ√ Function **ˣ√** (root) returns the real or complex root of a real or complex number.

nth_root **ˣ√***value*

For example, **5ˣ√32** returns **2**, the fifth root of 32.

The eval Function **eval** (evaluation) returns a list of the values of any selected functions in the current graphing MODE for the specified real value of the independent variable. **eval** is not valid in a graphing function.

eval *value*

The INTER (Interpolation) Feature

The TI-85 can interpolate or extrapolate a value linearly, given two known pairs and the x or y value of the unknown. Selecting ⟨INTER⟩ from the MATH menu displays a full-screen editor for entering values and displaying interpolated results.

The MATH INTER Editor

Select ⟨INTER⟩ from the MATH menu to display the INTERPOLATE editor.

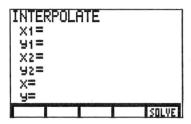

Interpolating a Value

1. Enter real values (which can be expressions) for (**x1,y1**), the first known pair.

2. Enter values for (**x2,y2**), the second known pair.

3. Enter a value for either the **x** or the **y** value of the unknown.

4. Move the cursor to the value for which you want to solve (**x** or **y**) and select ⟨SOLVE⟩.

The result is interpolated or extrapolated and displayed; the variables **x** and **y** are not changed. A square dot in the first column indicates the interpolated value. You can store individual values with the [STO▶] key.

For example, press **3** [ENTER] **5** [ENTER] to enter (3,5), then press **4** [ENTER] **4** [ENTER] to enter (4,4). To extrapolate the **y** value at **x**=1, press **1** [ENTER] and select ⟨SOLVE⟩. The result is **y=7**.

Further Solutions

After solving for a value, you can continue to enter values and interpolate from this display.

Using the Interpolation Function from a Command Line

You can use the interpolate feature from the Home screen or from a program to find a **y** value:

inter($x1,y1,x2,y2,x$**)**

To interpolate for **x**, enter **inter(**$y1,x1,y2,x2,y$**)**

The CALC (Calculus) Menu

The CALC menu displays calculus functions. Press [MORE] to move around the menu. When you select an item from the menu, the name is copied to the cursor location.

The CALC Menu

When you press [2nd] [CALC], the menu keys are labeled with the calculus menu.

evalF	nDer	der1	der2	fnInt
fMin	fMax	arc		

The calculus functions return values with respect to any nonsystem variable, to system variables **eqn** and **exp**, and to graphing variables such as **x**, **t**, and θ. The result is calculated using the current values of all variables. MODE must be **Dec**.

The calculus functions are valid in graphing equations.

The evalF Function

evalF (evaluate a function) returns the value of an expression with respect to the named variable.

evalF requires three arguments: an expression, the name of a variable, and a value to use for evaluation. The variable value can be a real number, a complex number, or a real or complex list.

evalF(*expression,variablename,value*)

For example, **evalF(A^3,A,5)** returns **125**.

evalF is not valid in the expression argument.

The nDer Function

nDer (numerical derivative) returns an approximate numerical derivative of an expression with respect to the named variable.

nDer requires two arguments: an expression and a variable name. An optional third argument gives a value to use for the variable; otherwise the current value is used. The variable value can be a real number, a complex number, or a real or complex list.

nDer(*expression,variablename,value*)

The numerical derivative value is the slope of the secant line through the points (*value* − δ,f(*value* − δ)) and (*value* + δ,f(*value* + δ)). This is an approximation of the numerical derivative. As δ gets smaller, the approximation usually gets more accurate.

For example, **nDer(A^3,A,5)** returns **75.0001** if δ = **.01**, but returns **75** if δ = **.0001**.

der1 and **der2** (page 3–14) can be used in the expression argument. **nDer** can be used once in the expression argument. A good approximation for the fourth derivative at the current value of **x** can be obtained by **nDer(nDer(der2(x^4,x),x),x)**. The accuracy is controlled by the variable δ (page 3–17) for step size. Because of the method, **nDer** can return a derivative value at a nondifferentiable point.

The CALC (Calculus) Menu (Continued)

The der1 and der2 Functions

The TI–85 uses the rules of differentiation to calculate the first and second derivatives exactly to 14 digits.

der1 (first derivative) returns the value of f', **der2** (second derivative) returns the value of f" with respect to the named variable.

der1 and **der2** require two arguments: an expression and a variable name. An optional third argument gives a value to use for the variable; otherwise the current value is used. The variable value can be a real number, a complex number, or a real or complex list.

der1 (*expression,variablename,value*)

For example, **der1(AB^3,AB,5)** returns **75** and **der2(AB^3,AB,5)** returns **30**.

der1 and **der2** are valid for the single-argument functions: **sin**, **cos**, **tan**, **sin⁻¹**, **cos⁻¹**, **tan⁻¹**, the hyperbolic functions, **log**, **ln**, **10^**, **e^**, **⁻¹**, **²**, $\sqrt{\ }$, **abs**, and negation. The two-argument functions **+** , **−** , **∗**, **/**, and **^** are valid in the expression argument, but other multiargument functions requiring parentheses are not. **evalF**, **der1**, **der2**, **fnInt**, **fMin**, **fMax**, **arc**, **nDer**, and **seq** are not valid in the expression argument. Matrices, vectors, and strings are not valid in the expression argument.

The fnInt Function

fnInt (function integral) returns the numerical integral.

fnInt requires four arguments: an expression, the name of the variable with respect to which to calculate the integral, and the lower and upper limits.

fnInt($expression$**,**$variablename$**,**$lower$**,**$upper$**)**

For example, **fnInt(A²,A,0,1)** returns **.333333333333**.

fnInt and **arc** are not valid in the expression argument. The accuracy is controlled by the variable **tol** (page 3–17). A value is stored to **fnIntErr** that is indicative of possible solution error.

Example

Use **nDer** and **fnInt** to demonstrate that:

$$D_x \left[\int_0^x f(A) \, dA \right] = f(A)$$

1. On the Home screen, enter and evaluate the expression $f(A) = A^2$ at $A = 3$.

   3→A:A² returns **9**.

2. Press [2nd] [CALC] to display the CALC menu and then enter and evaluate:

   nDer(fnInt(A²,A,0,x),x,3)

This returns **9.00003333332** at $\delta = .01$. You can change δ to increase the accuracy of the solution.

The CALC (Calculus) Menu (Continued)

The fMin and fMax Functions

fMin (function minimum) and **fMax** (function maximum) return the value at which the minimum or maximum value of an expression occurs, between specified lower and upper endpoints.

fMin and **fMax** require four arguments: an expression, the name of the variable with respect to which to calculate the minimum or maximum, and the lower and upper endpoints.

fMin(*expression,variablename,lower,upper*)

For example, **fMin(sin A,A,** $-\pi,\pi$ **)** returns **-1.57079717108**, the **A** value where the minimum occurs.

lower must be less than *upper*. **fMin** and **fMax** are not valid in the expression argument. The accuracy is controlled by the variable **tol** (page 3–17). If there is no finite minimum or maximum in the interval, usually (depending on the expression argument) an error occurs.

The arc Function

arc returns the length along a curve between two points on the curve.

arc requires four arguments: an expression to define the curve, the name of the independent variable, and the two values of the variable.

arc(*expression,variablename,value1,value2*)

For example, **arc(A^2,A,0,1)** returns **1.47894285752**.

arc and **fnInt** are not valid in the expression argument. **evalF**, **der1**, **der2**, **fMin**, **fMax**, **nDer**, and **seq** are not valid in the expression argument in **dxDer1** MODE. The accuracy is controlled by the variable **tol** in **dxNDer** or **dxDer1** MODE and by δ in **dxNDer** MODE (page 3–17).

The TOLER (Tolerance) Settings

The accuracy of the computations of certain functions is controlled by the variables δ and tol. The value may have an effect on calculating and plotting speed. The values of the variables can be viewed and edited on the TOLERANCE screen.

The TOLERANCE Editor

When you press [2nd] [TOLER], the TOLERANCE editor is displayed. The values shown are the default settings.

```
TOLERANCE
tol=1ᴇ⁻5
δ=.001
```

Editing a Value

1. Enter a positive real value (which can be an expression), but not zero:

    • Type the new value. The original value is cleared automatically when you begin typing.

    • Use [►] or [◄] to position the cursor and then make the changes.

2. Press [ENTER], [▼], or [▲]. If you entered an expression, it is evaluated. The new value is stored.

The δ Variable

The variable δ defines the step size in calculating the functions **arc** (in **dxNDer** MODE) and **nDer**, and in the GRAPH MATH operations dy/dx, dr/dθ, dy/dt, dx/dt, INFLC, TANLN, and ARC in **dxNDer** MODE (Chapter 4). δ must be a positive value.

The tol Variable

The variable **tol** defines the tolerance in calculating the functions **fnInt**, **fMin**, **fMax**, and **arc**, and the GRAPH MATH operations ∫f(x), FMIN, FMAX, and ARC (Chapter 4). **tol** must be a positive value.

Setting δ or tol from the Home Screen or a Program

You can store a value to δ or **tol** on the Home screen or in a program using the store instruction. When you press [2nd] [TOLER] in the program editor, the menu keys are labeled δ and **tol** for convenience.

The TEST (Relational) Menu

The TEST menu displays relational operations that compare two values and return 1 or 0. Press [MORE] to move around the menu. When you select from the menu, the name is copied to the cursor location.

The TEST Menu

When you press [2nd] [TEST], the menu keys are labeled with the first five items of the relational menu.

==   <   >   ≤   ≥
≠

The == (equals relational function) distinguishes it from the = (assignment) character on the keyboard.

The Relational Functions

The relational functions are valid for two lists of the same length. They return a list of results calculated on an element-by-element basis.

The == Function

== (equals) returns **1** if the arguments are equal, **0** if not equal. The arguments can be real or complex numbers, matrices, vectors, or lists, or strings.

For example {**1,2,3**} = = {**3,2,1**} returns {**0 1 0**}.

The <, >, ≤, and ≥ Functions

< (less than), > (greater than), ≤ (less than or equal), and ≥ (greater than or equal) return **1** if the test is true and **0** if the test is false. Both arguments must be real values or lists (which can be expressions).

The ≠ Function

≠ (not equal) returns **1** if the arguments are not equal, **0** if equal. The arguments can be real or complex numbers, matrices, vectors, or lists, or strings.

Using Tests in Expressions and Instructions

Only the Boolean operators are below relational functions in the EOS evaluation hierarchy.

- The expression **2 + 2 = = 2 + 3** evaluates to **0**. EOS first performs the addition and then compares 4 to 5.

- The expression **2 + (2 = = 2) + 3** evaluates to **6**. EOS first performs the test because it is in parentheses and then adds 2, 1, and 3.

Relational functions can be used to control program flow (Chapter 16).

Chapter 4: Function Graphing

This chapter describes function graphing on the TI–85 in detail. It also lays the foundation for using the other graphing modes of the TI–85.

Defining a Graph

To define a graph, select the graphing mode, set the graph format, enter and select functions to be graphed, and define the viewing rectangle. Once a graph is defined, it can be displayed and explored.

Steps in Defining a Graph

There are five basic steps to defining a graph. You may not need to do all of the steps each time you define a graph. The procedures are described in detail on the following pages.

1. Set the MODE to **Func** graphing.

2. Set the graph FORMT.

3. Enter or edit expressions to define a function or functions in the y(x) list.

4. Select the function or functions in the y(x) list to graph.

5. Set values for the RANGE variables to define the viewing rectangle.

Once a graph has been defined, you can display it and use several tools of the TI–85 to explore the behavior of the function or functions. These tools are described later in this chapter.

Graph Databases

You can store the elements that define the current graph in a graph database that has a user-defined name. At a later time, you can recall that database as the current graph (page 4–40).

Graph Pictures

You can store a picture of the current display in a graph picture that has a user-defined name. At a later time, you can superimpose the picture on the current graph (page 4–41).

Graphing Modes

The TI-85 has four graphing modes: function graphing, polar graphing, parametric graphing, and differential equation graphing.

The Graphing MODE

Each of the four graphing modes (function, polar, parametric, and differential equations) is independent of the others. Each MODE has a current graph, defined by its elements:

- The functions
- The graph FORMT
- The RANGE variables

Changes made to a graph element apply to that element in the current graphing MODE only. For example, changes to the RANGE variables in **Func** graphing do not affect the RANGE variables in **Pol** graphing.

Note: ZOOM factors, MODE settings, and tolerances are global.

Checking and Changing the Graphing MODE

To display or change the current MODE settings, press [2nd] [MODE]. The graphing modes are:

- **Func** (function graphing)
- **Pol** (polar graphing)
- **Param** (parametric graphing)
- **DifEq** (differential equation graphing)

To graph functions, you must be in **Func** MODE. The number base setting must be **Dec**. The **Radian/Degree** and **dxDer1/dxNDer** settings affect how some y(x) functions are interpreted.

Setting the Graphing MODE from a Program

You can set the graphing mode in a program through an interactive selection screen (Chapter 16) or by selecting the name from the CATALOG.

The GRAPH Menu and Display

[GRAPH] displays the GRAPH menu. It also displays the most recent graph, if no changes affecting the graph have been made.

The GRAPH Menu

When you press [GRAPH], the menu keys are labeled with the first five items of the graph menu. Press [MORE] to move around the menu.

y(x)=	RANGE	ZOOM	TRACE	GRAPH
MATH	DRAW	FORMT	STGDB	RCGDB
EVAL	STPIC	RCPIC		

Item	Accesses
y(x)=	The y(x) editor (page 4–8).
RANGE	The RANGE editor (page 4–12).
ZOOM	Operations to change the viewing rectangle (page 4–18).
TRACE	Displays graph to trace functions (page 4–17).
GRAPH	Displays graph with GRAPH menu (page 4–14).
MATH	Menu of operations to explore a graph mathematically (page 4–24).
DRAW	Operations to draw on graph (page 4–30).
FORMT	Graph format selection screen (page 4–6).
STGDB	Stores current graph database (page 4–40).
RCGDB	Recalls stored graph database (page 4–40).
EVAL	Displays graph and accesses an operation to evaluate functions (page 4–29).
STPIC	Stores current graph picture (page 4–41).
RCPIC	Recalls stored graph picture (page 4–41).

Displaying the GRAPH Menu

If you have selected an item, such as TRACE, that does not display menus, press [EXIT] to display the GRAPH menu.

**The "Smart
Graph" Feature**

The "Smart Graph" feature automatically keeps track of whether any element of a graph has been changed and replots only if you have done one or more of the following:

- Changed a function or the value of a variable that is used in a selected function.

- Selected or unselected a function.

- Changed a MODE setting for graphing MODE, number base MODE, **Radian/Degree**, or calculus MODE.

- Changed the value of a RANGE variable.

- Changed a graph FORMT setting other than an axis label or coordinate.

- Cleared drawings.

**The GRAPH
Screen**

When you press (GRAPH), "Smart Graph" controls what is displayed on the screen.

- If you have changed one or more of the above, "Smart Graph" does not display a graph. The display is not changed; the menu keys are labeled with the GRAPH menu.

  You can continue to make changes to the graph elements. "Smart Graph" will plot the new graph when you select ⟨GRAPH⟩, ⟨TRACE⟩, ⟨EVAL⟩, ⟨STGDB⟩, or a ZOOM, DRAW, MATH, or PIC operation.

- If you have not changed any of the above since the graph was displayed previously, "Smart Graph" displays the graph immediately, and the menu keys are labeled with the GRAPH menu.

Setting the Graph Format

The graph format determines how a graph appears on the display. The FORMT settings for function graphing apply only to Func MODE.

Checking FORMT Settings

To display the FORMT selection screen, select ⟨FORMT⟩ from the GRAPH menu. The GRAPH menu remains on the bottom line. The current settings are highlighted. The FORMT settings are described on the following page.

Setting	Meaning
RectGC PolarGC	Type of coordinates.
CoordOn CoordOff	Coordinates on or off.
DrawLine DrawDot	Connected or discrete points.
SeqG SimulG	How to plot functions.
GridOff GridOn	Graph grid off or on.
AxesOn AxesOff	Axes on or off.
LabelOff LabelOn	Axes labels off or on.

y(x)= | RANGE | ZOOM | TRACE | GRAPH

Changing FORMT Settings

To change any of the settings:

1. Move the cursor to the line of the setting you want to change. The setting the cursor is on blinks.

2. Move the cursor to the setting you want. Press [ENTER].

Leaving the FORMT Selection Screen

- To continue defining the graph, select ⟨y(x)=⟩ or ⟨RANGE⟩ from the GRAPH menu.

- To display the graph, select ⟨GRAPH⟩, ⟨TRACE⟩, ⟨EVAL⟩, ⟨STGDB⟩, or a ZOOM, DRAW, MATH, or PIC operation.

- To display the Home screen, press [2nd] [QUIT], [EXIT], or [CLEAR].

Rectangular or Polar Graphing Coordinate Display	**RectGC** (rectangular) displays the cursor coordinate in terms of the rectangular coordinates **x** and **y**.
	PolarGC displays the cursor coordinate in terms of the polar coordinates **r** and θ.
Cursor Coordinate On or Off	**CoordOn** (coordinate on) displays the cursor coordinate above the menu(s).
	CoordOff (coordinate off) does not display the cursor coordinate.
DrawLine or DrawDot Graph Display	**DrawLine** draws a line between the points calculated for the functions in the y(x) list.
	DrawDot plots only the calculated points for the functions.
Sequential or Simultaneous Graphing	**SeqG** (sequential graphing) evaluates and plots one function completely before the next function is evaluated and plotted.
	SimulG (simultaneous graphing) evaluates and plots all functions for a single value of **x** before the next value of **x** is evaluated and plotted.
Grid Off or Grid On	**GridOff** does not display grid points.
	GridOn displays grid points. Grid points correspond to the axis tick marks.
Axes On or Axes Off Display	**AxesOn** displays the axes.
	AxesOff does not display the axes. It overrides the Axis Label setting.
Axis Label Off or Axis Label On	**LabelOff** does not label the axes.
	LabelOn labels the axes with the variables (**x** and **y** for **Func**, **Pol**, and **Param** MODE; the labels vary in **DifEq** MODE).

Defining Functions in the y(x) List

Functions to be graphed are entered on the y(x) editor. Up to 99 functions can be stored in the current graph or in each database, limited only by available memory. One or more of these functions can be graphed at a time.

Displaying the Functions in the y(x) List

To display the y(x) editor, select ⟨y(x)=⟩ from the GRAPH menu. If no functions are defined, **y1 =** is displayed. In the example below, the **y1** and **y2** functions are defined.

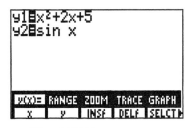

Adding a Function to the y(x) List

Use ▼ or ENTER to move the cursor to the line after the final defined function. The next function name is displayed automatically. Enter the expression to define the function.

Note: To move quickly from the first function to the final function in the list, press ▲.

Inserting a Function in the y(x) List

You can insert a function in the y(x) list only where there are gaps in the number sequence. For example, if only **y1** and **y4** are defined, you can insert **y3**.

1. Move the cursor to the function above which you want to insert.

2. Select ⟨INSf⟩ from the y(x) editor menu. The name of the immediately previous function is inserted.

3. Enter the expression to define the function.

Deleting a Function from the y(x) List

1. Move the cursor to the function in the y(x) list.

2. Select ⟨DELf⟩ from the y(x) editor menu. The function, including the name, is deleted.

**Entering
an Expression
to Define
a New Function**

- The independent variable must be **x**. You may select
  ⟨x⟩ from the y(x) editor menu, press x-VAR, or press
  2nd [alpha] ⊠.

- If the value of y(x) is not real or is undefined for a
  specified **x**, no point is plotted for that **x**; it is not an
  error.

- You may use functions, variables, constants, matrix
  elements, vector elements, list elements, or lists (page
  4–15) in the expression.

- You may use entire matrices or vectors in the
  expression, but the expression must evaluate to a real
  number at each point to be plotted.

- You may use complex values in the expression, but the
  expression must evaluate to a real number at each
  point to be plotted.

- You may use equation variables in the expression. For
  example, you may use one function in the y(x) list to
  define another, such as **y2 = 3y1**. You may select ⟨y⟩
  from the y(x) editor menu and then type the number of
  the function.

- You may recall equation variables into the expression
  (page 4–10).

The expression is stored as an equation variable as you
enter it. If an expression is longer than one line, it scrolls.
2nd ◄ and 2nd ► move the cursor to the beginning
and end of the expression.

When you complete the expression, press ENTER to
move to the beginning of the next y(x) function.

Note: If you press a key that displays a menu, the y(x)
editor menu moves to the seventh line (if it is not already
there), and the selected menu is displayed on the eighth
line.

Defining Functions in the y(x) List (Continued)

Editing an Existing Function in the y(x) List

1. Move the cursor to the function in the y(x) list. [2nd] [▶] and [2nd] [◀] move the cursor to the end or beginning of the expression quickly.

2. Edit the function in one of the following ways:

   • Position the cursor and make the changes.

   • Press [CLEAR] to clear (blank) the expression and then enter a new expression.

Recalling an Equation Variable into a Function

You can copy an expression in an equation variable, including another y(x) function, into a function.

1. Press [2nd] [RCL]. The cursor is positioned after **Rcl** on the prompt line. The keyboard is set in ALPHA-lock.

2. Enter the name of the variable. Press [ENTER]. The contents of the variable are inserted at the cursor location in the function, whether the calculator is in insert mode or not.

You can edit the characters you have recalled.

Leaving the y(x) Editor

• To continue defining the graph, select ⟨FORMT⟩ or ⟨RANGE⟩ from the GRAPH menu.

• To display the graph, select ⟨GRAPH⟩, ⟨TRACE⟩, ⟨EVAL⟩, ⟨STGDB⟩, or a ZOOM, DRAW, MATH, or PIC operation.

• To display the Home screen, press [2nd] [QUIT] or [EXIT] [EXIT].

Entering a y(x) Function from the Home Screen or a Program

You can enter a function in the y(x) list on the Home screen or in the program editor regardless of the current graphing MODE. Use an assignment instruction to store an expression to a function name:

yn = *expression*

Selecting Functions

Only functions that are selected are graphed. Any number of functions may be selected at one time. You select and unselect ("turn on" and "turn off") functions for graphing on the y(x) editor.

Turning a Function "On" or "Off"

The equal sign on a selected function is highlighted. To change the selection status of a function:

1. If the y(x) editor is not displayed, select ⟨y(x)=⟩ from the GRAPH menu to display the functions. In the example below, only the y1 function is selected.

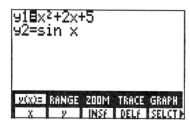

2. Move to the function you want to turn on or off.

3. Select ⟨SELCT⟩ from the y(x) editor menu. The status of the function is reversed.

Note: When you enter or edit a function, it is selected automatically. When you clear a function, it is unselected.

Turning All Functions "On" or "Off"

Press MORE if necessary and select the appropriate option from the y(x) editor menu. ALL+ turns all functions on in the y(x) list. ALL− turns all functions off.

Selecting Functions from the Home Screen or a Program

To select functions on the Home screen or from a program, use the instructions **FnOn** or **FnOff**, which can be accessed from the CATALOG.

If **FnOn** and **FnOff** have no arguments, they turn all the functions on or off. If **FnOn** and **FnOff** have arguments, they act on those functions. For example, **FnOn 1,3** turns on functions **y1** and **y3**.

Defining the Viewing Rectangle

The RANGE variables determine the boundaries and other attributes of the viewing rectangle. The RANGE variables associated with function graphing are retained if another type of graphing is used or if the calculator is off.

The RANGE Variables

The viewing rectangle of the TI–85 is the portion of the coordinate plane defined by the RANGE variables **xMin**, **xMax**, **yMin**, and **yMax**.

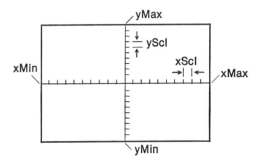

Checking the Viewing Rectangle

To display the values of the current RANGE variables, select ⟨RANGE⟩ from the GRAPH menu. The values shown below are the standard defaults.

```
RANGE
 xMin=-10
 xMax=10
 xScl=1
 yMin=-10
 yMax=10
 yScl=1
 y(x)= RANGE ZOOM TRACE GRAPH▶
```

Leaving the RANGE Editor

- To continue defining the graph, select ⟨y(x)=⟩ or ⟨FORMT⟩ from the GRAPH menu.

- To display the graph, select ⟨GRAPH⟩, ⟨TRACE⟩, ⟨EVAL⟩, ⟨STGDB⟩, or a ZOOM, DRAW, MATH, or PIC operation.

- To display the Home screen, press [2nd] [QUIT] or [EXIT].

Editing the RANGE Variables	1. Use ▼, ▲, or ENTER to move to the variable.
	2. Enter a real value (which can be an expression) in one of the following ways:

• Type a new value. The original value is cleared automatically when you begin typing.

• Use ► or ◄ to position the cursor and then make the changes.

3. Press ENTER, ▼, or ▲. If you entered an expression, it is evaluated. The new value is stored.

Note: **xMin** must be less than **xMax**, and **yMin** must be less than **yMax**. To turn the tick marks off, set **xScl** or **yScl** to zero.

Setting a RANGE Variable from the Home Screen or a Program

You can store a value to a RANGE variable for the current graphing mode on the Home screen or in the program editor, using the store instruction.

△x and △y

The variables △**x** and △**y** define the distance between the center of two adjoining points on a graph (graphing accuracy).

$$\triangle x = \frac{(xMax - xMin)}{126} \qquad \triangle y = \frac{(yMax - yMin)}{62}$$

△**x** and △**y** are not on the RANGE screen; they are accessible through the VARS RANGE screen. You can store values to △**x** and △**y** on the Home screen or in the program editor. When the value is stored, a new value for **xMax** or **yMax** is calculated and stored.

Note: △**x** and △**y** are calculated from **xMin**, **xMax**, **yMin**, and **yMax** at the time a graph is plotted.

Displaying a Graph

Once you have set the MODE, set the graph format, entered and selected functions, and defined the viewing rectangle in order to define a graph, you can display the graph with or without the menu.

**Displaying
a New Graph**

Press [GRAPH] to display the GRAPH menu, if necessary. To display the graph, select ⟨GRAPH⟩. The graph is displayed with the GRAPH menu on line eight. Press [CLEAR] to see the graph with no menus.

The TI–85 graphs all selected functions.

- Functions with undefined values graph without causing an error. For example, an error occurs if you evaluate **1/x** at **x** = 0, but no error occurs when you graph **y1 = 1/x** for -10 ≤ **x** ≤ 10.

- The current graph FORMT settings apply, and the current values of the RANGE variables define the viewing rectangle.

- As a graph is plotted, the TI–85 updates the variables **x** and **y** with the coordinate values of the function.

- As a graph is plotted, the busy indicator in the upper right of the display is on. No menu is displayed until the graph is complete.

- To pause graphing temporarily as a graph is being plotted, press [ENTER]. The busy indicator changes to a dotted line. To resume graphing, press [ENTER] again. To discontinue graphing after pausing, press [ON] .

- To stop graphing as a graph is being plotted, press [ON] until the graphing stops. Select ⟨GRAPH⟩ to start over.

Note: Smart Graph plots the current graph, if necessary, when you select ⟨TRACE⟩, ⟨EVAL⟩, ⟨STGDB⟩, or a ZOOM, DRAW, MATH, or PIC operation.

**Graphing from
the Home Screen
and Programs**

You can display and explore a graph from a program (pages 4–42 and 4–43). You can access graphing commands on the Home screen from the CATALOG.

Displaying More of a Graph

To see parts of the graph that may be "hidden" by the cursor, coordinate values, or menus:

- Press [CLEAR]. The cursor, coordinate values, **lower** and **upper** indicators, and menu(s) disappear. TRACE, ZOOM, or MATH operations are cancelled. To display the menu(s) after you press [CLEAR], press [EXIT] or [GRAPH].

- Press [ENTER] (except during TRACE). The cursor and coordinate values disappear, but the menu(s), if any, remain.

- Select ⟨GRAPH⟩ from the GRAPH menu or press [GRAPH]. The cursor and coordinate values disappear, but the menu(s) remain.

When you press a cursor-movement key, the cursor moves from its current position and the coordinate values display.

Graphing a Family of Curves

If you enter a list as an element in an expression, the TI–85 plots the function for each value in the list, graphing a family of curves. (In **SimulG**, it graphs all functions for the first element, then for the second element, and so on.) For example, entering **{1,2,3}sin x** as a function in the y(x) editor graphs three functions: **1 sin x**, **2 sin x**, and **3 sin x**.

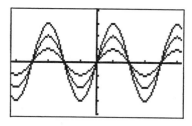

Exploring a Graph with the Free-Moving Cursor

While a graph is displayed, the free-moving cursor can be moved anywhere on the graph to identify the coordinate of any location on the graph.

The Free-Moving Cursor

You can use ◄, ►, ▲, and ▼ to move the cursor around the graph. When you first display the graph, no cursor is visible. As soon as you press a cursor-movement key, the cursor moves from the center of the viewing rectangle.

- In **RectGC** FORMT, moving the cursor updates the variables **x** and **y**. In **PolarGC** FORMT, the variables **r** and θ are updated also.

- If the FORMT is **CoordOn**, the coordinate values of the cursor location are displayed on the lowest available line just above the menu line or lines (if any), as you move the cursor around the graph. Coordinate values generally are displayed with 11 digits in normal floating-decimal format. The numeric display MODE settings do not affect coordinate display.

Note: The free-moving cursor moves from point to point on the display. If you move the cursor to a point that appears to be "on" the function, it may be near, but not necessarily on, the function; therefore, the coordinate value displayed at the bottom of the screen is not necessarily a point on the function. To move the cursor along a function, use the TRACE feature.

Graphing Accuracy

The display coordinate values approximate actual math coordinates accurate to within the width/height of a point, $\triangle x$ and $\triangle y$ (page 4–13).

As the values of **xMax** and **xMin** (and **yMax** and **yMin)** get closer together (after a ZOOM command, for example), $\triangle x$ and $\triangle y$ become smaller, the graphing accuracy of the calculator increases, and the display coordinate values more closely approximate the math coordinates.

Exploring a Graph with the TRACE Feature

The TRACE feature moves the cursor from one plotted point to the next along a function. When you select ⟨TRACE⟩ from the GRAPH menu, Smart Graph displays the current graph, if necessary. The cursor coordinate may be displayed at the bottom of the screen. No menus are displayed during TRACE.

Beginning a TRACE

Select ⟨TRACE⟩ to begin a TRACE. If the graph is not displayed, the TI–85 displays it. The TRACE cursor is on the first selected function in the y(x) list at the middle **x** value on the display. The number of the function shows in the upper right of the display.

Moving along a Function

Use ▶ or ◀ to move the cursor along the function. Each press moves the cursor from one plotted point (**x**, **y** =f(**x**)) to the next and updates the variables **x** and **y**.

Panning Left or Right

If you trace a function to the left or right edge of the display, the viewing rectangle automatically pans to the left or right. The RANGE variables **xMin** and **xMax** are updated accordingly.

Tracing a Function above or below the Display

If you trace a function above or below the viewing rectangle, the cursor disappears, but the coordinate is displayed (if **CoordOn**) and the variables **x** and **y** are updated.

QuickZoom

While tracing, you can press ENTER to adjust the viewing rectangle so that the cursor location is the center of the new viewing rectangle, even if the cursor is above or below the display.

Moving from Function to Function

To trace another function starting at the same **x** value, use ▼ or ▲ to move to that function. The function number in the upper right corner changes. The order is based on the order of the functions in the y(x) list, not the appearance of the functions as graphed on the display.

Tracing a Family of Curves

If a selected function graphs a family of curves (page 4–15), ▼ moves the cursor to each curve in the list before moving to the next y(x) function. ▲ moves in the reverse order.

Cursor Coordinate Display

You must select **CoordOn** on the FORMT screen to display the coordinate values **x** and **y** for **RectGC** (**r** and θ for **PolarGC**). The **y** value is calculated from the **x** value; that is, **y** =f(**x**). If the function is nonreal or undefined at an **x** value, the **y** value is blank.

Leaving TRACE

To leave TRACE and display the GRAPH menu, press EXIT or GRAPH.

Exploring a Graph with the ZOOM Features

Selecting ⟨ZOOM⟩ accesses operations to adjust the viewing rectangle. BOX, ZIN, ZOUT, ZOOMX, ZOOMY, and ZINT prompt you to move the cursor to define a new viewing rectangle. ZSTD, ZPREV, ZFIT, ZSQR, ZTRIG, ZRCL, and ZDECM plot the new graph immediately.

The GRAPH ZOOM Menu

When you select ⟨ZOOM⟩ from the GRAPH menu, the menu keys are labeled with the first five items of the menu. Press [MORE] to move around the menu.

BOX	ZIN	ZOUT	ZSTD	ZPREV
ZFIT	ZSQR	ZTRIG	ZDECM	ZRCL
ZFACT	ZOOMX	ZOOMY	ZINT	ZSTO

Item	Action
BOX	Draws box to define viewing rectangle (page 4–19).
ZIN	Magnifies graph (page 4–20).
ZOUT	Displays more of graph (page 4–20).
ZSTD	Sets default RANGE variables (page 4–22).
ZPREV	Sets RANGE variables to values prior to executing previous ZOOM operation (page 4–22).
ZFIT	Sets **yMin** and **yMax** to include minimum and maximum **y** values for **xMin** ≤ **x** ≤ **xMax** (page 4–22).
ZSQR	Sets aspect ratio to one (page 4–22).
ZTRIG	Sets built-in trig RANGE variables (page 4–22).
ZDECM	Sets size of points to .1 (page 4–22).
ZRCL	Sets user-defined RANGE variables (page 4–23).
ZFACT	Displays ZOOM FACTORS editor (page 4–21).
ZOOMX	Displays more of graph using **xFact** only (page 4–20).
ZOOMY	Displays more of graph using **yFact** only (page 4–20).
ZINT	Sets integer values on axes (page 4–22).
ZSTO	Sets user-defined RANGE variables to current values (page 4–23).

When a ZOOM operation is executed, the TI–85 updates the values of the RANGE variables and displays the graph in the new viewing rectangle.

Using ZOOM Box

ZOOM Box uses the cursor to select diagonal corners of a rectangle. The TI-85 then plots the selected functions again, using that rectangle (box) to define the new viewing rectangle.

Defining the ZOOM Box

1. Select ⟨BOX⟩ from the GRAPH ZOOM menu. The menus disappear.

   Notice the special cursor at the center of the display. It indicates that you are using a ZOOM operation.

2. Move the cursor to any corner of the box you want to define. Press [ENTER]. The cursor changes to a small square.

3. Move the cursor to the diagonal corner of the box you want to define. As you move the cursor, the boundaries of the box change on the display.

   Note: You can cancel the ZOOM BOX procedure any time before you press [ENTER] in one of the following ways:

   • To display the GRAPH menu, press [EXIT] or [GRAPH].

   • Press [CLEAR] to leave ZOOM, but not display the GRAPH menu.

   • To return to the Home screen, press [2nd] [QUIT].

   • To select another screen or menu, press the appropriate key(s).

4. When the box is defined as you want it, press [ENTER].

   The TI-85 updates the RANGE variables and plots the selected functions in the new viewing rectangle defined by the box.

Zooming In or Out

ZIN (zoom in) magnifies the graph. ZOUT (zoom out) displays more of the graph. ZOOMX and ZOOMY display more of the graph horizontally or vertically. Changes are centered around the cursor location. The xFact and yFact settings determine the extent of the magnification.

Zooming In on a Graph

1. After checking or changing the ZOOM factors (page 4–21), select ⟨ZIN⟩ from the GRAPH ZOOM menu. Notice the special cursor. It indicates that you are using a ZOOM operation.

2. Move the cursor to the point you want as the center of the new viewing rectangle. Press ⌑ENTER⌑.

   The TI–85 adjusts the viewing rectangle by **xFact** and **yFact**, updates the RANGE variables, and plots the selected functions again, centered around the cursor location.

3. You can zoom in on the graph again:

   • To zoom in at the same point, press ⌑ENTER⌑.

   • To zoom in at a new point, move the cursor to the new point and press ⌑ENTER⌑.

   You can press ⌑ENTER⌑ to zoom in on a graph repeatedly. ZIN is not cancelled until you press a key other than ⌑ENTER⌑ or a cursor-movement key.

Using ZOUT

The procedure for ZOUT is the same as for ZIN.

ZOOMX and ZOOMY

The procedure to zoom out on a graph using only **xFact** or only **yFact** is the same as for ZIN.

• ZOOMX adjusts the horizontal axis of the viewing rectangle by **xFact**, updates the RANGE variables, and plots the selected functions again, centered around the cursor location. **yMin** and **yMax** are not changed.

• ZOOMY adjusts the vertical axis of the viewing rectangle by **yFact**, updates the RANGE variables, and plots the selected functions again, centered around the cursor location. **xMin** and **xMax** are not changed.

Setting ZOOM Factors

ZOOM factors determine the extent of the change for the viewing rectangle created by ZIN, ZOUT, ZOOMX, or ZOOMY on a graph. You can review or edit the ZOOM factors.

ZOOM Factors

ZOOM factors are positive numbers (not necessarily integers) greater than or equal to 1. They define the magnification or reduction factor used to zoom in or out around a point (page 4–20). ZOOM factors are global; they apply to all graphing modes. **xFact** is the variable name for the horizontal factor; **yFact** is the variable name for the vertical factor.

Checking xFact and yFact

Select ⟨ZFACT⟩ from the GRAPH ZOOM menu to display the ZOOM FACTORS screen (values shown are defaults).

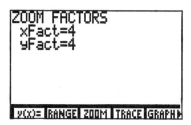

Editing xFact and yFact

1. Enter a real value (which can be an expression) in one of the following ways:

   • Type a new value. The original value is cleared automatically when you begin typing.

   • Use ▶ or ◀ to position the cursor and then make the changes.

2. Press [ENTER], ▼, or ▲. If you entered an expression, it is evaluated. The new value is stored.

Setting ZOOM Factors from the Home Screen or a Program

You can store a value to **xFact** or **yFact** on the Home screen or in the program editor. Select the variable name from the VARS ALL screen or type it from the keyboard.

value→**xFact** or *value*→**yFact**

Other ZOOM Features

The TI-85 has a variety of additional ZOOM features for exploring a graph. Some reset the RANGE variables to predefined values and some use factors to adjust the RANGE variables. All except ZINT plot the selected functions as soon as the menu selection is made.

Previous   ZPREV (zoom previous) returns to the RANGE values defined prior to the most recent ZOOM.

Standard   ZSTD (zoom standard) changes the RANGE variables to the standard default values:

xMin = -10	yMin = -10
xMax = 10	yMax = 10
xScl = 1	yScl = 1

Fit   ZFIT (zoom to fit) recalculates **yMin** and **yMax** to include the minimum and maximum **y** values of the selected functions between the current **xMin** and **xMax**. **xMin** and **xMax** are not changed. (The busy indicator displays as the new viewing rectangle is calculated.)

Square   ZSQR (zoom square) redefines the viewing rectangle based on the current RANGE variables. The RANGE variables are adjusted in only the x direction or y direction. The midpoint of the current graph (not the axis) becomes the midpoint of the new graph. ZSQR makes the graph of a circle look like a circle.

Trig   ZTRIG (zoom trig) changes the RANGE variables to values appropriate for trig functions ($\triangle \mathbf{x} = \pi/24$). The trig RANGE variables in **Radian** MODE are:

xMin = -8.24668071567	yMin = -4
xMax = 8.24668071567	yMax = 4
xScl = 1.5707963267949 ($\pi/2$)	yScl = 1

Decimal   ZDECM (zoom decimal) changes the RANGE variables to values that set $\triangle \mathbf{x}$ and $\triangle \mathbf{y} = .1$.

xMin = -6.3	yMin = -3.1
xMax = 6.3	yMax = 3.1
xScl = 1	yScl = 1

Integer   ZINT (zoom integer) plots the selected functions, redefining the viewing rectangle so that $\triangle \mathbf{x} = 1$, $\triangle \mathbf{y} = 1$, the mid-point of each point is an integer, **xScl = 10**, and **yScl = 10**. Move the cursor to the point you want as the center of the new viewing rectangle, and press ENTER.

The User-Defined ZOOM

ZSTO stores the values of the current RANGE variables to
user-defined ZOOM RANGE variables. ZRCL changes the
viewing rectangle to the values stored with ZSTO.

**User-Defined
ZOOM RANGE
Variables**

In **Func** MODE there are six ZOOM RANGE variables that are
user-defined: **zxMin**, **zxMax**, **zxScl**, **zyMin**, **zyMax**, and
zyScl. These variables are global; they apply to all
graphing modes. Changing the value of **zxMin**, for
example, in **Func** MODE also changes it in **Param** MODE.

In **Pol** MODE, the user-defined variables also include
zθMin, **zθMax**, and **zθStep**. In **Param** MODE, the
user-defined variables also include **ztMin**, **ztMax**, and
ztStep. In **DifEq** MODE, the user-defined variables also
include **ztMin**, **ztMax**, **ztStep**, and **ztPlot**.

**Setting
User-Defined
ZOOM RANGE
Variables**

To store the current viewing rectangle, select ⟨ZSTO⟩
(zoom store) from the GRAPH ZOOM menu. The values of
the current RANGE variables are stored in the user-
defined ZOOM RANGE variables.

The user-defined ZOOM RANGE variables contain the
standard default values until you edit them the first time.

**Setting a
User-Defined
ZOOM RANGE
Variable from
the Home Screen
or a Program**

You can store a value to a user-defined ZOOM RANGE
variable, such as **zxMin**, from the Home screen or in a
program. Select the variable name from the VARS RANGE
screen or type it from the keyboard.

value→zoomrange

**Recalling the
User-Defined
Viewing
Rectangle**

When you select ⟨ZRCL⟩ from the GRAPH ZOOM menu,
ZRCL (zoom recall) updates the RANGE variables to the
values of the user-defined ZOOM RANGE variables. The
selected functions are plotted as soon as the menu
selection is made.

The GRAPH MATH Menu

The GRAPH MATH operations analyze the graph that is
displayed. The current graph is displayed when the GRAPH
MATH operation is selected.

The GRAPH MATH Menu When you select ⟨MATH⟩ from the GRAPH menu, the
menu keys are labeled with the first five items of the
menu. Press MORE to move around the menu.

LOWER	UPPER	ROOT	dy/dx	∫f(x)
FMIN	FMAX	INFLC	YICPT	ISECT
DIST	ARC	TANLN		

Item	Accesses
LOWER	Defines lower bound of interval (page 4–25).
UPPER	Defines upper bound of interval (page 4–25).
ROOT	Finds root of a function in interval (page 4–26).
dy/dx	Finds derivative (slope) of a function at a point (page 4–26).
∫f(x)	Finds definite integral of a function in interval (page 4–26).
FMIN	Finds minimum of a function in interval (page 4–27).
FMAX	Finds maximum of a function in interval (page 4–27).
INFLC	Finds inflection point of a function in interval (page 4–27).
YICPT	Finds y-intercept of a function (page 4–26).
ISECT	Finds intersection of two functions in interval (page 4–27).
DIST	Finds distance between two points on the display (page 4–28).
ARC	Finds distance along a function between two points on a function (page 4–28).
TANLN	Draws tangent line at a point (page 4–28).

Setting an Interval for MATH Operations

The MATH operations ROOT, ∫f(x), ISECT, FMIN, FMAX, and INFLC analyze a function between two values of x, identified by the variables lower and upper.

lower and upper

On a graph, the values of **lower** and **upper** are always between **xMin** and **xMax**. **lower** changes to **xMin** and **upper** changes to **xMax** if:

- You execute a ZOOM operation.

- You change **xMin** or **xMax** in the RANGE editor or from a command line.

First define the viewing rectangle, and then set **lower** and **upper** from the GRAPH MATH menu or from a command line.

Setting an Interval from a Graph

You can select the interval in which to analyze the graph. If you do not explicitly define the interval, **lower** is set to **xMin** and **upper** is set to **xMax**.

1. Select ⟨MATH⟩ from the GRAPH menu. The GRAPH MATH menu is displayed.

2. Select ⟨LOWER⟩ from the GRAPH MATH menu. The selection cursor is displayed on the current graph.

3. Position the cursor on the **x** value for the lower endpoint of the interval. Press ENTER. A right-arrow indicator at the top of the display shows the lower endpoint and the **x**-coordinate value is stored in the variable **lower**. (When **lower** = **xMin**, the indicator is a single point.)

4. Set **upper** in the same way.

Setting an Interval from the Home Screen or a Program

To use an exact value for **lower** or **upper**, store a value to the variable from the Home screen before you press GRAPH. In a program, store a value to **lower** or **upper** to define the interval.

Using the MATH Operations

The GRAPH MATH operations provide a number of mathematical graph-analysis features to use directly on a graph. When you select any of these operations from the menu, the graph is displayed without menus, and the cursor is in TRACE. Restrictions are the same as for the CALC functions.

The ROOT Operation

ROOT uses the SOLVER (page 14–7) to find a root of a function.

Set values for **lower** and **upper**, if desired. Select 〈ROOT〉, use ▲ or ▼ to move the TRACE cursor to the desired function. Use ► or ◄ to move to a point between **lower** and **upper** to serve as an initial guess. Press [ENTER]. The result cursor is displayed at the solution point, the cursor coordinate value is the result, and **x** is stored in **Ans**.

The dy/dx Operation

dy/dx (derivative) finds the derivative (slope) of a function at a point. The accuracy is affected by the differentiation MODE (Chapter 1) and the variable δ (Chapter 3).

Select 〈dy/dx〉. Use ▲ or ▼ to move the TRACE cursor to the desired function. Use ► and ◄ to move to the desired point. Press [ENTER]. The result **dy/dx =** is displayed and stored in **Ans**.

The ∫f(x) Operation

∫f(x) (numerical integral) finds the numerical integral of a function between **lower** and **upper**. The accuracy is affected by the variable **tol** (Chapter 3).

Select 〈∫f(x)〉. Use ▲ or ▼ to move the TRACE cursor to the desired function. Use ► or ◄ to move to the desired value for **lower**. Press [ENTER]. Repeat for **upper** (must be on the display). The result ∫**f(x) =** is displayed and stored in **Ans**. A value indicative of possible solution error is stored in **fnIntErr**.

The YICPT Operation

YICPT (**y** intercept) calculates the value of **y** at **x** = 0 for a function.

Select 〈YICPT〉. Use ▲ or ▼ to move the TRACE cursor to the desired function. Press [ENTER]. The result cursor is displayed at the solution point, the cursor coordinate value is the result, and **y** is stored in **Ans**.

The FMIN and
FMAX Operations   FMIN (function minimum) and FMAX (function maximum) find the minimum or maximum value of a function. The accuracy is affected by the variable **tol** (Chapter 3).

Set values for **lower** and **upper**, if desired. Select ⟨FMIN⟩ or ⟨FMAX⟩, use ▲ or ▼ to move the TRACE cursor to the desired function. Press ENTER. The result cursor is displayed at the solution point, the cursor coordinate value is the result, and **x** is stored in **Ans**.

The ISECT
Operation   ISECT (intersection) uses the SOLVER (page 14–7) to find an intersection of two functions.

Set values for **lower** and **upper**, if desired. Select ⟨ISECT⟩. Use ▲ or ▼ to move the TRACE cursor to the desired first function. Press ENTER. The cursor automatically moves to the next function in the list. If necessary, use ▲ or ▼ to move to the desired function. Use ◄ or ► to move the cursor to a point near the intersection, between **lower** and **upper**, to serve as an initial guess. The result cursor is displayed at the solution point, the cursor coordinate value is the result, and **x** is stored in **Ans**.

The INFLC
Operation   INFLC (inflection) finds an inflection point for a function. The accuracy is affected by the differentiation MODE and by δ in **dxNDer** MODE.

Set values for **lower** and **upper**, if desired. Select ⟨INFLC⟩. Use ▲ or ▼ to move the TRACE cursor to the desired function. Press ENTER. Use ◄ or ► to move the cursor to a point near the intersection, between **lower** and **upper**, to serve as an initial guess. Press ENTER. The result cursor is displayed at the solution point, the cursor coordinate value is the result, and **x** is stored in **Ans**.

The DIST Operation

DIST (distance) finds the straight-line distance between two points on a function or functions.

Select ⟨DIST⟩. Use ▲ or ▼ to move the TRACE cursor to the desired function. Use ► or ◄ to move the TRACE cursor to the first point (on the display). Press ENTER. The point is marked. Use ▲ or ▼ (if necessary) and ► or ◄ to move to the second point (on the display). A line displays as you move the cursor, but disappears if you TRACE off the display. Press ENTER. The result **DIST=** is displayed and stored in **Ans**.

The ARC Operation

ARC finds the distance along a function between two points on the function. The accuracy is affected by the variables **tol** and sometimes δ (Chapter 3) and the differentiation MODE (Chapter 1).

Select ⟨ARC⟩. Use ▲ or ▼ to move the TRACE cursor to the desired function. Use ► or ◄ to move the TRACE cursor to the first point. Press ENTER. The point is marked. Use ► or ◄ to move to the second point (on the display). Press ENTER. The result **ARC=** is displayed and stored in **Ans**.

The TANLN Operation

TANLN (tangent line) draws a tangent line at a point on a function. The accuracy is affected by the differentiation MODE and the variable δ (Chapter 3).

Select ⟨TANLN⟩. Use ▲ or ▼ to move the TRACE cursor to the desired function. Use ► and ◄ to move to the desired point. Press ENTER. The tangent line is drawn, and the result **dy/dx =** is displayed and stored in **Ans**. (Select ⟨CLDRW⟩ from the DRAW menu to remove the line.)

Results

Coordinate value results are displayed for ROOT, YICPT, ISECT, FMAX, FMIN, and INFLC even if you have selected **CoordOff** on the FORMT screen. The coordinate values of the results cursor are stored in **x** and **y**.

When a cursor-movement key is pressed, the result cursor disappears and the free-moving cursor appears near the location of the result.

Using EVAL to Analyze a Graph

EVAL evaluates currently selected functions for a specified value of x. You can use EVAL directly on a graph. You also can use eval from the Home screen or a program.

Using EVAL on a Graph

1. Select ⟨EVAL⟩ from the GRAPH menu. The graph displays. The cursor is positioned after **Eval x =** on the prompt line.

2. Enter a real value for **x** between **xMin** and **xMax** (which can be an expression).

   If there is a value entered for **Eval x =** , CLEAR clears it. If there is no value for **x**, CLEAR cancels EVAL.

3. Press ENTER. The result cursor is on the first selected function in the list at the entered **x** and the coordinate values are displayed. (Coordinates are displayed even if you have selected **CoordOff** on the FORMT screen.) Use ▲ or ▼ to move the cursor between functions at the entered **x** value.

   When ► or ◄ is pressed, the free-moving cursor appears. It cannot necessarily move back to the EVAL **x** value.

Using the eval Function from the Home Screen or a Program

The **eval** (evaluate) function returns the value of any selected functions, evaluated at the specified **x** value. The only argument is the real **x** value at which to evaluate the functions (which can be an expression).

eval *xvalue*

The results are returned as a list. If any of the functions are defined as a family of curves, each value is given in the list.

For example, if **y1 = x^3** and **y2 = 1/x** and both are selected, then **eval 5** returns {**125 .2**}.

Note: **eval** cannot be used in a y(x) expression.

The DRAW Menu

The GRAPH DRAW menu accesses operations that draw
points, lines, circles, and shaded areas on a graph. You can
draw directly on a graph using the cursor to identify
coordinates or you can enter these instructions on the Home
screen or in the program editor.

The GRAPH DRAW Menu When you select ‹DRAW› from the GRAPH menu, the
menu keys are labeled with the first five items of the
menu. Press [MORE] to move around the menu.

Shade	LINE	VERT	CIRCL	DrawF
PEN	PTON	PTOFF	PTCHG	CLDRW
TanLn	Drlnv			

Item	Accesses
Shade	Instruction that shades part of the graph (Home screen or program only) (page 4–32).
LINE	Operation that draws a straight line (page 4–34).
VERT	Operation that draws a vertical line (page 4–35).
CIRCL	Operation that draws a circle (page 4–36).
DrawF	Instruction that draws a function (Home screen or program only) (page 4–37).
PEN	Operation that accesses a free-form drawing tool (interactive only) (page 4–38).
PTON	Operation that turns on a point (page 4–39).
PTOFF	Operation that turns off a point (page 4–39).
PTCHG	Operation that toggles a point on and off (page 4–39).
CLDRW	Operation that clears drawings (page 4–31).
TanLn	Instruction that draws a tangent line (Home screen or program only) (page 4–35).
Drlnv	Instruction that draws the inverse of a function (Home screen or program only) (page 4–37).

The DRAW operations, except **Drlnv**, can draw on **Func**,
Polar, **Param**, and **DifEq** graphs. The coordinates for
DRAW instructions are always the **x**-coordinate and
y-coordinate values of the display.

Drawing on a Graph

The DRAW operations let you draw points, lines, circles, and shading on the current graph. These drawings are temporary.

The DRAW Operations

Access the DRAW operations through:

- The GRAPH menu to draw on a graph interactively.

- The CATALOG to enter DRAW instructions on the Home screen or in the program editor.

- The GRAPH menu in the program editor.

All points, lines, and shading drawn on a graph with DRAW operations are temporary. When the "Smart Graph" feature (page 4–5) plots a graph, all drawn points, lines, and shading are erased. A family of curves (page 4–15) cannot be drawn with **Shade**, **DrawF**, **DrInv**, or **TanLn**.

Before Drawing on a Graph

Because the DRAW operations draw on top of the graph of the currently selected functions, the following steps may be appropriate before drawing on a graph.

1. Change the MODE settings (page 4–3).

2. Change the graph FORMT (pages 4–6 and 4–7).

3. Enter or edit expressions to define functions in the y(x) list (pages 4–8 through 4–10).

4. Select or unselect functions in the y(x) list (page 4–11).

5. Edit RANGE variables (pages 4–12 and 4–13).

Clearing a Drawing from a Graph

To clear drawings from the currently displayed graph, select ⟨CLDRW⟩ from the GRAPH DRAW menu. The current graph is plotted and displayed with no drawn elements.

Clearing a Drawing from the Home Screen or a Program

The **ClDrw** (clear drawing) instruction clears drawings from the current graph. It displays the message **Done**. The next time you display the graph, all drawn points, lines, circles, and shaded areas will be gone. **ClDrw** has no arguments.

Note: You can store drawings with **StPic** (page 4–41).

Shading Areas on a Graph

The Shade instruction shades the area on a graph that is below one specified function and above another. It also draws the two functions.

The Shading Parameters

The **Shade** instruction can have four arguments. Only the areas where the first argument is less than the second argument are shaded. The first two arguments are required. The final two arguments are optional.

The first argument defines the bottom boundary of the shaded area and the function to be drawn. The argument can be any of the following:

- An expression in terms of **x**. For example, $x^2 + 1$ shades the area above the curve $y = x^2 + 1$.

- A real value (which can be an expression). For example, **3** shades the area above the line $y = 3$.

- An expression stored in an equation variable or a function in the y(x) list and referenced by name. For example, if $y2 = x^2 + 5$, **y2** shades the area above the curve $y = x^2 + 5$.

The second argument defines the top boundary of the shaded area and the function to be drawn. The argument can be any of the types described for the first argument.

The third argument (optional) defines the left boundary of the shaded area (the beginning **x**). It is a real value (which can be an expression). If the argument is not specified, the default is the current value of **lower** (or **xMin** if the MODE is not **Func**).

The fourth argument (optional) defines the right boundary of the shaded area (the ending **x**). It is a real value (which can be an expression). If the argument is not specified, the default is the current value of **upper** (or **xMax** if the MODE is not **Func**).

**Drawing a
Shaded Area
on a Graph**

To shade an area on a graph, enter the instruction on a
blank line on the Home screen or in the program editor.

1. Select ⟨DRAW⟩ from the GRAPH menu.

2. Select ⟨Shade⟩ from the GRAPH DRAW menu. **Shade(** is
   copied to the cursor location. (If you select ⟨Shade⟩
   while the graph is displayed, the Home screen is
   displayed.)

3. Enter the first argument. Press ⎡,⎤.

4. Enter the second argument.

   - If you do not want to enter the third or fourth
     arguments, go to step 6.

   - If you want to enter the third and fourth
     arguments, press ⎡,⎤, and then go to step 5.

5. Enter the optional arguments, separated by commas.

6. Press ⎡)⎤ and ⎡ENTER⎤.

When the instruction is executed, the shaded area and
the two functions, as defined by the arguments, are
drawn on the current graph:

Shade(*lowerfunc,upperfunc,xbeg,xend***)**

For example, **Shade(x+1,x^3 – 8x,-5,5)** displays:

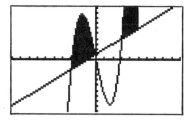

Drawing Lines

While a graph is displayed, the LINE operation lets you define a line on the graph using the cursor. You also can enter an instruction on the Home screen or in the program editor to draw a line on a graph.

Drawing a Line from a Graph

1. Select ⟨LINE⟩ from the GRAPH DRAW menu. The current graph is displayed.

2. Position the cursor at the beginning point of the line you want to draw. Press ENTER.

3. Move the cursor to the end point of the line you want to draw. The line is displayed as you move the cursor. Press ENTER. The line is drawn on the graph between the two selected points.

Repeat steps 2 and 3 to continue to draw lines. To cancel LINE and display the menus, press EXIT.

Drawing a Line from the Home Screen or a Program

The **Line** instruction on the Home screen or in the program editor has four real value arguments (which can be expressions): the **x** value and **y** value of the beginning coordinate and the **x** value and **y** value of the ending coordinate.

Line(*xbeg,ybeg,xend,yend*)

When the instruction is executed, the line is drawn on the current graph.

For example, **Line(1,1,6,8)** displays:

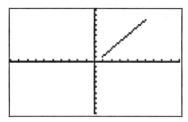

Drawing Vertical Lines and Tangent Lines

While a graph is displayed, the VERT operation lets you define a vertical line on the graph using the cursor. You also can enter the instruction on the Home screen or in the program editor. Using the TanLn instruction, you can draw the tangent line of a function at a specified point.

Drawing a Vertical Line from a Graph

1. Select ⟨VERT⟩ from the GRAPH DRAW menu. The current graph is displayed.

2. Position the cursor where you want to draw the vertical line. A line is displayed as you move the cursor. Press ENTER. The line is drawn.

Repeat step 2 to continue to draw vertical lines. To cancel VERT and display the menus, press EXIT.

Drawing a Vertical Line from the Home Screen or a Program

The **Vert** (vertical line) instruction on the Home screen or in the program editor requires one argument, the real **x** value at which to draw the vertical line (which can be an expression).

Vert x

Drawing a Tangent Line

TanLn (tangent line) draws a line tangent to a function at a specified point. When you select ⟨TanLn⟩ from the GRAPH DRAW menu, the instruction is copied to the Home screen. The **TanLn** instruction requires two arguments: an expression in terms of **x** and the real **x** value at which to draw the tangent line (which can be an expression). The expression is interpreted as being in **Func** MODE.

TanLn(*expression,value***)**

For example, if **y1 = .2x^3 − 2x + 6** is the only selected function, **TanLn(y1,3)** plots **y1** and draws the tangent line:

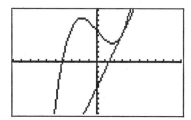

Note: You can draw a tangent line interactively through the GRAPH MATH menu (page 4–28).

Drawing Circles

While a graph is displayed, the CIRCL operation lets you define a circle on the graph using the cursor. You also can enter an instruction on the Home screen or in the program editor to draw a circle on a graph.

Drawing a Circle from a Graph

1. Select ⟨CIRCL⟩ from the GRAPH DRAW menu. The current graph is displayed.

2. Position the cursor at the center of the circle you want to draw. Press [ENTER].

3. Move the cursor to a point on the circumference. Press [ENTER]. The circle is drawn on the graph.

Because this circle is drawn on the display and is independent of the RANGE values (unlike the **Circl** instruction, see below), it appears as a circle.

Repeat steps 2 and 3 to continue to draw circles. To cancel CIRCL and display the menus, press [EXIT].

Drawing a Circle from the Home Screen or a Program

The **Circl** instruction on the Home screen or in the program editor requires three real arguments (which can be expressions): the **x**-coordinate and **y**-coordinate values of the center, and the radius of the circle.

Circl($x,y,radius$**)**

When the instruction is executed, the circle is drawn on the current graph.

Note: When the **Circl** instruction is used from the Home screen, the drawn circle may not look like a circle because it is drawn with respect to the current RANGE values. For example, in the standard viewing rectangle, **Circl(0,0,5)** displays:

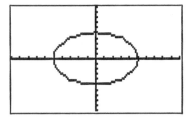

To make the drawn circle look like a circle, execute **ZSqr** first.

Drawing Functions and Inverses

The DrawF instruction draws a function on the current graph from the Home screen or in the program editor. The DrInv instruction draws an inverse of a function on the current graph from the Home screen or a program.

Drawing a Function

DrawF (draw function) draws a function on the current graph. When you select ‹DrawF› from the GRAPH DRAW menu, the instruction is copied to the Home screen. The **DrawF** instruction requires one argument, an expression in terms of **x**:

DrawF *expression*

For example, if **y1 = .2x^3 – 2x + 6** is the only selected function, **DrawF   y1 – 5** plots **y1** and draws the function:

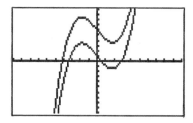

Drawing an Inverse of a Function

DrInv (draw inverse) draws the inverse of a function on the current graph. When you select ‹DrInv› from the GRAPH DRAW menu, the instruction is copied to the Home screen. You must be in **Func** MODE. The **DrInv** instruction requires one argument, an expression in terms of **x**:

DrInv *expression*

For example, if **y1 = .2x^3 – 2x + 6** is the only selected function, **DrInv   y1** plots **y1** and draws its inverse:

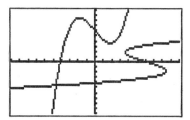

Using PEN to Draw on a Graph

While a graph is displayed, the PEN feature lets you draw directly on the graph with the cursor.

Using the PEN Feature

PEN can only draw directly on a graph. It is not an instruction.

1. Select <PEN> from the GRAPH DRAW menu. The current graph is displayed.

2. Position the cursor where you want to begin drawing. Press [ENTER] to turn the pen on.

3. As you move the cursor, it draws on the graph, turning on each point that the cursor crosses.

4. Press [ENTER] to turn the pen off. Move the cursor to a new position where you want to begin drawing again.

Repeat steps 2, 3, and 4 to continue to draw on the graph with the pen. To cancel PEN and display the menus, press [EXIT].

Drawing Points

While a graph is displayed, the PT (point) operations let you turn on, turn off, or reverse a point on the graph using the cursor. You also can enter an instruction on the Home screen or in the program editor to execute these instructions.

Drawing a Point from a Graph

1. Select ⟨PTON⟩ from the GRAPH DRAW menu. The current graph is displayed.

2. Position the cursor at the location on the display where you want to draw the point. Press [ENTER]. The point is drawn.

Repeat step 2 to continue to draw points. To cancel PTON and display the menus, press [EXIT].

Drawing a Point from the Home Screen or a Program

The **PtOn** (point on) instruction on the Home screen or in the program editor requires two real arguments (which can be expressions): the **x** value of the coordinate and the **y** value of the coordinate.

PtOn(x,y**)**

When the instruction is executed, the point is drawn on the current graph.

The PTOFF and PTCHG Instructions

The procedure for using PTOFF (point off) to turn off (erase) a point is the same as for PTON.

The procedure for using PTCHG (point change) to toggle (reverse) a point on and off is the same as for PTON.

Storing and Recalling Graph Databases

A graph database is the elements that define a particular graph. The graph can be recreated from these elements. You can store these elements with a user-assigned name and recall it as the current graph at a later time. Graph databases do not include any drawn items.

Graph Databases The elements of a graph database are:

- Graphing MODE, graph FORMT settings, and RANGE variables.

- All functions in the y(x) list, and whether they are selected.

Storing a Graph Database
1. Select ⟨STGDB⟩ (store graph database) from the GRAPH menu.

2. The cursor is positioned after **Name=** on the prompt line. The menu keys are labeled with the names of existing databases for the current graphing MODE in alphabetical order. You may type a name or select one from the menu.

3. Press [ENTER]. The elements of the current database are stored.

Recalling a Graph Database
Caution: When you recall a graph database, all existing y(x) functions are replaced. You may want to store the current y(x) functions to another database before recalling a stored database.

1. Select ⟨RCGDB⟩ (recall graph database) from the GRAPH menu.

2. Enter the name as above.

3. Press [ENTER]. The new database replaces the current graph database.

- If you recall a graph database while a graph is displayed, the graphing mode of the recalled database must match the current graphing mode. The new graph is plotted.

- If you recall a graph database from the Home screen or a program (page 4–43), the TI–85 changes graphing MODE automatically, if necessary. The new graph is not plotted.

Deleting a Graph Database Graph databases are deleted from memory through the memory management menu (Chapter 18.)

Storing and Recalling Graph Pictures

You can store an image of the current display with a user-assigned name and superimpose that image onto a displayed graph at a later time from the Home screen or a program.

Storing a Graph Picture

A picture includes drawn elements, plotted functions, axes, and tick marks. The picture does not include menus, axis labels, **lower** and **upper** indicators, prompts, or cursor coordinates. Any parts of the display "hidden" by these are stored with the picture.

1. Select ⟨STPIC⟩ from the GRAPH menu. The current graph is displayed if necessary.

2. The cursor is positioned after **Name =** on the prompt line, and the menu keys are labeled with the names of existing pictures in alphabetical order. You may type a name or select one from the menu.

3. Press [ENTER]. The most recently displayed picture is stored.

Recalling a Graph Picture

1. Select ⟨RCPIC⟩ from the GRAPH menu. The current graph is displayed if necessary.

2. The cursor is positioned after **Name =** on the prompt line. Enter the name as above.

3. Press [ENTER]. The picture is superimposed on the current graph.

Note: Pictures are drawings. You cannot TRACE any curve on a picture.

Deleting a Graph Picture

Graph pictures are deleted from memory through the memory management menu (Chapter 18.)

GRAPH Menu Items in the Program Editor

You can access the graphing capabilities of the TI–85 in the program editor (Chapter 16). To enter graphing instructions, type the name, copy it from CATALOG, or select it from the GRAPH menu in the program editor.

The GRAPH Menu in the Program Editor

When you press GRAPH in the program editor, the menu keys are labeled with the PRGM GRAPH menu.

VARS	RANGE	ZOOM	Trace	DispG
MATH	DRAW	FORMT	StGDB	RcGDB
eval	StPic	RcPic		

The VARS Menu

When you select ⟨VARS⟩, the menu keys are labeled with the names of the graphing variables and some instructions.

y	x	xt	yt	t
r	θ	Q	Q′	t
FnOn	FnOff	Axes	QI	

The RANGE Menu

When you select ⟨RANGE⟩, the menu keys are labeled with the names of all the RANGE variables:

xMin	xMax	xScl	yMin	yMax
yScl	tMin	tMax	tStep	θMin
θMax	θStep	tPlot	difTol	

The ZOOM Instructions

When you select ⟨ZOOM⟩, the menu keys are labeled:

ZInt	ZIn	ZOut	ZStd	ZPrev
ZFit	ZSqr	ZTrig	ZDecm	ZRcl

When a ZOOM instruction is executed, the current graph is displayed. **ZInt**, **ZIn**, **ZOut** and **ZSqr** use the midpoint of the current graph as the new midpoint. If **Pause** (Chapter 16) is the next program command, the program halts so you can examine the display. Execution resumes when you press ENTER.

The Trace Instruction

When you select ⟨Trace⟩, **Trace** is copied to the cursor location.

When the **Trace** instruction is executed, the current graph is displayed with cursor coordinate values, the TRACE cursor is on the midpoint of the first selected function, and the special program input busy signal is displayed. Use the cursor movement keys to move the cursor. Press ENTER to resume program execution.

The DispG Instruction	**DispG** displays a graph of currently selected functions during program execution. The graph has no cursor and no menu. In the program editor, press [GRAPH] and then select ⟨DispG⟩. **DispG** is copied to the cursor location. You can use the **Pause** instruction (Chapter 16) to halt the program so you can examine the display. Execution resumes when you press [ENTER].
The MATH Menu	When you select ⟨MATH⟩, the menu keys are labeled with the CALC functions that correspond to the interactive GRAPH MATH operation.

fMin	fMax	arc	fnInt

The DRAW Instructions	When you select ⟨DRAW⟩ the menu keys are labeled:

Shade	Line	Vert	Circl	DrawF
PtOn	PtOff	PtChg	ClDrw	TanLn
DrInv				

The DRAW instructions are described on pages 4–30 through 4–39.

FORMT Settings	You can set graph FORMT settings in a program through a TI–85 interactive selection screen (Chapter 16).
The eval Function	When you select ⟨eval⟩, **eval** is copied to the cursor location. The **eval** function is described on page 4–29.
Graph Databases and Pictures	When you select a store or recall instruction, the name of the instruction is copied to the cursor location. Type the name of the database or picture or copy it from the VARS GDB or VARS PIC screen.

StGDB *databasename*	and	**RcGDB** *databasename*
StPic *picturename*	and	**RcPic** *picturename*

GRAPH Menu Chart

You can access all graphing
operations by pressing $\boxed{\text{GRAPH}}$

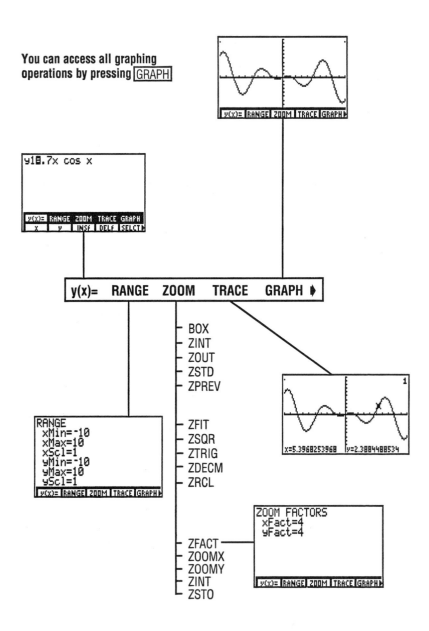

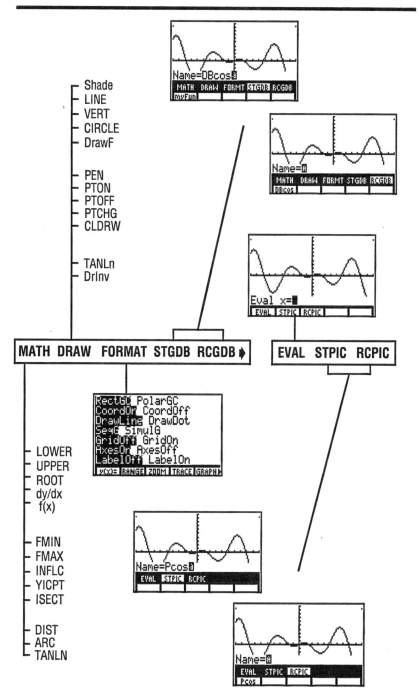

- Shade
- LINE
- VERT
- CIRCLE
- DrawF

- PEN
- PTON
- PTOFF
- PTCHG
- CLDRW

- TANLn
- DrInv

Name=DBcos█

| MATH | DRAW | FORMT | STGDB | RCGDB |
| myFun | | | | |

Name=█

| MATH | DRAW | FORMT | STGDB | RCGDB |
| DBcos | | | | |

Eval x=█

| EVAL | STPIC | RCPIC | | |

MATH DRAW FORMAT STGDB RCGDB ▶   **EVAL STPIC RCPIC**

RectGC PolarGC
CoordOn CoordOff
DrawLine DrawDot
SeqG SimulG
GridOff GridOn
AxesOn AxesOff
LabelOff LabelOn

| Y(X)= | RANGE | ZOOM | TRACE | GRAPH▶ |

- LOWER
- UPPER
- ROOT
- dy/dx
- f(x)

- FMIN
- FMAX
- INFLC
- YICPT
- ISECT

- DIST
- ARC
- TANLN

Name=Pcos█

| EVAL | STPIC | RCPIC | | |

Name=█

| EVAL | STPIC | RCPIC | | |
| Pcos | | | | |

Example: Using Lists in Graphing

The TI–85 uses lists to graph a family of curves. The function is evaluated and plotted once for each element of the list. Plot the functions $2x - \{0,2,4\}$ and $\{1,2,3\} \sin (2x - \{0,2,4\})$.

Procedure

1. Press $\boxed{\text{GRAPH}}$, select ⟨y(x)=⟩ and enter the functions:

   y1 = 2x – {0,2,4}
   y2 = {1,2,3} sin y1

   Note: { and } are on the LIST menu.

2. Place the cursor anywhere on **y1** and select ⟨SELCT⟩ to turn off the function so it will not graph.

3. Select ⟨RANGE⟩ from the GRAPH menu and set the RANGE variables:

xMin = -10	**yMin = -3**
xMax = 10	**yMax = 3**
xScl = 1	**yScl = 1**

4. Select ⟨GRAPH⟩ to graph the functions:

   $f_1(x) = \sin 2x$
   $f_2(x) = 2 \sin (2x - 2)$
   $f_3(x) = 3 \sin (2x - 4)$

5. Press $\boxed{\text{CLEAR}}$ to clear the menu from the display.

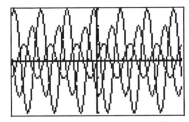

Chapter 5: Polar Graphing

This chapter describes how to graph polar equations on the TI-85. Polar graphs are completely independent of function, parametric, or differential equation graphs. Before doing polar graphing, you should be familiar with the graphing features in Chapter 4, Function Graphing.

Defining and Displaying a Polar Graph

Polar equations are defined in terms of the independent variable θ. Up to 99 polar equations can be defined and graphed at one time, limited by available memory.

Steps in Defining a Polar Graph	The steps for defining a polar graph are the same as those for defining a function graph. Differences are noted below. Graph formats, equations, and RANGE variables in **Pol** graphing are independent of the other graphing modes.
Setting the Graphing MODE	To graph polar equations, you must select **Pol** on the MODE screen.
The Pol GRAPH Menu	The **Pol** GRAPH menu is:

r(θ)=	**RANGE**	**ZOOM**	**TRACE**	**GRAPH**
MATH	**DRAW**	**FORMT**	**STGDB**	**RCGDB**
EVAL	**STPIC**	**RCPIC**		

Setting the Graph Format	Select ⟨FORMT⟩ to display the FORMT screen. In **Pol** graphing, you may select **RectGC** or **PolarGC** graph coordinate display; **PolarGC** shows the cursor coordinates in terms of the variables that define the equations, **r** and θ. **DrawLine** usually presents a more meaningful **Pol** graph.
Displaying Polar Equations	Select ⟨r(θ)=⟩ from the GRAPH menu to display the r(θ) editor, where you display and enter polar equations. You can enter up to 99 equations. If no equations are defined, **r1 =** is displayed.

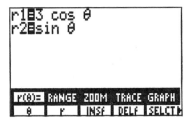

Defining a Polar Equation	Enter or edit the polar equation(s).
	• The independent variable in each equation must be θ. You may select $\langle\theta\rangle$ from the menu.
	• You can reference another equation; for example, **r2 = r1 + 1**. You may select $\langle r \rangle$ from the menu, and then type the number of the equation.
Selecting a Polar Equation	Only the polar equations you select are graphed. The procedure for selecting equations in **Pol** graphing is the same as in **Func** graphing.
Defining the Viewing Rectangle	Select $\langle$RANGE$\rangle$ to display and change the RANGE variables. The values shown below are the standard defaults in **Radian** MODE.

Setting	Meaning
θMin=0	Smallest θ value to evaluate
θMax=6.28318530718	Largest θ value to evaluate (2π)
θStep=.13089969389957	Increment between θ values ($\pi/24$)
xMin=-10	Smallest **x** value to display
xMax=10	Largest **x** value to display
xScl=1	Spacing between **x** tick marks
yMin=-10	Smallest **y** value to display
yMax=10	Largest **y** value to display
yScl=1	Spacing between **y** tick marks

Displaying the Graph	Select $\langle$GRAPH$\rangle$, $\langle$TRACE$\rangle$, $\langle$EVAL$\rangle$, $\langle$STGDB$\rangle$, or a ZOOM, MATH, DRAW, or PIC operation to plot the selected polar equations. The TI–85 evaluates **r** for each value of θ (from θ**Min** to θ**Max** in intervals of θ**Step**) and then plots each point. As the graph is plotted, the variables θ, **r**, **x**, and **y** are updated.
Graph Databases and Pictures	Storing or recalling a graph database or graph picture in **Pol** graphing works as it does in **Func** graphing.

Exploring and Analyzing a Polar Graph

As in Function graphing, several tools are available for exploring a Polar graph: using the free-moving cursor, tracing an equation, zooming, and drawing.

The Free-Moving Cursor

The free-moving cursor works in **Pol** graphing just as it does in **Func** graphing. The variables **x** and **y** are updated (**r** and θ also are updated in **PolarGC** FORMT). If FORMT is **CoordOn**:

• In **PolarGC** FORMT, the cursor coordinate values for **r** and θ are displayed.

• In **RectGC** FORMT, the cursor coordinate values for **x** and **y** are displayed.

The TRACE Feature

The TRACE feature lets you move the cursor along polar equations. When you begin a trace, the TRACE cursor is on the first selected equation at θ**Min**. Use ▶ or ◀ to move the cursor along an equation, increasing θ by θ**Step** with each keystroke. Use ▲ or ▼ to move between equations. The variables **r**, θ, **x**, and **y** are updated. If FORMT is **CoordOn**:

• In **PolarGC** FORMT, the cursor coordinate values for **r** and θ are displayed.

• In **RectGC** FORMT, the cursor coordinate values for **x**, **y**, and θ are displayed.

If you have graphed a family of curves, ▼ or ▲ moves through each curve before moving to the next r(θ) function.

If the cursor moves off the display, the coordinate values at the bottom of the display continue to change appropriately.

In **Pol** graphing, automatic panning does not occur if the cursor moves off the display to the left or right.

The QuickZoom feature is available in **Pol** graphing. If you TRACE an equation and then press [ENTER], the viewing rectangle is adjusted so that the cursor location becomes the center of the new viewing rectangle, even if you have traced off the display.

The ZOOM Features

The ZOOM features work in **Pol** graphing as they do in **Func** graphing, except ZFIT, which adjusts the viewing rectangle in both the **x** and the **y** directions. The **Pol** GRAPH ZOOM menu is:

BOX	ZIN	ZOUT	ZSTD	ZPREV
ZFIT	ZSQR	ZTRIG	ZDECM	ZRCL
ZFACT	ZOOMX	ZOOMY	ZINT	ZSTO

Only the **x** and **y** RANGE variables are affected. The θ RANGE variables (θ**Min**, θ**Max**, and θ**Step**) are not affected, except by ZSTD and ZRCL.

Drawing on a Polar Graph

The DRAW instructions work in **Pol** graphing as they do in **Func** graphing. The **Pol** GRAPH DRAW menu is:

Shade	LINE	VERT	CIRCL	DrawF
PEN	PTON	PTOFF	PTCHG	CLDRW
TanLn				

Note: The coordinates for DRAW instructions in **Pol** graphing are the **x**-coordinate and **y**-coordinate values of the display, just as they are in **Func** graphing.

Evaluating Equations for a Given θ

The EVAL operation evaluates currently selected polar equations for a given value of θ directly on a graph.

The **eval** function in a program or from the Home screen, returns a list of **r** values.

The MATH Features

The MATH operations work in **Pol** graphing as they do in **Func** graphing. The **Pol** GRAPH MATH menu is:

DIST	dy/dx	dr/dθ	ARC	TANLN

The distances calculated by DIST and ARC are distances in the rectangular coordinate plane. dy/dx and dr/dθ are independent of the **RectGC** or **PolarGC** FORMT.

TANLN at a point where the derivative is undefined will draw the line, but no result is displayed or stored in **Ans**.

Example: Graphing a Limaçon

The polar equation r=a+b cos θ graphs a limaçon. Graph the
equation for a=3 and b= -5 and find the length of the arc that
defines the limaçon.

Procedure

1. Press [2nd] [MODE]. Select **Pol** MODE. Choose the
   defaults for the other modes.

2. Press [GRAPH] [MORE] and select ⟨FORMT⟩. Select
   PolarGC to show cursor coordinates **r** and θ.

3. Select ⟨r(θ)=⟩. Enter the polar equation:

   r1 = 3 – 5 cos θ

4. Select ⟨ZOOM⟩ from the GRAPH menu. Select ⟨ZSTD⟩
   from the GRAPH ZOOM menu to graph the equation in
   the standard default viewing rectangle.

5. Select ⟨TRACE⟩ and trace the equation.

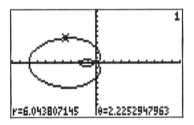

6. To calculate the arc length from θ=0 to θ=2π. Press
   [GRAPH] [MORE] ⟨MATH⟩ ⟨ARC⟩. The cursor is on the
   function at **r** = -2 and θ=0.

7. Press [ENTER] to mark the beginning of the arc at θ=0.

8. Press and hold [▶] until you have traced the curve
   back to the beginning, θ=2π (6.2831853072). Press
   [ENTER] to mark the end of the arc.

   The busy indicator displays while the arc length is
   calculated. The result, ARC=34.313687101, is displayed
   at the bottom of the screen.

Chapter 6: Parametric Graphing

This chapter describes how to graph parametric equations on the TI-85. Parametric graphs are completely independent of function, polar, or differential equation graphs. Before doing parametric graphing, you should be familiar with the graphing features in Chapter 4, Function Graphing.

Defining and Displaying a Parametric Graph

Parametric equations have an x component and a y component, each expressed in terms of the independent variable t. They often are used to graph equations over time. Up to 99 pairs of parametric equations can be defined and graphed at one time, limited by available memory.

Steps in Defining a Parametric Graph

The steps for defining a parametric graph are the same as those for defining a function graph. Differences are noted below. Graph formats, equations, and RANGE variables in **Param** graphing are independent of the other graphing modes.

Setting the Graphing Mode

To graph parametric equations, you must select **Param** on the MODE screen.

The Param GRAPH Menu

The **Param** GRAPH menu is:

E(t) =	RANGE	ZOOM	TRACE	GRAPH
MATH	DRAW	FORMT	STGDB	RCGDB
EVAL	STPIC	RCPIC		

Setting the Graph Format

Select ⟨FORMT⟩ to display the FORMT screen. **DrawLine** usually presents a more meaningful **Param** graph.

Displaying the Components of Parametric Equations

Select ⟨E(t)=⟩ from the GRAPH menu to display the E(t) editor, where you display and enter parametric equations. You can enter up to 99 pairs of equations, each defined in terms of t. If no equations are defined, **xt1 =** and **yt1 =** are displayed.

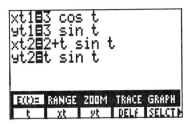

Press [MORE] to access ⟨INSf⟩, ⟨ALL+⟩ and ⟨ALL−⟩.

Deleting Parametric Equations

To delete a parametric equation, place the cursor on either component and select ⟨DELf⟩. Both components are deleted. To delete a parametric equation from the MEM DELET menu, delete the **xt** component.

Graph Databases and Pictures

Storing or recalling a graph database or graph picture in **Param** graphing works as it does in **Func** graphing.

Defining Components of Parametric Equations	Enter or edit both the **x** and **y** components in a pair to define a parametric equation.
	• The independent variable in each component must be **t**. You may select ⟨t⟩ from the menu.
	• You can reference a component of a parametric equation in the expression; for example, **xt2 = 3 xt1**. You may select ⟨xt⟩ or ⟨yt⟩ from the menu and then type the number of the equation.
Selecting Parametric Equations	Only the parametric equations you select are graphed. To select a parametric equation, you may place the cursor on either the **x** or **y** component and select ⟨SELCT⟩; both components are selected.
Defining the Viewing Rectangle	Select ⟨RANGE⟩ to display and change the RANGE variables. The values shown below are the standard defaults in **Radian** MODE.

Setting	Meaning
tMin=0	Smallest **t** value to evaluate
tMax=6.28318530718	Largest **t** value to evaluate (2π)
tStep=.13089969389957	Increment between **t** values (π/24)
xMin=-10	Smallest **x** value to display
xMax=10	Largest **x** value to display
xScl=1	Spacing between **x** tick marks
yMin=-10	Smallest **y** value to display
yMax=10	Largest **y** value to display
yScl=1	Spacing between **y** tick marks

Displaying the Graph	Select ⟨GRAPH⟩, ⟨TRACE⟩, ⟨EVAL⟩, ⟨STGDB⟩, or a ZOOM, DRAW, MATH, or PIC operation to plot the selected parametric equations. The TI–85 evaluates both the **x** and the **y** component for each value of **t** (from **tMin** to **tMax** in intervals of **tStep**) and then plots each point. As the graph is plotted, the variables **x**, **y**, and **t** are updated.

Exploring and Analyzing a Parametric Graph

As in Function graphing, several tools are available for exploring a Parametric graph: using the free-moving cursor, tracing an equation, zooming, and drawing.

The Free-Moving Cursor

The free-moving cursor works in **Param** graphing just as it does in **Func** graphing. The variables **x** and **y** are updated (**r** and θ also are updated in **PolarGC** FORMT). If FORMT is **CoordOn**:

- In **PolarGC** FORMT, the cursor coordinate values for **r** and θ are displayed.

- In **RectGC** FORMT, the cursor coordinate values for **x** and **y** are displayed.

The TRACE Feature

The TRACE feature lets you move the cursor along parametric equations. When you begin a trace, the TRACE cursor is on the first selected equation at **tMin**. Use ▶ or ◀ to move the cursor along an equation, one **tStep** at a time. Use ▲ or ▼ to move between equations. The variables **x**, **y**, and **t** are updated (**r** and θ also are updated in **Polar GC** FORMAT). If FORMT is **CoordOn**:

- In **PolarGC** FORMT, the cursor coordinate values for **r**, θ, and **t** are displayed.

- In **RectGC** FORMT, the cursor coordinate values for **x**, **y**, and **t** are displayed.

If you have graphed a family of curves, ▼ or ▲ moves through each curve before moving to the next E(t) function.

If the cursor moves off the display, the coordinate values at the bottom of the display continue to change appropriately.

In **Param** graphing, automatic panning does not occur if the cursor moves off the display to the left or right.

The QuickZoom feature is available in **Param** graphing. If you TRACE an equation and then press ENTER, the viewing rectangle is adjusted so that the cursor location becomes the center of the new viewing rectangle, even if you have traced off the display.

The ZOOM Features	The ZOOM features work in **Param** graphing as they do in **Func** graphing, except ZFIT, which adjusts the viewing rectangle in both the **x** and the **y** directions. The **Param** GRAPH ZOOM menu is:

BOX	ZIN	ZOUT	ZSTD	ZPREV
ZFIT	ZSQR	ZTRIG	ZDECM	ZRCL
ZFACT	ZOOMX	ZOOMY	ZINT	ZSTO

Only the **x** (**xMin**, **xMax**, and **xScl**) and **y** (**yMin**, **yMax**, and **yScl**) RANGE variables are affected. The **t** RANGE variables (**tMin**, **tMax**, and **tStep**) are not affected, except for ⟨ZSTD⟩ and ⟨ZRCL⟩.

Drawing on a Parametric Graph	The DRAW instructions work in **Param** graphing as they do in **Func** graphing. The coordinates for DRAW instructions are the **x**-coordinate and **y**-coordinate values of the display. The **Param** GRAPH DRAW menu is:

Shade	LINE	VERT	CIRCL	DrawF
PEN	PTON	PTOFF	PTCHG	CLDRW
TanLn				

Evaluating Equations for a Given t

EVAL evaluates currently selected parametric equations for a given value of **t**. It is used directly on the graph.

In a program or from the Home screen, the **eval** function returns a list of **x** and **y** values in the form {**xt1**(**t**) **yt1**(**t**) **xt2**(**t**) **yt2**(**t**) ...}.

The MATH Features

The MATH operations work in **Param** graphing as they do in **Func** graphing. The **Param** GRAPH MATH menu is:

DIST	dy/dx	dy/dt	dx/dt	ARC
TANLN				

The distances calculated by DIST and ARC are distances in the rectangular coordinate plane.

TANLN at a point where the derivative is undefined will draw the line, but no result is displayed and no result is stored in **Ans**.

Example: Simulating Motion

Graph the parametric equation that describes the position over time of a ball that has been kicked.

Problem

Graph the position of a ball kicked at an angle of 52° with an initial velocity of 40 feet per second. (Ignore air resistance.) What is the maximum height and when is it reached? How far away and when does the ball strike the ground?

If v_0 is the initial velocity and θ is the angle, then the horizontal component of the position of the ball as a function of time is described by

$$x(t) = t \, v_0 \cos \theta$$

The vertical component of the position of the ball as a function of time is described by

$$y(t) = -16 \, t^2 + t \, v_0 \sin \theta$$

Procedure

1. Press [2nd] [MODE]. Select **Param** and **Degree** MODE.

2. Press [GRAPH]. Select ⟨FORMT⟩. Select **DrawLine** and **RectGC**.

3. Select ⟨E(t)=⟩ from the GRAPH menu. Enter the expressions to define the parametric equation in terms of **t**.

   xt1 = 40t cos 52
   yt1 = 40t sin 52 – 16t²

3. Select ⟨RANGE⟩. Set the RANGE variables.

tMin = 0	**xMin = -5**	**yMin = -5**
tMax = 2.5	**xMax = 50**	**yMax = 20**
tStep = .02	**xScl = 5**	**yScl = 5**

4. Select ⟨TRACE⟩ to graph the position of the ball as a function of time and to explore the graph. The values for **x**, **y**, and **t** are displayed at the bottom of the screen. These values change as you trace the graph.

   Move the cursor along the path of the ball to investigate these values.

Chapter 7: Differential Equation Graphing

This chapter describes how to solve numerically and graph
differential equations on the TI-85. DifEq graphs are
completely independent of function, polar, or parametric
graphs. Before doing DifEq graphing, you should be familiar
with the graphing features in Chapter 4, Function Graphing.

Defining a DifEq Graph

DifEq graphing can graph a system of up to nine first-order differential equations.

Steps in Defining a Graph

The steps for defining a differential equation graph are similar to those for defining a function graph, but also include setting initial conditions and selecting the axes. To graph any differential equation above first order, transform it to an equivalent system of first-order differential equations. Each equation in the system requires an initial condition.

Setting the Graphing Mode

To graph a differential equation, you must select **DifEq** on the MODE screen.

The DifEq GRAPH Menu

The **DifEq** GRAPH menu is:

Q'(t)=	RANGE	INITC	AXES	GRAPH
FORMT	DRAW	ZOOM	TRACE	EVAL
STGDB	RCGDB	STPIC	RCPIC	

Setting the Graph Format

Select ⟨FORMT⟩ to display and change the FORMT options: coordinate, axes, grid, and label display.

Displaying the Equations

Select ⟨Q'(t)=⟩ from the GRAPH menu to display the Q'(t) editor, where you display and enter differential equations. You can enter up to 9 equations. The independent variable in **DifEq** is **t**. If no equations are defined, **Q'1 =** is displayed.

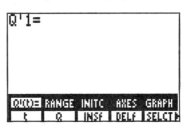

Defining a Differential Equation

Enter or edit the differential equation as a system of first-order equations.

- In **DifEq** graphing, the equations must be defined from **Q'1** through **Q'***n*.

- You may select ⟨t⟩, the independent variable, from the menu.

- You can reference another differential equation variable in the expression; for example, **Q'2 = Q1**. You may select ⟨Q⟩ from the menu and then type the number of the variable.

- Lists are not valid in the equations in **DifEq** MODE.

Selecting Equations

Select equations in **DifEq** graphing as in **Func** graphing. All equations are used in the calculation, but only the selected equations appropriate for the selected axes are graphed.

Setting the Initial Conditions

You must set a real initial value (at **t = tMin**) for each first-order equation entered on the Q'(t) editor. Select ⟨INITC⟩ from the GRAPH menu. The INITIAL CONDITIONS editor is displayed. Any previously defined initial conditions are shown. A square dot to the left of an initial condition value indicates that an equation exists in the Q'(t) list, and an initial condition is required for it.

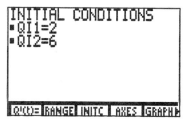

Graph Databases and Pictures

Storing or recalling a graph database or graph picture in **DifEq** graphing works as it does in **Func** graphing. Initial conditions and axes selection are part of a **DifEq** database.

Differential Equation Graphing   **7–3**

Displaying and Selecting the Axes

You can specify the **x** and **y** axes (as **t**, **Q**, **Q'**, **Q**$_n$, or **Q'**$_n$) of the graph in order to see the planes of the solution. Note that, if the axes are **t** and **Q**n (or **Q'**n), only the **Q**n (or **Q'**n) solution is plotted, regardless of which equations are selected. Select ⟨AXES⟩ from the GRAPH menu to display the AXES editor.

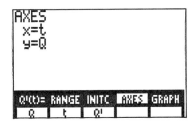

Defining the Viewing Rectangle

Select ⟨RANGE⟩ to display and change the RANGE variables. The values shown below are the standard defaults in **Radian** MODE. **x** and **y** settings correspond to the variables selected as the axes.

Setting	Meaning
tMin=0	Smallest **t** value to solve
tMax=6.28318530718	Largest **t** value to solve (2π)
tStep=.13089969389957	TRACE increment between **t** values ($\pi/24$)
tPlot=0	Point at which plotting usually begins
xMin=-10	Smallest **x** value to display
xMax=10	Largest **x** value to display
xScl=1	Spacing between **x** tick marks
yMin=-10	Smallest **y** value to display
yMax=10	Largest **y** value to display
yScl=1	Spacing between **y** tick marks
difTol=.001	Tolerance to help select the step size for solving. **difTol** must be ≥ 1E-12.

Displaying and Exploring a DifEq Graph

As in Func graphing, several tools are available for exploring a DifEq graph: using the free-moving cursor, tracing an equation, zooming, and drawing.

Displaying a Graph

Select ⟨GRAPH⟩, ⟨TRACE⟩, ⟨EVAL⟩, ⟨STGDB⟩, or a ZOOM, DRAW, or PIC operation to plot the selected differential equations. The TI–85 solves each equation from **tMin** to **tMax**. If **t** is not an axis, it plots each point beginning at **tPlot**, otherwise it begins at **tMin**. As a graph is plotted, the variables **x**, **y**, **t**, and **Q1**n are updated.

tStep affects the TRACE resolution and appearance of the graph, but not the accuracy of the TRACE values. **tStep** does not determine the step size for solving; the algorithm (Runge-Kutta 2–3) determines the step size. If the **x** axis is **t**, setting **tStep**<(**xMax** − **xMin**)/126 increases plotting time without increasing accuracy.

The Free-Moving Cursor

The free-moving cursor works in **DifEq** graphing as it does in **Func** graphing. The cursor coordinate values for **x** and **y** are displayed and the variables are updated.

The TRACE Feature

The TRACE feature lets you press ▶ to move the cursor along the equation one **tStep** at a time. When you begin a TRACE, the TRACE cursor is on the first selected equation at or near **tPlot** (or **tMin** if **t** is an axis) and the coordinate values of **x**, **y**, and **t** are displayed at the bottom of the screen. ◀ returns the cursor to the beginning point on the same equation.

As you trace an equation, the values of **x**, **y**, and **t** are updated and displayed. **x** and **y** are calculated from **t**.

If the cursor moves off the screen, the coordinate values of **x**, **y**, and **t** displayed at the bottom of the screen continue to change appropriately.

Automatic panning does not occur in **DifEq** graphing if the cursor moves off the screen to the left or right.

The QuickZoom feature is available in **DifEq** graphing. If you TRACE an equation and then press ENTER, the viewing rectangle is adjusted so that the cursor location becomes the center of the new viewing rectangle, even if you had traced off the screen.

Exploring and Analyzing a DifEq Graph (Continued)

The ZOOM Features

The ZOOM features work in **DifEq** graphing as they do in **Func** graphing, except ZFIT, which adjusts the viewing rectangle in both the **x** and **y** directions. The **DifEq** GRAPH ZOOM menu is:

BOX	**ZIN**	**ZOUT**	**ZSTD**	**ZPREV**
ZFIT	**ZSQR**	**ZTRIG**	**ZDECM**	**ZRCL**
ZFACT	**ZOOMX**	**ZOOMY**	**ZINT**	**ZSTO**

Only the **x** (**xMin**, **xMax**, and **xScl**) and **y** (**yMin**, **yMax**, and **yScl**) RANGE variables are affected. The **t** RANGE variables (**tMin**, **tMax**, and **tPlot**) are not affected, except for ZSTD and ZRCL. You may want to change the **t** RANGE variables to ensure that sufficient points are plotted. ZSTD sets **difTol = .001** and **t** and **Q** as axes.

Drawing on a DifEq Graph

The DRAW instructions work in **DifEq** graphing as they do in **Func** graphing. The coordinates for DRAW instructions are the **x**-coordinate and **y**-coordinate values of the display. The **DifEq** GRAPH DRAW menu is:

Shade	**LINE**	**VERT**	**CIRCL**	**DrawF**
PEN	**PTON**	**PTOFF**	**PTCHG**	**CLDRW**
TanLn				

The MATH Features

The MATH features are not available in **DifEq** graphing.

Evaluating Equations for a Given t

EVAL evaluates currently selected differential equations for a given value of **t**, **tMin** ≤ **t** ≤ **tMax**. It can be used directly on the graph. In a program or from the Home screen, **eval** returns a list of **Q** values.

Example: Transforming a Differential Equation

To use differential equations on the TI-85, you must transform the differential equation into a system of first-order differential equations. In general, an nth order differential equation can be transformed to an equivalent system of n first-order differential equations.

Problem

Convert $y^{(4)} - y = e^{-x}$ to an equivalent system of four first-order differential equations.

Procedure

Define the variables:

$$\mathbf{Q1} = y$$
$$\mathbf{Q2} = y'$$
$$\mathbf{Q3} = y''$$
$$\cdots \quad \cdots$$
$$\mathbf{Q9} = y^{(8)}$$

Therefore, by differentiation

$$\mathbf{Q'1} = y'$$
$$\mathbf{Q'2} = y''$$
$$\mathbf{Q'3} = y'''$$
$$\cdots \quad \cdots$$
$$\mathbf{Q'9} = y^{(9)}$$

You can use the variable definitions above to convert the differential equation to a system of first-order equations (no derivatives on the right-hand side of the system).

1. From the second chart, $\mathbf{Q1} = y'$ and from the first chart, $y' = \mathbf{Q2}$. Therefore, by substitution, $\mathbf{Q1} = \mathbf{Q2}$.

2. Similarly, $\mathbf{Q'2} = y'' = \mathbf{Q3}$ and $\mathbf{Q'3} = y''' = \mathbf{Q4}$.

3. From the original differential equation, $\mathbf{Q'4} = y^{(4)} = e^{-x} + y = e^{-t} + \mathbf{Q1}$. (In differential equations on the TI-85, **t** is the independent variable.)

4. Press [2nd] [MODE] and select **DifEq**.

5. Press [GRAPH] ⟨Q′(t)=⟩. Enter the equations.

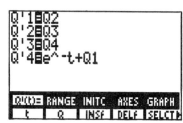

(Continued)

Example: Solving a Differential Equation

Consider the differential equation $y^{(4)} - y = e^{-x}$ entered on the previous page. Solve the initial value problem by setting the RANGE variables, entering initial conditions: $y(0) = 3$, $y'(0) = -5.25$, $y''(0) = 7.5$, $y'''(0) = -5.75$, and graphing the differential equation.

Procedure

1. Use ⟨SELCT⟩ to turn off **Q'2**, **Q'3**, and **Q'4**.

2. Select ⟨RANGE⟩. Set the RANGE variables to:

tMin=0	**xMin=0**	**yMin=-4**
tMax=10	**xMax=10**	**yMax=4**
tStep=.01	**xScl=1**	**yScl=1**
tPlot=0		**difTol=.001**

3. Select ⟨INITC⟩. Enter the initial conditions.

   QI1=3
   QI2=-5.25
   QI3=7.5
   QI4=-5.75

4. Select ⟨AXES⟩. Set the axes to **x=t** and **y=Q**.

5. Select ⟨TRACE⟩ to graph and to explore graphically the solution to the differential equation.

6. From analytic methods, we know that the solution to this differential equation is $y = (5 - (1/4)x)e^{-x} - 2\cos x$. Select **DrawF** from the GRAPH DRAW menu. On the Home screen execute:

   DrawF $(5 - (1/4)x)e^{\wedge}-x - 2\cos \; x$

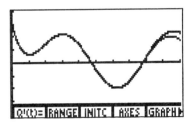

7. Note that the graphic solution is not good for **t**>8. Change **difTol** to .00001 and repeat step 6.

Example: Linear Harmonic Oscillator

Plot the solution to the linear harmonic oscillator second-order diffential equation: $y'' + y = 0$ with initial conditions $y(0) = 0$ and $y'(0) = 5.0$.

Procedure

Transform this second-order differential equation to the equivalent system of first-order equations:

Let **Q1 = y** and let **Q2 = y'**. By substitution, **Q'1 = Q2** and **Q'2 = -Q1**.

1. Press [2nd] [MODE]. Select **DifEq** mode. Choose the defaults for the other modes.

2. Press [GRAPH] and select ⟨Q'(t)=⟩. Enter the expressions to define the equation in terms of **t**.

   Q'1 = Q2
   Q'2 = -Q1

3. Use ⟨SELCT⟩ to unselect **Q'2**.

4. Use ⟨DELf⟩ to delete **Q'3** and **Q'4**.

5. Select ⟨RANGE⟩. Set the values to:

tMin = 0	xMin = -10	yMin = -10
tMax = 2π	xMax = 10	yMax = 10
tStep = π/24	xScl = 2	yScl = 5
tPlot = 0		difTol = .001

6. Select ⟨INITC⟩. Enter the initial conditions.

   QI1 = 0
   QI2 = 5

   Note: All four initial conditions from the earlier problem remain if you have not deleted them through MEM DELET. The square dots next to **QI1** and **QI2** indicate that they are the initial conditions required.

7. Select ⟨AXES⟩. Set the axes to **x = t** and **y = Q**.

(Continued)

Example: Linear Harmonic Oscillator (Continued)

**Procedure
(Continued)**

8. Select ⟨TRACE⟩ to graph the solution and begin tracing. The TRACE values are the numerical solutions to the differential equation.

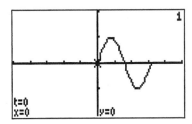

9. Select ⟨DrawF⟩ from the GRAPH DRAW menu. Use it to overlay the function **5 sin x** and visually compare it to the solution of the differential equation.

   DrawF 5 sin x

10. Select ⟨AXES⟩ from the GRAPH menu. Define **x = Q1** and **y = Q2**.

11. Select ⟨ZSQR⟩ from the GRAPH ZOOM menu. This is the phase plane of the solution.

12. Select ⟨RANGE⟩ from the GRAPH menu. Set **tPlot = π** to begin the plot at π.

13. Select ⟨GRAPH⟩. Notice that it plots only half of the equation in the phase plane.

Chapter 8: Constants and Conversions

This chapter describes how to use built-in constants, user-defined constants, and built-in conversions on the TI-85.

The CONS (Constants) Menu

The CONS menu accesses built-in and user-defined constants for use in expressions. You also can create and edit user-defined constants through the CONS menu.

The CONS Menu   When you press [2nd] [CONS], the menu keys are labeled with the constants menu.

BLTIN   EDIT   USER

Item	Accesses
BLTIN	Menu of names of the built-in constants.

Na	**k**	**Cc**	**ec**	**Rc**
Gc	**g**	**Me**	**Mp**	**Mn**
μ0	**ε0**	**h**	**c**	**u**

EDIT	The constant editor, where you create or edit user-defined constants (page 8–4).
USER	Menu of user-defined constants (page 8–3).

π and e π (pi) and **e** (natural log) are stored as constants in the TI–85. π, 3.1415926535898, is accessible from the keyboard. **e**, 2.718281828459, is accessible from the keyboard as lowercase **e**.

Built-In Constants   The TI–85 has 15 built-in constants that you can select from the CONS BLTIN (built-in) menu or type from the keyboard and CHAR GREEK menu.

Na	Avagadro's number	$6.0221367\text{E}23$ mole^{-1}
k	Boltzman's constant	$1.380658\text{E}-23$ J/K
Cc	Coulomb constant	$8.9875517873682\text{E}9$ N m^2/C^2
ec	Electron charge	$1.60217733\text{E}-19$ C
Rc	Gas constant	8.31451 J/mole K
Gc	Gravitational constant	$6.67259\text{E}-11$ N m^2/kg^2
g	Earth acceleration due to gravity	9.80665 m/sec^2
Me	Mass of an electron	$9.1093897\text{E}-31$ kg
Mp	Mass of an proton	$1.6726231\text{E}-27$ kg
Mn	Mass of an neutron	$1.6749286\text{E}-27$ kg
μ0	Permeability of a vacuum	$1.2566370614359\text{E}-6$ N/A^2
ε0	Permittivity of a vacuum	$8.8541878176204\text{E}-12$ F/m
h	Planck's constant	$6.6260755\text{E}-34$ J sec
c	Speed of light	$299{,}792{,}458$ m/sec
u	Atomic mass unit	$1.6605402\text{E}-27$ g

Using Constants

The values for built-in constants cannot be changed, and the values for user-defined constants can be changed only in the CONSTANT editor. Otherwise, constants are used like variables in expressions.

Entering and Editing Constants

User-defined constants can be entered and edited only in the constant editor (see page 8–4). [STO▶] and [2nd] [=] are not used to store values to constants. Built-in constants cannot be edited.

Using a Constant in an Expression

To use a constant in an expression, you may:

• Type the name of the built-in or user-defined constant (case-sensitive).

• Select the name of a user-defined constant from the VARS CONS screen.

• Select the name from the CONS USER menu or the CONS BLTIN menu.

Example

Calculate the time in seconds for light to travel from the sun to Mercury, a distance of 57,924,000 km.

57924000 [×] **1000** [÷]
[2nd] [CONS] ⟨BLTIN⟩
[MORE] [MORE] ⟨c⟩   57924000∗1000/c
[ENTER]   193.213666503

Creating and Editing User-Defined Constants

On the TI–85 you can create real or complex user-defined constants. Use the CONSTANT editor to create a new user-defined constant, change the value of an existing user-defined constant, or delete a user-defined constant.

Defining a New User-Defined Constant

1. Press [2nd] [CONS] to display the CONS menu.

2. Select ‹EDIT› to display the constant editor. The menu keys are labeled with the names of the existing user-defined constants in alphabetical order.

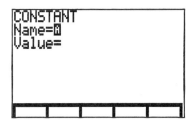

3. Type the name of the new constant. It must follow the rules for naming variables (Chapter 2). The keyboard is set in ALPHA-lock. You cannot move to the value until you have entered a name.

4. Press [ENTER]. The value is blank, and the menu keys are labeled:

    PREV   NEXT   DELET

5. Enter the real or complex value of the new constant (which can be an expression). The new constant is created and the value stored.

Note: If you press a key that displays a menu, the constant editor menu moves to the seventh line (if it is not already there), and the selected menu is displayed on the eighth line.

Displaying an Existing User-Defined Constant

1. Select ⟨EDIT⟩ from the CONS menu. The menu keys are labeled with the names of the existing user-defined constants in alphabetical order.

2. Enter the name of the constant to change in one of two ways.

   • Select the name from the menu.

   • Type the name, up to eight characters (case-sensitive). The keyboard is set in ALPHA-lock.

3. Press ENTER. The value of the constant is displayed, and the menu keys are labeled:

   PREV   NEXT   DELET

   • To display the previous constant (alphabetically) and value, select ⟨PREV⟩.

   • To display the next constant (alphabetically) and value, select ⟨NEXT⟩.

Editing an Existing User-Defined Constant

1. Display the constant as described above.

2. Enter the new real or complex value (which can be an expression).

Deleting a User-Defined Constant

You can delete a user-defined constant in one of two ways:

   • Through the MEM DELET menu (Chapter 18).

   • Through the constant editor. Select ⟨DELET⟩ when the constant is displayed as described above. The constant is deleted immediately, and the next constant (alphabetically) is displayed.

The CONV (Conversions) Menu

The TI-85 has built-in conversion functions for the most commonly used conversions. The conversion functions, which are accessed from the CONV menu, convert between any two defined units within the same conversion type. Press [MORE] to move around the menu.

The CONV Menu   When you press [2nd] [CONV], the menu keys are labeled with the conversion types. When you select a type, the menu keys are labeled with the units for that type.

LNGTH	AREA	VOL	TIME	TEMP
MASS	FORCE	PRESS	ENRGY	POWER
SPEED				

Item	Accesses
LNGTH	Menu of units of length.

mm	cm	m	in	ft
yd	km	mile	nmile	lt-yr
mil	Ang	fermi	rod	fath

(**nmile**=nautical mile, **lt-yr**=light year, **Ang**=Angstrom, **fath**=fathom)

Item	Accesses
AREA	Menu of units of area.

ft^2	m^2	mi^2	km^2	acre
in^2	cm^2	yd^2	ha	

(**ha**=hectare)

Item	Accesses
VOL	Menu of units of volume.

liter	gal	qt	pt	oz
cm^3	in^3	ft^3	m^3	cup
tsp	tbsp	ml	galUK	ozUK

Item	Accesses
TIME	Menu of units of time.

sec	mn	hr	day	yr
week	ms	μs	ns	

(**ms**=millisecond, μ**s**=microsecond, **ns**=nanosecond)

Item	Accesses
TEMP	Menu of units of temperature.

°C	°F	°K	°R

The CONV	Item	Accesses
Menu (Continued)	**MASS**	Menu of units of mass.

gm	kg	lb	amu	slug
ton	mton			

(**ton** = 2000 lb, **mton** = metric ton, **amu** = atomic mass unit)

FORCE	Menu of units of force.

N	dyne	tonf	kgf	lbf

(**tonf** = ton force, **kgf** = kg force, **lbf** = pound force)

PRESS	Menu of units of pressure.

atm	bar	N/m^2	lb/in^2	mmHg
mmH^2	inHg	inH_2O		

ENRGY	Menu of units of energy.

J	cal	Btu	ft-lb	kw-hr
eV	erg	l-atm		

(**ft-lb** = foot-pound, **eV** = electron Volt)

POWER	Menu of units of power.

hp	W	ftlb/s	cal/s	Btu/m

(**W** = watts, **ftlb/s** = foot-pound per second, **Btu/m** = Btu per minute)

SPEED	Menu of units of speed.

ft/s	m/s	mi/hr	km/hr	knot

Note: ⟨mmH_2⟩ is copied to the cursor location as **mmH_2O**.
⟨Btu/m⟩ is copied as **Btu/mn**.

Values of conversion factors generally use internationally defined values.

Using Conversions

The functions to convert between units on the TI-85 must be accessed from the CONV menu. Units are grouped by conversion types. You can convert between any pair of units within a conversion type.

Using a Conversion Function in an Expression

You cannot type the name of a conversion function in an expression or obtain it from the catalog. To enter the name of a conversion function in an expression, you must "build" the name of the function through the CONV menu. The name consists of three parts: the "from" unit, the conversion symbol, and the "to" unit. Both units must be from the same conversion type. You cannot, for example, convert **ft** to **gal**.

1. Enter the real value to be converted (which can be an expression).

2. Press [2nd] [CONV] to display the conversion menu. The menu keys are labeled with the types.

3. Select the type of conversion. The menu keys are labeled with the units within that conversion type in alphabetical order.

4. Select the "from" unit. The name of the "from" unit and the conversion symbol ▶ are copied to the cursor location.

5. Select the "to" unit. The name of the "to" unit is copied to the cursor location.

   value from_unit▶to_unit

For example, **2 in▶mm** returns **50.8**.

Notes about Conversions

Once a conversion function has been entered, you can edit the alphabetic characters in it, but the special characters °, ^{2}, ^{3}, $_2$, -, /, and ▶ are accessible only through the CONV menu.

To convert values expressed as rates, you must use parentheses. For example, to convert 12 miles in 7 hours to meters per second, enter **(12/7) mi/hr▶m/s** or **12 mile▶m/7 hr▶sec**, which returns **.766354285714**.

Conversions are higher than negation in the EOS hierarchy (page 1–8). For functions such as temperature conversion, when the value to be converted is negative, use parentheses. For example, **(-1)°C▶°F** returns **30.2**.

Chapter 9: Strings and Characters

This chapter describes strings and how to manipulate them. It also describes the miscellaneous characters, Greek letters, and accented international letters available through menus for use in display text and variable names.

Chapter Contents

Entering and Using Strings

On the TI-85, you can enter and use strings. Strings are used primarily in programming to display and enter characters. Strings are entered, stored, and displayed directly on a command line.

Strings

A string is a sequence of characters that is enclosed between quotation (") marks. Strings are not evaluated. To evaluate a string, it must first be converted to an equation using the **St▶Eq** instruction (page 9-5).

Strings on the TI-85 have two primary applications.

- They define text for display in a program.

- They accept input from the keyboard in a program.

Entering a String

1. Press [2nd] [STRNG] to display the STRNG menu.

"	sub	lngth	Eq▶St	St▶Eq

2. Select ⟨ " ⟩ to indicate the beginning of the string.

3. Enter the characters in the string. Press [ALPHA] or [2nd] [alpha], as appropriate.

4. Select ⟨ " ⟩ from the STRNG menu to indicate the end of the string. This is not necessary at the end of a command or preceding the [STO▶] key.

The completed expression is:

"string"

For example, **"Hello"**.

String Variables On the TI–85, strings can be stored to and represented by variables.

Storing a String To store a string, press [STO▶] following the string and then enter the name of the variable to which to store the string. The completed instruction is:

"characters"▸stringname

For example, **"Hello"▸GREETING**.

Displaying a String Variable To display the contents of a string variable, enter the name of the string on a blank line on the Home screen and press [ENTER].

The STRNG (String) Menu

The STRNG menu displays additional functions and
instructions to manipulate strings. When you select from the
STRNG menu, the character or the name of the function or
instruction is copied to the cursor location.

The STRNG Menu   When you press [2nd] [STRNG], the menu keys are labeled
with the string menu.

"	sub	lngth	Eq►St	St►Eq

The " character is used to enter strings (page 9–3).

Finding a Subset   **sub** (subset) returns a string created from a subset of a
of a String   string. **sub** has three arguments: a string or the name of a
string variable, the beginning position (1, 2, 3, etc.) of the
subset, and the number of characters (including blanks)
in the subset. When the expression is evaluated, the
subset of the string is returned as a string.

sub(*string,begin,length*)

For example, if **STRING** contains **"The answer is 33"**, then
sub(STRING,15,2) returns **33**.

Finding the   **lngth** (length) returns the number of characters of a
Length of a   string. The string can be a variable containing a string, or
String   you can enter the string directly. When the expression is
evaluated, the number of characters (including blanks)
in the string is returned. The quotation marks are not
included in the length.

lngth *"string"* or **lngth** *stringname*

For example, if **STRING** contains **"The answer is 33"**, then
lngth STRING returns **16**.

Concatenating   To concatenate strings, use the **+** function.
Strings
For example, **"St" + "ring"** returns **String**.

Converting an Equation to a String

Eq►St (equation to string) is used primarily in programming to convert an equation to a string. It has two arguments: the name of the variable containing the equation and the name of the variable to which to store the string. When the instruction is executed, the equation in the equation variable is stored as a string in the string variable.

Eq►St (*equationname,stringname*)

The **Disp** programming instruction displays the string in the string variable.

Converting a String to an Equation

St►Eq (string to equation) is used primarily in programming to convert a string entered using the **InpSt** programming instruction into an equation to use in an expression. It has two arguments: the name of the variable containing the string and the name of the variable to which to store the equation. When the instruction is executed, the string in the string variable is converted to an equation and stored in the equation variable.

St►Eq(*stringname,equationname*)

Program Example

In a program, the following commands allow the user to enter a function to graph during execution.

:InpSt "Enter y1: ",STR:St►Eq(STR,y1)

The CHAR (Character) Menu

The CHAR menu accesses additional characters to use in variable names and display text.

The CHAR Menu When you press [2nd] [CHAR], the menu keys are labeled with the CHAR (character) menu.

MISC   GREEK   INTL

Item	Accesses
MISC	Menu of miscellaneous characters (page 9–7).

?	#	&	%	′
!	@	$	~	|
¿	Ñ	ñ	Ç	ç

Item	Accesses
GREEK	Menu of Greek characters (page 9–7).

α	β	γ	Δ	δ
ε	θ	λ	μ	ϱ
Σ	σ	τ	φ	Ω

Item	Accesses
INTL	Menu of accent marks to create international characters (page 9–8).

′	`	^	¨

Note that the space character is the ALPHA function of the negation key.

Accessing Miscellaneous and Greek Characters

The CHAR MISC and CHAR GREEK menus display miscellaneous characters and the most commonly used Greek characters for use in variable names, strings, and display text. When you select an item from the MISC or GREEK menu, the character is copied to the cursor location.

Using Miscellaneous Characters

To use a miscellaneous character in a name or text:

1. Press [2nd] [CHAR] to display the CHAR menu.

2. Select ⟨MISC⟩. The menu keys are labeled with the first five items of the miscellaneous character menu. Press [MORE] to move around the menu.

?	#	&	%	'
!	@	$	~	|
¿	Ñ	ñ	Ç	ç

3. Select the character, which is copied to the cursor location. You can continue to select characters from this menu.

Note: Ñ, ñ, Ç, and ç, are the only miscellaneous characters that are valid in a variable name. !, %, and ' are functions.

Using Greek Characters

To use a Greek character in a name, expression, or text:

1. Press [2nd] [CHAR] to display the CHAR menu.

2. Select ⟨GREEK⟩. The menu keys are labeled with the first five items of the Greek letter menu. Press [MORE] to move around the menu.

α	β	γ	Δ	δ
ε	θ	λ	μ	ϱ
Σ	σ	τ	ϕ	Ω

3. Select the character, which is copied to the cursor location. You can continue to select characters from this menu.

Note: π is on the keyboard. On the TI–85, π is not a character and is not valid in variable names. Aπ is implied multiplication.

Accessing International Characters

The CHAR INTL menu item accesses accent marks that can be combined with uppercase or lowercase vowels to create international characters for use in variable names and display text.

Using International Characters in an Expression

To use an international character in a name, expression, or text:

1. Press 2nd [CHAR] to display the CHAR menu.

2. Select ‹INTL›. The menu keys are labeled with the accent marks.

    ´   ˋ   ˆ   ¨

3. Use the menu keys to select an accent mark.

4. The keyboard is automatically set in ALPHA-lock (or alpha-lock if you manually set it for alpha or alpha-lock). To change to alpha-lock, press 2nd [alpha].

    Press the key for the vowel.

    The character that is copied to the cursor location includes the accent mark; for example, **á**, **Ä**, or **è**. The keyboard remains in ALPHA-lock or alpha-lock.

Chapter 10: Number Bases

This chapter describes functions, instructions, and designators to enter and use numbers in binary, hexadecimal, octal, or decimal number bases on the TI-85.

Chapter Contents

Using Number Bases

You can enter and display numbers on the TI–85 in binary, hexadecimal, octal, or decimal number base.

Number Bases

The MODE number-base setting (Chapter 1) controls how an entered number is interpreted and how results are displayed on the Home screen. However, you can enter numbers in any number base using number-base designators, and you can display the result on the Home screen in any number base using number base conversions.

All numbers are stored internally as decimal. If you perform an operation in a MODE setting other than **Dec**, the TI–85 performs integer math, truncating after every calculation and expression. For example, in **Hex** MODE **1/3 + 7** returns **7h** (1 divided by 3, truncated to 0, and then added to 7).

Number Base Ranges

Binary, octal, and hexadecimal numbers on the TI–85 are defined in the following ranges:

Type	High Value Low Value	Decimal Equivalent
Binary	0111 1111 1111 1111b 1000 0000 0000 0000b	32,767 -32,767
Octal	2657 1420 3643 7777o 5120 6357 4134 0001o	99,999,999,999,999 -99,999,999,999,999
Hexadecimal	0000 5AF3 107A 3FFFh FFFF A50C EF85 C001h	99,999,999,999,999 -99,999,999,999,999

One's and Two's Complements

To obtain the one's complement of a binary number, enter the **not** function (page 10–7) before the number. For example, **not 111100001111** in **Bin** MODE returns **1111000011110000b**.

To obtain the two's complement of a binary number, press (-) before entering the number. For example, **-111100001111** in **Bin** MODE returns **1111000011110001b**.

The BASE (Number Base) Menu

The BASE menu accesses characters, designators, functions, and instructions to use with numbers in binary, hexadecimal, and octal number bases, in addition to decimal number base.

The BASE Menu   When you press [2nd] [BASE], the menu keys are labeled with the number base menu.

A – F	TYPE	CONV	BOOL	BIT

Item	Accesses
A – F	Hexadecimal characters (page 10–5).

A				
B	C	D	E	F

TYPE	Number base designators (page 10–4).

b	h	o	d

CONV	Display conversion instructions (page 10–6).

►Bin	►Hex	►Oct	►Dec

BOOL	Boolean operators (page 10–7).

and	or	xor	not

BIT	Bit-manipulation functions (page 10–8).

rotR	rotL	shftR	shftL

Designating Number Bases

The BASE TYPE menu accesses the number base designators. You can enter a number in any number base using the number base designators: b (binary), h (hexadecimal), o (octal), or d (decimal). They must be entered from the BASE TYPE menu and cannot be typed from the keyboard.

Designating the Base of a Number

In an expression, you can enter a number in any number base, regardless of MODE. Enter the number, followed by the base designator.

1. Enter the number.

2. Press 2nd [BASE] to display the number base menu.

3. Select ‹TYPE›. The menu keys are labeled with the number base designators.

b   h   o   d

4. Select the type of number base.

   The designator is copied to the cursor location.

5. Continue entering the expression.

Example of Number Base Entry

Set **Dec** (default) MODE	10b+10	
		12
	10h+10	
		26
Set **Bin** MODE	10h+10	
		10010b
	10d+10	
		1100b
Set **Oct** MODE	10b+10	
		12o
	10d+10	
		22o
Set **Hex** MODE	10b+10	
		12h
	10d+10	
		1Ah

Accessing Hex Digits

The BASE A–F menu accesses the hexadecimal digits **A** through **F**, which are special characters on the TI–85. They must be entered from the BASE A–F menu and cannot be typed from the keyboard. The hexadecimal digits 0 through 9 can be typed from the keyboard.

Entering Hexadecimal Digits

To enter a hexadecimal number, type the digits 0 through 9 from the keyboard, just as you would for a decimal number. If one of the digits **A** through **F** is required:

1. Press [2nd] [BASE] to display the number base menu.

2. Select **<A–F>**. The menu keys are labeled with the hexadecimal characters. Notice that they are slightly different from the letters **A** through **F**.

   • If you are on the Home screen, the menu keys are labeled:

A				
B	C	D	E	F

   To enter **A**, press [2nd] [M1].

   • If you are in an editor, the menu keys are labeled:

A–B	C	D	E	F

   To enter **A** or **B**, press [F1] and the menu keys are labeled:

A	B	C	D	E–F

3. Press the menu key associated with the character. The hexadecimal character is copied to the cursor location.

4. Continue entering the number. You may continue to select characters from this menu.

Note: If the MODE is not **Hex**, you must enter the **h** designator, even if the number contains a special hexadecimal character.

Displaying Results in Another Number Base

The BASE CONV menu accesses display conversion instructions. They are valid only at the end of a command and control how results are displayed, regardless of MODE setting. The expression is interpreted based on the MODE base setting. In all but ►Dec, the result is truncated to an integer.

The BASE CONV Menu

When you select ⟨CONV⟩ from the BASE menu, the menu keys are labeled with the base conversion menu.

►**Bin**   ►**Hex**   ►**Oct**   ►**Dec**

The ►Bin Instruction

►**Bin** (display as binary) displays a real result in binary number base, including the **b** suffix. (Results outside the binary range are displayed according to the base MODE.)

result►**Bin**

The ►Hex Instruction

►**Hex** (display as hexadecimal) displays a real result in hexadecimal number base, including the **h** suffix.

result►**Hex**

The ►Oct Instruction

►**Oct** (display as octal) displays a real result in octal number base, including the **o** suffix.

result►**Oct**

The ►Dec Instruction

►**Dec** (display as decimal) displays a real result in decimal number base, including the **d** suffix in **Bin, Hex,** or **Oct** MODE.

result►**Dec**

Example of Number Base Display

In **Dec** MODE, solve $10b + Fh + 10o + 10$, then increment by one and display in other number bases.

Set **Dec** MODE	10b+Fh+10o+10	35
Binary display	Ans+1►Bin	100100b
Hex display	Ans+1►Hex	25h
Octal display	Ans+1►Oct	46o
Decimal display (current MODE)	Ans+1	39

Using Boolean Operators

The BASE BOOL menu accesses Boolean operators, which are functions that compare two arguments bit by bit.

The BASE BOOL Menu

When you select ⟨BOOL⟩ from the BASE menu, the menu keys are labeled with the Boolean operators.

and   **or**   **xor**   **not**

The Boolean Operators and, or, and xor

The operators **and**, **or**, and **xor** (exclusive or) require two real arguments (which can be expressions).

value **and** *value*

The Boolean Operator not

The operator **not** requires one real argument (which can be an expression).

not *value*

Results

When the expression is evaluated, the arguments are converted to hexadecimal integers and the corresponding bits of the arguments are compared. The results are returned according to this table:

First Argument	Second Argument	Result			
		and	or	xor	not (arg1)
1	1	1	1	0	0
1	0	0	1	1	0
0	1	0	1	1	1
0	0	0	0	0	1

The result is displayed according to the current MODE setting. For example:

- In **Bin** MODE, **101 and 110** returns **100b**.

- In **Hex** MODE, **5 and 6** returns **4h**.

Manipulating Number Base Digits

The BASE BIT menu accesses functions that manipulate bits in number base digits. These functions are valid in Bin, Oct, and Hex MODE.

The BASE BIT Menu

When you select ⟨BIT⟩ from the BASE menu, the menu keys are labeled with the bit manipulation functions.

rotR **rotL** **shftR** **shftL**

Note: Both the argument and the result must be within defined number ranges (page 10–2). Rotate and shift operate on 16 base digits. It is possible, especially if the argument is not entered in binary, to overflow on these calculations.

The Rotate Functions

rotR (rotate to the right) and **rotL** (rotate to the left) take one real argument (which can be an expression).

When the expression is evaluated, the argument is truncated to an integer, converted to the current base MODE, and the bits rotated.

rotR *value* or **rotL** *value*

For example, in **Bin** MODE, **rotL 0000111100001111** returns **1111000011110b**.

In **Hex** MODE, **rotR A6** (1010 0110) returns **53h** (0101 0011).

The Shift Functions

shftR (shift to the right) and **shftL** (shift to the left) take one real argument (which can be an expression).

When the expression is evaluated, the argument is truncated to an integer, converted to the current base MODE, and the bits shifted.

shftL *value* or **shftR** *value*

For example, in **Bin** MODE, **shftR 0000111100001111** returns **11110000111b**.

In **Oct** MODE, **shftL 5** (101) returns **12o** (001 010).

Chapter 11: Complex Numbers

This chapter describes how to enter and use complex
numbers, describing additional functions and instructions to
use with complex numbers on the TI-85.

Entering and Using Complex Numbers

Complex numbers begin and end with parentheses, and have two elements separated by either a comma (rectangular format) or an angle symbol (polar format).

Complex Numbers

A complex number has two components. On the TI-85, the complex number $a + bi$ is entered as (a,b). In this guidebook, this is expressed as $(real,imag)$ in rectangular format or $(magnitude \angle angle)$ in polar format.

Lists, matrices, and vectors can have complex elements.

Entering Complex Numbers

Complex numbers are stored in rectangular format, but you can enter a complex number in rectangular or polar format, regardless of the format specified by the MODE setting. The separators, which are entered from the keyboard, determine the format. The components can be real numbers or expressions that evaluate to real numbers; the expression is evaluated when the command is executed.

Complex Number Variables

On the TI-85, complex numbers can be stored to and represented by variables.

Complex Results

Complex numbers in results, including list, matrix, and vector elements, are displayed in the format (rectangular or polar) specified by the MODE setting or by a display conversion instruction (page 11-4):

$(real,imag)$ or $(magnitude \angle angle)$

For example, in **PolarC** and **Degree** MODE, **(2,1) − (1 ∠45)** returns **(1.32565429614 ∠ 12.7643896828)**.

Using a Complex Number in an Expression

To use a complex number in an expression, you may:

• Type the complex number directly.

• Type the name of the complex-number variable (case-sensitive).

• Select the name from the VARS CPLX screen.

The CPLX (Complex Number) Menu

The CPLX menu accesses additional functions and instructions to use with complex numbers. Press [MORE] to move around the menu. When you select from the CPLX menu, the name of the function or instruction is copied to the cursor location. These examples assume Radian MODE.

The CPLX Menu

When you press [2nd] [CPLX], the menu keys are labeled with the first five items of the complex menu.

conj   real   imag   abs   angle
►Rec   ►Pol

Lists are valid arguments for all of these functions and instructions, returning a list of results calculated on an element-by-element basis.

The conj Function

conj (conjugate) returns the complex conjugate of a complex number or list.

conj (*real,imag*) returns (*real,-imag*) in **RectC** MODE.

conj (*magnitude ∠ angle*) returns (*magnitude ∠ -angle*) in **PolarC** MODE.

For example, **conj (3,4)** returns **(3,-4)** or **(5∠-.927295218002)**.

The real Function

real returns the real portion(s) of a complex number or list as a real number.

real (*real,imag*) returns *real*.

real (*magnitude ∠ angle*) returns *magnitude* **∗cos** *angle*.

For example, **real (3,4)** returns **3** and **real (3∠4)** returns **-1.96093086259**.

The imag Function

imag (imaginary) returns the imaginary (nonreal) portion(s) of a complex number or list as a real number.

imag (*real,imag*) returns *imag*.

imag (*magnitude ∠ angle*) returns *magnitude* **∗sin** *angle*.

For example, **imag (3,4)** returns **4** and **imag (3∠4)** returns **-2.27040748592**.

The CPLX (Complex Number) Menu (Continued)

The abs
Function

abs (absolute value) returns the magnitude (modulus), $\sqrt{(real^2 + imag^2)}$, of a complex number or list.

abs (*real,imag*) returns $\sqrt{(real^2 + imag^2)}$.

abs (*magnitude ∠ angle*) returns *magnitude*.

For example, **abs (3,4)** returns **5** and **abs (3 ∠ 4)** returns **3**.

The angle
Function

angle returns the polar angle of a complex number or list, calculated as tan⁻¹(*imag/real*) (adjusted by $+\pi$ in the second quadrant or $-\pi$ in the third quadrant).

angle (*real,imag*) returns tan⁻¹(*imag/real*).

angle (*magnitude ∠ angle*) returns *angle*, $-\pi < angle \le \pi$.

For example, **angle (3,4)** returns **.927295218002** and **angle (3 ∠ 4)** returns **-2.28318530718**.

The ▶Rec
Instruction

▶Rec (display as rectangular) displays a complex result in rectangular format. It is valid only at the end of a command. It is not valid if the result is real.

complexresult▶**Rec** displays (*real,imag*).

For example, $\sqrt{-2}$▶**Rec** displays **(0,1.41421356237)**, even if the MODE is **PolarC**.

The ▶Pol
Instruction

▶Pol (display as polar) displays a complex result in polar format. It is valid only at the end of a command. It is not valid if the result is real.

complexresult▶**Pol** displays (*magnitude ∠ angle*).

For example, even if the MODE is **RectC**, $\sqrt{-2}$▶**Pol** displays **(1.41421356237 ∠ 1.57079632679)** in **Radian** MODE.

Chapter 12: Lists

This chapter describes functions and instructions to use with lists on the TI-85. Lists on the TI-85 can be any length, limited only by available memory.

Entering and Using Lists

On the TI-85, you can enter and use real or complex lists of any length. You can enter lists, which begin with a { and end with a }, in an expression directly from the keyboard. You also can define and edit lists in the LIST editor.

Lists

Lists on the TI-85 have three primary applications:

- To provide a list of values as function arguments.

- To graph a family of curves.

- To store and manipulate statistical data.

Using a List in an Expression

To use a list in an expression:

- Type the list directly.

- Type the name of the list variable (case-sensitive).

- Select the name from the VARS LIST screen.

- Select the name from the LIST NAMES menu.

Entering a List

You can enter, edit, and store a list in the LIST editor (page 12-6). You also can enter a list directly in an expression.

1. Press [2nd] [LIST] to display the LIST menu, and select ⟨{⟩ to indicate the beginning of the list. { is copied to the cursor location.

2. Enter each element in the list, separated by commas. An element can be a real or complex number or an expression that evaluates to a real or complex number; the expression is evaluated when the command is executed. Commas are required on entry to separate elements, but are not displayed on output.

3. Select ⟨}⟩ from the LIST menu to indicate the end of the list. } is copied to the cursor location. This is not necessary at the end of a command or preceding the [STO▶] key.

The completed expression for a list is in the form:

$\{element_1, element_2, \ldots, element_n\}$

Storing a List On the TI–85, lists can be stored to and represented by variables.

To store a list or a list result, press $\boxed{\text{STO►}}$ following the list and then enter the name of the variable to which to store it. The completed instruction is in the form:

$\{element_1,element_2,\ldots,element_n\}$→$listname$

Displaying a List Variable To display the contents of a list variable, use the LIST editor or enter the name of the list variable on a blank line on the Home screen and press $\boxed{\text{ENTER}}$.

Results of List Calculations If a list result is too long to be displayed in its entirety, ellipsis marks (…) are shown at the left or right. Use $\boxed{\blacktriangleright}$ and $\boxed{\blacktriangleleft}$ to scroll the list. Lists are displayed in the form:

$\{element_1 \quad element_2 \quad \ldots \quad element_n\}$

Lists as Arguments Lists can be arguments for certain functions. The function returns a list of results calculated on an element-by-element basis. If two arguments of a function are lists, they must be the same length.

For example $\{1,2,3\}^2$ returns $\{1 \quad 4 \quad 9\}$.

List Elements A list element can be a real or complex number. If any element of a list is complex, all elements in the list are complex and are displayed as complex.

For example, $\{1,2,\sqrt{(-4)}\}$ returns $\{(1,0) \quad (2,0) \quad (0,2)\}$.

Accessing List Elements To use an individual list element in an expression, enter the name of the list, followed by the number of the element in parentheses:

$listname(element\#)$

Note: The TI–85 does not interpret this as implied multiplication.

The LIST Menu

The LIST menu accesses the LIST identifier characters, the
LIST editor (where you create, enter, and edit lists), and a
menu of additional list functions and instructions.

The LIST Menu　　When you press [2nd] [LIST], the menu keys are labeled
with the LIST menu.

{	}	**NAMES**	**EDIT**	**OPS**

Item	Accesses
{	List identifier character.
}	List identifier character.
NAMES	Menu of existing lists.
EDIT	LIST editor, where you enter and edit lists (page 12–5).
OPS	Menu of list functions and instructions (page 12–8).

dimL	sortA	sortD	min	max
sum	prod	seq	li▶vc	vc▶li
Fill				

Names of Lists　　The LIST NAMES menu displays the names of existing lists
in alphabetical order. Press [MORE] to move around the
menu. When you select an item, the name of the list is
copied to the cursor location.

Selecting a List

To define a new list or edit an existing one, you first must enter or select the list name. You can then use the LIST editor to define a new list or edit an existing list (page 12-5).

Selecting a List

1. Select ⟨EDIT⟩ from the LIST menu to display the list selection screen. The menu keys are labeled with the names of existing lists in alphabetical order.

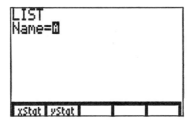

2. Enter the name of the list.

   • Select an existing name from the menu.

   • Type the name of a new or existing list of up to eight characters (case-sensitive). The keyboard is set in ALPHA-lock.

3. Press [ENTER]. If you selected an existing list, the LIST editor displays its elements. In a new list, only the first element is displayed; the value is blank. A ↓ is displayed at the left of the line above the menu(s) if there are more elements in the list than can be displayed at one time.

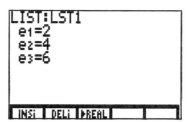

Defining and Editing Lists with the Editor

After you have entered or selected the name of the list, the LIST editor prompts you to enter or edit the elements.

Editing a List with the LIST Editor

Enter new real or complex values (which can be expressions) for the list elements, as appropriate. Expressions are evaluated when you move off the element or leave the editor.

When you press [ENTER] or [▼] at the bottom of a list, a prompt for a new element is added automatically.

Note: If you press a key that accesses a menu, the LIST editor menu moves to the seventh line (if it is not already there), and the selected menu is displayed on the eighth line.

Moving around the LIST Editor

Key	Action
[►] [◄]	Moves the cursor within a list element.
[▲] [▼]	Moves the cursor between list elements.
[ENTER]	Moves the cursor to the next list element.
⟨INSi⟩	Inserts a new element above the cursor.
⟨DELi⟩	Deletes the element where the cursor is located.
⟨►REAL⟩	Truncates the list in the editor to a real list.

Note: To move quickly to the final element in the list, press [▲] from the first element.

Using Math Functions with Lists

A list can be used to input several values to serve as arguments for certain functions. The function is evaluated for each element in the list and a list of results is returned. The examples below assume the default MODE settings.

Using Math Functions with Lists

Function	Display
Addition and subtraction	$\{1,7,1\}-\{1,2,3\}$
	$\{0\ \ 5\ \ -2\}$
	$3+\{1,7,(2,1)\}$
	$\{(4,0)\ \ (10,0)\ \ (5,1)\}$
Multiplication	$\{1,7,(2,1)\}*\{1,2,3\}$
	$\{(1,0)\ \ (14,0)\ \ (6,3)\}$
	$3\{1,7,2\}$
	$\{3\ \ 21\ \ 6\}$
Division	$\{1,7,2\}/\{1,2,4\}$
	$\{1\ \ 3.5\ \ .5\}$
	$\{1,7,2\}/.5$
	$\{2\ \ 14\ \ 4\}$
Single-argument function	$\{1,7,2\}^2$
	$\{1\ \ 49\ \ 4\}$
	$\ln\ \{1,7,2\}$
	$\{0\ \ 1.94591014906\ \ .69\dots$
Relational operators	$\{1,7,2\}<\{5,5,5\}$
	$\{1\ \ 0\ \ 1\}$

Notes about Using Math Functions with Lists

• If a list is used as an argument to a function, the function must be valid for every element in the list, except in graphing.

• If two lists are used as arguments of two-argument functions, the length of the lists must be the same. The result is a list in which each element is the result of evaluating the function using the corresponding elements in the lists.

For example, {**1,2,3**}+{**4,5,6**}returns {**5 7 9**}, evaluated as {**1+4,2+5,3+6**}.

• If a list and a value are used as arguments of two-argument functions, the value is used with each element in the list.

For example, {**1,2,3**}+**4** returns {**5 6 7**}.

List Functions

The LIST OPS menu accesses functions and instructions to use with lists. Press MORE to move around the menu. When you select an item from the menu, the name is copied to the cursor location.

The LIST OPS Menu

When you select ⟨OPS⟩ from the LIST menu, the menu keys are labeled with the first five items of the LIST operations menu.

dimL	sortA	sortD	min	max
sum	prod	seq	li►vc	vc►li
Fill				

dimL is explained on page 12–10.

The Sort Functions

sortA (sort ascending) and **sortD** (sort descending) return lists with elements sorted in ascending or descending numerical order. Complex lists are sorted based on magnitude (modulus).

sortA {$element_1, element_2, \ldots$} or **sortA** *list_name*

For example, **sortD** {2,7,-8,0} returns {7 2 0 -8}.

The min and max Functions

min (minimum) and **max** (maximum) return the smallest or largest element of a list. For a complex list, the element with smallest or largest magnitude (modulus) is returned. The parentheses are required.

min({$element_1, element_2, \ldots$}**)** or **max(***listname***)**

For example, **min(**{2,7,-8,0}**)** returns -8.

The sum Function

sum (summation) returns the sum of the elements of a real or complex list.

sum {$element_1, element_2, \ldots$} or **sum** *list_name*

For example, **sum** {2,7,-8,0} returns 1.

| **The prod Function** | **prod** (product) returns the multiplicative product of the elements of a real or complex list. |
| | |

prod {$element_1, element_2, \ldots$} or **prod** *listname*

For example, **prod** {**2,7,-8**} returns **-112**.

| **The seq Function** | **seq** (sequence) returns a real list, in which each element is the value of the expression, evaluated at increments for the specified variable from the beginning value to an ending value. The increment can be negative. **seq** is not valid within the expression. |

seq(*expression, variablename, begin, end, increment*)

For example, **seq(M^2,M,1,11,3)** returns {**1 16 49 100**}.

| **The li►vc Function** | **li►vc** (convert list to vector) returns a real or complex vector converted from a list. |

li►vc {$element_1, element_2, \ldots$} or **li►vc** *listname*

For example, **3li►vc** {**2,7,-8,0**} returns [**6 21 -24 0**].

| **The vc►li Function** | **vc►li** (convert vector to list) returns a real or complex list converted from a vector. |

vc►li [$element_1, element_2 \ldots$] or **vc►li** *vectorname*

For example, **(vc►li [2,7,-8,0])^2** returns {**4 49 64 0**}.

| **The Fill Instruction** | **Fill** stores a real or complex value to every element in an existing list. |

Fill(*value, listname*)

Defining and Recalling List Dimensions

You can access the dimension (length) of a list using the dimL function on the LIST OPS menu. If used as a function, dimL returns the number of elements of a list. Combined with the store instruction, you can use dimL to change the length of a list.

The List Dimension Function

dimL (list dimension) has three uses:

- To return the length (number of elements) of a list.

  dimL *list*

  For example, **1/dimL** {**2,7,-8,0**} returns **.25**.

- To create a new list of a specified length. The elements of the new list are zeros.

  length→**dimL** *listname*

  For example, **3→dimL** **NEWLIST** creates **NEWLIST** {**0 0 0**}.

- To redimension an existing list. The elements of the old list that are within the new length are not changed. Any additional elements that are created are zeros.

  length→**dimL** *listname*

  For example, if **MYLIST** contains {**2 7 -8 0**}:

  5→dimL **MYLIST** changes **MYLIST** to {**2 7 -8 0 0**}.

  2→dimL **MYLIST** changes **MYLIST** to {**2 7**}.

Chapter 13: Matrices and Vectors

This chapter describes how to use matrices and vectors on the TI-85. The number of matrices and vectors that you can store in the TI-85 is limited only by available memory. Matrices have up to 255 rows and 255 columns. Vectors can have up to 255 elements.

Entering and Using Matrices

A matrix is a two-dimensional real or complex array. Matrices, which begin with [[, can be entered directly in an expression. They also can be defined and edited in the matrix editor.

Using a Matrix in an Expression

To use a matrix in an expression:

- Type the matrix directly.

- Type the name of the matrix variable (case-sensitive).

- Select the name from the VARS MATRX screen.

- Select the name from the MATRX NAMES menu.

Entering a Matrix

You can enter, edit, and store a matrix in the MATRX editor (page 13–6). You also can enter a matrix directly in an expression.

1. Press [2nd] [[] to indicate the beginning of the matrix.

2. Press [2nd] [[] to indicate the beginning of a row.

3. Enter each element in the row, separated by commas. An element is a real or complex value (which can be an expression); the expression is evaluated when the command is executed. Commas are required on entry to separate elements, but are not displayed on output.

4. Press [2nd] []] to indicate the end of a row.

5. Repeat steps 2 through 4 to enter all of the rows.

6. Press [2nd] []] to indicate the end of the matrix.

The closing]] is not necessary at the end of a command or preceding the [STO▶] key. The completed expression is in the form:

$[[element_{1,1}, \dots, element_{1,n}] \dots [element_{m,1}, \dots, element_{m,n}]]$

Note: Each row in a matrix is a vector; therefore, a vector can be used to define a row. For example,
[1,2,3]▸V1:[[V1][V1]] is equivalent to **[[1,2,3][1,2,3]]**

Storing a Matrix

On the TI–85, matrices can be stored to and represented by variables.

To store a matrix or a matrix result, press $\boxed{\text{STO}\blacktriangleright}$ following the matrix and then enter the name of the variable to which to store it. When the instruction is executed, the TI–85 evaluates any elements entered as expressions and then stores the matrix to the variable. For example:

[[5 – 4,1,0][2,3,1][7,0,0][1,1,1]]▸MM

Displaying a Matrix Variable

To display the contents of a matrix variable, enter the name of the matrix on a blank line on the Home screen and press $\boxed{\text{ENTER}}$.

Results of Matrix Calculations

Matrix results are displayed in tabular form on the right of the screen.

- If all columns of a matrix do not fit in the display, as indicated by ellipsis marks (…) in the left or right column of the display, use $\boxed{\blacktriangleright}$ and $\boxed{\blacktriangleleft}$ to display the rest of the columns.

- If all rows of a matrix do not fit in the display, as indicated by ↑ in the right column of the top row or ↓ in the right column of the bottom row, use $\boxed{\blacktriangle}$ and $\boxed{\blacktriangledown}$ to display the rest of the rows.

For example:

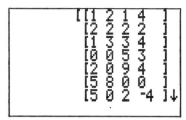

Example

Calculate 2 times the matrix: $\begin{bmatrix} 5 & 3-2 \\ 2 & (2,1) \end{bmatrix}$

Store it to a variable and recall element 1,2.

2 [2nd] [[] [2nd] [[] **5** [,]	
3 [−] **2** [2nd] []]	
[2nd] [[] **2** [,] [(] **2** [,] **1** [)]	
[2nd] []] [2nd] []]	`2[[5,3-2][2,(2,1)]]`
[ENTER]	`[[(10,0) (2,0)]`
	`[(4,0)  (4,2)]]`
[STO▶] **MAT**	`Ans→MAT`
[ENTER]	`[[(10,0) (2,0)]`
	`[(4,0)  (4,2)]]`
[ALPHA] [ALPHA] **MAT** [ALPHA]	
[(] **1** [,] **2** [)]	`MAT(1,2)`
[ENTER]	`(2,0)`

Matrix Elements   A matrix element can be a real or complex value.

If any element of a matrix is complex, all elements in the matrix are complex.

Note: The TI–85 does not interpret the name of a matrix followed by an open parenthesis as implied multiplication. It accesses specific elements in the matrix (page 13–19).

The MATRX (Matrix) Menu

The MATRX menu accesses additional matrix capabilities of the TI-85. From this menu you create and enter matrices, change matrix elements, change the dimension of a matrix, and access additional matrix functions.

The MATRX Menu When you press [2nd] [MATRX], the menu keys are labeled with the matrix menu.

NAMES	EDIT	MATH	OPS	CPLX

Item	Accesses
NAMES	Menu of existing matrices.
EDIT	The matrix editor, where you enter and edit matrices (page 13–6).
MATH	Matrix math functions (page 13–12).

det	ᵀ	norm	eigVl	eigVc
rnorm	cnorm	LU	cond	

OPS	Matrix row functions and other matrix functions and instructions (page 13–14).

dim	Fill	ident	ref	rref
aug	rSwap	rAdd	multR	mRAdd
randM				

CPLX	Complex matrix functions (page 13–18).

conj	real	imag	abs	angle

Names of Matrices The MATRX NAMES menu displays the names of existing matrices in alphabetical order. Press [MORE] to move around the menu. When you select an item, the name of the matrix is copied to the cursor location.

Defining and Editing Matrices with the Editor

In addition to entering matrices directly in an expression, you can use the matrix editor to define a new matrix or to edit an existing matrix. To define a new matrix or edit an existing one, you must first select the matrix name.

Selecting a Matrix

1. Select ⟨EDIT⟩ from the MATRX menu to display the matrix selection screen. The menu keys are labeled with the names of existing matrices in alphabetical order.

2. Enter the name of the matrix.

   • Select an existing name from the menu.

   • Type the name of a new or existing matrix of up to eight characters (case-sensitive). The keyboard is set in ALPHA-lock.

3. Press ENTER. If you selected an existing matrix, its dimensions and elements are displayed.

Accepting or Changing Matrix Dimensions

The dimensions of the matrix (rows × columns) are displayed on the top line. The default dimension for a new matrix is 1 × 1. The cursor is on the row dimension. You must accept or change the row dimension value and the column dimension value each time you enter the matrix editor.

   • To accept the value, press ENTER.

   • To change the value, enter a number (up to 255) and press ENTER.

Note: You can use ▲ and ▼ to move onto and edit the matrix dimensions at any time in the editor.

Displaying Matrix Contents in the Editor

The matrix is displayed in the matrix editor one column at a time. For example, let **SAMPLE** be the 8 x 4 matrix:

$$\begin{bmatrix} 1 & 2 & 1 & 4 \\ 2 & 2 & 2 & 2 \\ 1 & 3 & 3 & 4 \\ 0 & 0 & 5 & 3 \\ 2 & 0 & 9 & 4 \\ 5 & 8 & 0 & 0 \\ 5 & 0 & 2 & -4 \\ 5 & 6 & 3 & 1.1 \end{bmatrix}$$

The six elements indicated in column 3 of **SAMPLE** would be displayed in the matrix editor as:

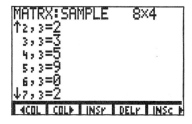

Editing a Matrix with the Matrix Editor

In a new matrix, all values are zero. ↓ is displayed at the left of the line above the menu(s) if there are more rows in the matrix than can be displayed at one time.

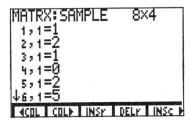

name & row × col
row, col = value

Enter new real or complex values (which can be expressions) for the matrix elements, as appropriate. Expressions are evaluated when you move off the element or leave the editor.

- Press ENTER after each value to enter the matrix row by row.

- Press ▼ after each value to enter the matrix column by column.

Note: If you press a key that accesses a menu, the matrix editor menu moves to the seventh line (if it is not already there), and the selected menu is displayed on the eighth line.

Moving around the Matrix Editor

When you select a matrix, the menu keys are labeled with the first five items of the matrix editing operations. Press MORE to move around the menu.

◄COL	COL►	INSr	DELr	INSc
DELc	►REAL			

Key	Action
► or ◄	Moves the cursor within a matrix element.
▲ or ▼	Moves the cursor within the current column. If the cursor is on the first element, ▲ moves the cursor onto the dimensions. If the cursor is on the bottom element, ▼ moves the cursor to the top of the next column.
ENTER	Moves the cursor to the next column, same row, except on the final column (moves to first column, next row for convenience in entering).
⟨◄COL⟩ or ⟨COL►⟩	Displays the adjacent column, with the cursor on the same row.
⟨INSr⟩	Inserts a new row above the cursor.
⟨DELr⟩	Deletes the row where the cursor is located.
⟨INSc⟩	Inserts a new column to left of the cursor.
⟨DELc⟩	Deletes the column where the cursor is located.
⟨►REAL⟩	Truncates the matrix in the editor to a real matrix.

To add a row at the bottom or a column on the right, change the dimensions. Each new element is zero.

Using Math Functions with Matrices

A matrix can be used in many expressions where a variable can be used. However, the dimensions of the matrices must be appropriate for the function. Math functions to use with matrices can be accessed from the keyboard, MATH menu, and TEST menu, in addition to the MATRX menus.

The Addition and Subtraction Functions

To add or subtract matrices, the dimensions must be the same.

$matrix + matrix$ or $matrix - matrix$

The Multiplication Function

To multiply matrices, the column dimension of the first matrix must match the row dimension of the second matrix.

$matrix * matrix$ or $matrix\ matrix$

You can multiply a value times a matrix or a matrix times a value.

$value\ matrix$ or $matrix\ value$

The Negation Function

Negating a matrix negates each element in the matrix.

$-matrix$

The Inverse Function

To invert a matrix, the matrix must be square and the determinant cannot equal zero.

$matrix^{-1}$

The Square Function

To square a matrix, the matrix must be square.

$matrix^2$

The Power Function

To raise a matrix to a power, the matrix must be square. The power must be a real integer between 0 and 255.

$matrix \wedge power$

The round Function

Rounding a matrix rounds each element in a real or complex matrix. The second argument (optional) is the number of decimal places (0 to 11) to round to. If there is no second argument, the number is rounded to twelve digits. The parentheses are required.

round(*matrix,decimals***)** or **round(***matrix***)**

For example, **round([[5.555,4.4][.001,0]],2)** returns
[[**5.56 4.4**]
  [**0   0**]]

The Relational Functions

To compare two matrices using the relational functions **= =** and **≠**, the matrices must have the same dimensions. The matrices are compared on an element-by-element basis, and a **1** if true or a **0** if false is returned. If the matrix is complex, the magnitude (modulus) of each element is compared.

matrix **= =** *matrix* returns **1** if every comparison is true; it returns **0** if any comparison is false.

matrix≠matrix returns **1** if at least one comparison is false.

The Exponential, sin, and cos Functions

e^x, **sin**, and **cos** return square, real matrices that are the matrix exponential, matrix sine, or matrix cosine of a square, real matrix. This is not the exponential, sine, or cosine of each element. The value returned for the exponential of a defective matrix may be incorrect.

e ^ *matrix*, **sin** *matrix*, or **cos** *matrix*

The iPart, fPart, and int Functions

iPart, **fPart**, and **int** return a real or complex matrix containing the integer part, fractional part, or greatest integer of each element of a real or complex matrix.

iPart *matrix*, **fPart** *matrix*, or **int** *matrix*

The MATRX MATH Menu

The MATRX MATH menu displays additional matrix math functions. Press MORE to move around the menu. When you select an item from the menu, the name is copied to the cursor location.

The MATRX MATH Menu

When you select ⟨MATH⟩ from the MATRX menu, the menu keys are labeled with the first five items of the menu.

det	T	norm	eigVl	eigVc
rnorm	cnorm	LU	cond	

The det Function

det (determinant) returns the determinant of a square matrix. The result is a real number if the matrix is real, a complex number if the matrix is complex.

det *matrix*

The Transpose Function

T (transpose) returns a transposed matrix. The result is a matrix in which element(*row,column*) is swapped with element(*column,row*). For complex matrices, the result is a matrix in which element(*row,column*) is swapped with element(*column,row*), and the conjugate is taken.

*matrix*ᵀ

The norm Function

norm returns the Frobenius norm, a number equal to $\sqrt{\Sigma (real^2 + imag^2)}$ where the sum is over all elements of a real or complex matrix.

norm *matrix*

The eigVl Function

eigVl (eigenvalues) returns a list of the eigenvalues of a real or complex square matrix. The eigenvalues of a real matrix may be complex.

eigVl *matrix*

The eigVc Function

eigVc (eigenvector) returns a matrix containing the eigenvectors for a real or complex square matrix, each column corresponding to an eigenvalue. The eigenvectors of a real matrix may be complex.

eigVc *matrix*

The rnorm Function	**rnorm** (row norm) returns the largest of the sums of the absolute values of the elements (magnitudes of complex elements) in each row.

rnorm *matrix*

The cnorm Function	**cnorm** (column norm) returns the largest of the sums of the absolute values of the elements (magnitudes of complex elements) in each column.

cnorm *matrix*

The LU Instruction	**LU** (lower-upper decomposition) calculates the permutation matrix resulting from the Crout LU decomposition of a square real or complex matrix. It stores the lower triangular matrix, the upper triangular matrix, and the permutation matrix in the variables specified by the second, third, and fourth arguments, respectively.

LU(*matrix,lmatrixname,umatrixname,pmatrixname*)

The cond Function	**cond** (condition) returns **norm** *matrix* $*$ **norm** *matrix*$^{-1}$. This number indicates how well-behaved a real or complex square matrix is expected to be for certain matrix functions, particularly inverse. The condition number for a well-behaved matrix is close to 1.

cond *matrix*

For a matrix with no inverse, **cond** returns an error.

The MATRX OPS (Operations) Menu

The MATRX OPS menu displays the matrix row operations, the dimension function, and several additional matrix functions and instructions. Press [MORE] to move around the menu. When you select an item from the menu, the name is copied to the cursor location.

The MATRX OPS Menu

When you select ⟨OPS⟩ from the MATRX menu, the menu keys are labeled with the first five items of the matrix operations menu.

dim	Fill	ident	ref	rref
aug	rSwap	rAdd	multR	mRAdd
randM				

dim is explained on page 13–15. The row operations are explained on pages 13–16 and 13–17.

The Fill Instruction

Fill stores a value to every element in an existing matrix.

Fill(*value,matrixname*)

Note: A real value stored to a complex matrix makes the matrix real, and vice versa.

The ident Function

ident (identity) returns the identity matrix of the dimension specified.

ident *dimension*

The aug Function

aug (augment) concatenates two matrices or a matrix and a vector (real or complex). The number of rows in the first matrix must equal the number of rows in the second matrix or the number of elements in the vector.

aug(*matrixA,matrixB*) or **aug**(*matrix,vector*)

For example, to augment [[1,2][3,4]] and [[5,6][7,8]], **aug**([[1,2][3,4]],[[5,6][7,8]]) returns
```
[[1  2  5  6]
 [3  4  7  8]]
```

The randM Function

randM (create random matrix) returns a matrix of random one-digit integers (-9 to 9) of the dimensions specified.

randM(*rows,columns*)

For example, **0→rand:randM(2,3)**
creates
```
[[4  -2  0]
 [-7  8  8]]
```

Defining and Recalling Matrix Dimensions

Matrix dimensions can be accessed using the dim function on the MATRX OPS menu. The dim function is used to recall or store the dimensions of a matrix.

The dim Function   **dim** (dimension) has three uses:

- To return a list containing the dimensions (number of rows and columns) of a matrix.

  dim *matrix*

  For example, **dim [[2,7,1][-8,0,1]]** returns { **2   3** } .

- To create a new matrix of specified dimensions (used with the store instruction). The elements in the new matrix are zeros.

  {*rows,columns*}→**dim** *matrixname*

  For example, **{2,2}→dim NEWMTRX**
  creates **NEWMTRX**   **[[0   0]**
                                                [0   0]]

- To redimension an existing matrix (used with the store instruction). The elements in the old matrix that are within the new dimensions are not changed. Any additional elements that are created are zeros.

  {*rows,columns*}→**dim** *matrixname*

  For example, if **MAT** contains   **[[2   7   7]**
                                                [-8   0   7]]

  {2,2}→dim MAT   changes **MAT** in
  memory to   **[[2   7]**
                                                [-8   0]]

  {2,3}→dim MAT changes **MAT** in
  memory to   **[[2   7   0]**
                                                [-8   0   0]]

The Row Functions

Six matrix row functions can be accessed from the MATRX OPS menu. These functions, which can be used in an expression, do not change the original matrix. The result of each function is a temporary matrix. The value for a multiplier or a row can be an expression.

The ref Function	**ref** (row echelon form) returns the row echelon form of a real or complex matrix. The number of columns must be greater than or equal to the number of rows.

ref *matrix*

The rref Function	**rref** (reduced row echelon form) returns the reduced row echelon form of a real or complex matrix. The number of columns must be greater than or equal to the number of rows.

rref *matrix*

The rSwap Function	**rSwap** (row swap) returns a matrix after swapping two rows. It requires three arguments: the matrix, the number of the first row to swap, and the number of the row to swap with it.

rSwap(*matrix,row1,row2*)

The rAdd Function	**rAdd** (row addition) returns a matrix after adding two rows and storing the results in the second row. It requires three arguments: the matrix, the number of the row to add, and the number of the row to add to and in which to store the results.

rAdd(*matrix,row1,row2*)

The multR Function	**multR** (row multiplication) returns a matrix after multiplying a row by a value and storing the results in the same row. It requires three arguments: the value, the matrix, and the number of the row to multiply.

multR(*value,matrix,row*)

The mRAdd Function	**mRAdd** (multiply and add row) returns a matrix after multiplying a row by a value, adding the results to a second row, and storing the results in the second row. It requires four arguments: the value, the matrix, the number of the row to multiply, and the number of the row to add to and in which to store the results.

mRAdd(*value,matrix,row1,row2*)

Function	Display

Enter matrix	`[[5,3,1,1][2,0,4,2][-`
	`3,-1,2,3]]→MTRX`
	`   [[5   3   1 1]`
	`    [2   0   4 2]`
	`    [-3 -1  2 3]]`

Swap row 2 and row 3	`rSwap(MTRX,2,3)`
	`   [[5   3   1 1]`
	`    [-3 -1  2 3]`
	`    [2   0   4 2]]`

Add row 2 to row 3	`rAdd(MTRX,2,3)`
	`   [[5   3   1 1]`
	`    [2   0   4 2]`
	`    [-1 -1  6 5]]`

Multiply row 2 by 5	`multR(5,MTRX,2)`
	`   [[5   3   1   1 ]`
	`    [10  0   20 10]`
	`    [-3 -1  2   3 ]]`

Multiply row 2 by 5,
add to row 3
	`mRAdd(5,MTRX,2,3)`
	`   [[5 3   1   1 ]`
	`    [2 0   4   2 ]`
	`    [7 -1 22 13]]`

Return row echelon form	`ref MTRX`
	`[[1  .6  .2 .2`
	` [0  1   -3 -1.3333333..`
	` [0  0   1   .933333333...`

Return reduced row
echelon form
	`rref MTRX`
	`[[1 0  0 -.8666666666...`
	` [0 1  0 1.4666666666..`
	` [0 0  1 .93333333333..`

The MATRX CPLX (Complex) Menu

The MATRX CPLX menu displays complex functions to use with complex matrices. If a matrix has any complex element, all elements in the matrix are complex. When you select an item from the menu, the name is copied to the cursor location.

The MATRX CPLX Menu

When you select ⟨CPLX⟩ from the MATRX menu, the menu keys are labeled with the matrix complex menu.

conj   real   imag   abs   angle

The conj Function

conj (conjugate) returns the complex conjugate of a complex matrix. The result is a complex matrix in which each element is the complex conjugate of the original.

conj *matrix*

The real Function

real returns a real matrix containing the real portion of each element.

real *matrix*

The imag Function

imag (imaginary) returns a real matrix containing the imaginary portion of each element.

imag *matrix*

The abs Function

abs (absolute value) returns a real matrix. If an element is real, **abs** returns the absolute value of the element. If an element is complex, **abs** returns the magnitude (modulus), $\sqrt{(real^2 + imag^2)}$, of the element.

abs *matrix*

The angle Function

angle returns a real matrix containing the polar angle of each element, calculated as $\tan^{-1}(imag/real)$, adjusted by $+\pi$ for the second quadrant or $-\pi$ for the third quadrant.

angle *matrix*

Creating a Complex Matrix

You can create a complex matrix from two real matrices of the same dimensions, one containing the real part of each element and one containing the imaginary part of each element. The dimensions of the matrices must be the same.

real_matrix **+ (0,1)** *imag_matrix*

Storing and Using Portions of a Matrix

A specific matrix element, row, or submatrix can be used in an expression. You can store to a specific matrix element, row, or submatrix from the Home screen or a program.

Accessing a Matrix Element

The name of a matrix followed by an open parenthesis accesses specific elements in the matrix. It does not indicate implied multiplication. The expression to access a matrix element is:

matrixname(row,column)

For example, if **MTRX** is

```
[[1  2  3]
 [4  5  6]]
```

MTRX(1,2) returns **2**.

Accessing a Matrix Row

A matrix row is a vector. The expression to access all of a matrix row is:

matrixname(row)

For example, **MTRX(1)** returns

```
[1  2  3]
```

Accessing a Submatrix

The expression to access a submatrix is:

matrixname(beginrow,begincol,endrow,endcol)

For example, **MTRX(1,1,2,2)** returns

```
[[1  2]
 [4  5]]
```

Changing a Matrix

7→MTRX(1,2) changes **MTRX** to

```
[[1  7  3]
 [4  5  6]]
```

[7,8,9]→MTRX(1) changes **MTRX** to

```
[[7  8  9]
 [4  5  6]]
```

The instruction to store to part of a matrix row is:

vector→matrixname(row,column)

[1,2]→MTRX(2,2) changes **MTRX** to

```
[[7  8  9]
 [4  1  2]]
```

To store a submatrix, specify the beginning row and column.

[[6,7][8,9]]→MTRX(1,2) changes **MTRX** to

```
[[7  6  7]
 [4  8  9]]
```

Entering and Using Vectors

A vector is a one-dimensional array. You can enter and use real or complex vectors of up to 255 elements on the TI–85. Vectors, which begin with [, can be entered in an expression directly from the keyboard. They also can be defined and edited in the vector editor.

Vectors

Vectors are treated as n × 1 arrays for calculation purposes, but are entered and displayed as 1 × n arrays for convenience. A 2-element or 3-element vector can define magnitude and direction in 2-dimensional or 3-dimensional space.

Vectors of more than three elements must be entered in rectangular format. 2-element and 3-element vectors can be entered and displayed in several formats:

Format	Entry	Display
2-element rectangular	$[\mathbf{x},\mathbf{y}]$	$[\,x \quad y\,]$
2-element cylindrical or spherical	$[\mathbf{r} \angle \theta\,]$	$[\,r \angle \theta\,]$
3-element rectangular	$[\mathbf{x},\mathbf{y},\mathbf{z}]$	$[\,x \quad y \quad z\,]$
3-element cylindrical	$[\mathbf{r} \angle \theta,\mathbf{z}]$	$[\,r \angle \theta \quad z\,]$
3-element spherical	$[\mathbf{r} \angle \theta \angle \Phi\,]$	$[\,r \angle \theta \angle \Phi\,]$

Note: Only real vectors are displayed in cylindrical or spherical format. Complex vectors are automatically displayed in rectangular format.

Using a Vector in an Expression

To use a vector in an expression:

• Type the vector directly.

• Type the name of the vector variable (case-sensitive).

• Select the name from the VARS VECTR screen.

• Select the name from the VECTR NAMES menu.

Entering a Vector	You can enter, edit, and store a vector in the VECTR editor (page 13–24). You also can enter a vector directly in an expression.

1. Press 2nd [[] to indicate the beginning of the vector.

2. Enter each element in the vector, separated by a comma or angle symbol (the 2nd function of ⌐,⌐]), depending on the preferred vector format. An element is a real or complex value (which can be an expression); the expression is evaluated when the command is executed.

3. Press 2nd []] to indicate the end of the vector. This is not necessary at the end of a command or preceding the STO► key.

The completed expression in rectangular form is:

$[element_1, \ldots, element_n]$

Storing a Vector	On the TI–85, vectors can be stored to and represented by variables.

To store a vector or a vector result, press STO► following the vector and then enter the name of the variable to which to store it. When the instruction is executed, the TI–85 evaluates any elements entered as expressions and then stores the vector to the variable. The completed instruction is in the form:

$[element_1, \ldots, element_n] \rightarrow vector\_name$

Displaying a Vector Variable	Real 2-element and 3-element vector results are displayed in the format specified by the MODE setting (**RectV**, **CylV**, or **SphereV**) or by a display conversion instruction (page 13–29).

Entering and Using Vectors (Continued)

Example of Entering a Vector	In **RectV** MODE, calculate .6 times the vector [5,1+1], store the result, and then find the fractional portion.

. 6 [2nd] [[] 5 [,] 1 [+] 1		
[2nd] [[]	.6[5,1+1]	
[ENTER]		[3 1.2]
[STO▶] **VECT**	Ans→VECT	
[ENTER]		[3 1.2]
[2nd] [MATH] ⟨NUM⟩ ⟨fPart⟩		
[ALPHA] [ALPHA] **VECT**	fPart VECT	
[ENTER]		[0 .2]

Vector Elements	An element of a vector can be a real or a complex number. If any element of a vector is complex, all elements of the vector are complex.

For example, **[1,2,(3,1)]** returns **[(1,0) (2,0) (3,1)]**. |
| **Using a Vector Element in an Expression** | A specific vector element can be used in an expression. You can store to a specific vector element from the Home screen or a program.

value→vectorname(element) |

The VECTR (Vector) Menu

The VECTR menu accesses additional vector instructions and functions. From this menu you create and enter vectors, change vector elements, change the dimension of a vector, and access additional vector functions.

The VECTR Menu When you press [2nd] [VECTR], the menu keys are labeled with the vector menu.

NAMES	EDIT	MATH	OPS	CPLX

Item	Accesses
NAMES	Menu of existing vectors.
EDIT	The vector editor, where you enter and edit vectors (page 13–24).
MATH	Vector math functions (page 13–27).

cross	unitV	norm	dot

OPS	Vector functions and display conversion instructions (pages 13–28 and 13–29).

dim	Fill	►Pol	►Cyl	►Sph
►Rec	li►vc	vc►li		

CPLX	Complex vector functions (page 13–30).

conj	real	imag	abs	angle

Names of Vectors The VECTR NAMES menu displays the names of existing vectors in alphabetical order. Press [MORE] to move around the menu. When you select an item, the name of the vector is copied to the cursor location.

Defining and Editing Vectors with the Editor

In addition to entering vectors directly in an expression, you can use the vector editor to define a new vector or to edit an existing vector. To define a new vector or edit an existing one, you must first select the vector name.

Selecting a Vector

1. Select ⟨EDIT⟩ from the VECTR menu to display the vector selection screen. The menu keys are labeled with the names of existing vectors in alphabetical order.

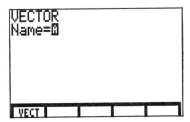

2. Enter the name of the vector.

   ,• Select an existing name from the menu.

   • Type the name of a new or existing vector of up to eight characters (case-sensitive). The keyboard is set in ALPHA-lock.

3. Press [ENTER]. If you selected an existing vector, its dimension and elements are displayed. In a new vector only the first element is displayed; the value is zero. ↓ is displayed at the left of the line above the menu(s) if there are more elements in the vector than can be displayed at one time.

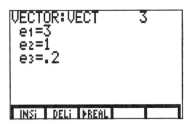

4. Change the dimension if desired. Press [ENTER].

Editing a Vector with the Vector Editor

Enter new real or complex values (which can be expressions) for the vector elements, as appropriate. The expression is evaluated when you move off the element or leave the editor.

Note: If you press a key that accesses a menu, the vector editor menu moves to the seventh line (if it is not already there), and the selected menu is displayed on the eighth line.

Moving around the Vector Editor

Key	Action
▶ ◀	Moves the cursor within a vector element.
▲ ▼	Moves the cursor between vector elements.
ENTER	Moves the cursor to next vector element.
⟨INSi⟩	Inserts a new element above the cursor.
⟨DELi⟩	Deletes the element where the cursor is located.
⟨▶REAL⟩	Truncates the vector in the editor to a real vector.

Note: To move quickly to the final element in the vector, press ▲ from the dimension.

Using Math Functions with Vectors

A vector can be used in many expressions where a variable can be used. Math functions to use with vectors can be accessed from the keyboard, from the MATH menu, and from the TEST menu.

The Addition and Subtraction Functions	To add or subtract real or complex vectors, the length must be the same. The result is a vector in which each element is the result of operating on the corresponding elements.

vector **+** *vector* or *vector* **−** *vector*

The Multiplication and Division Functions	You cannot multiply a vector times a vector, square a vector, or raise a vector to a power. You can multiply a vector times a real or complex value or vice versa. You can divide a vector by a real or complex value.

value vector or *vectorⳑvalue*

An m x n matrix multiplied by an n-element vector returns an m-element vector.

The Negation Function	Negating a vector negates each element in the vector.

-vector

The iPart, fPart, and int Functions	**iPart** (integer part), **fPart** (fractional part), and **int** (greatest integer) return a real or complex vector containing the integer part, fractional part, or greatest integer of each element of a real or complex vector.

iPart *vector*, **fPart** *vector*, or **int** *vector*

The round Function	**round** rounds each element of a vector. The parentheses are required.

round(*vector,decimals***)** or **round(***vector***)**

The Relational Functions	To compare two vectors of the same dimension, use the relational functions **= =** and **≠**. The vectors are compared on an element-by-element basis and a **1** if true or **0** if false is returned. If the vector is complex, the magnitude (modulus) of each element is compared.

vector **= =** *vector* returns **1** if every comparison is true; it returns **0** if any comparison is false.

vector≠vector returns **1** if at least one comparison is false.

The VECTR MATH Menu

The VECTR MATH menu displays additional vector math functions. Some vector functions are valid only for 2-element or 3-element vectors. When you select an item from the menu, the name is copied to the cursor location.

The VECTR MATH Menu

When you select <MATH> from the VECTR menu, the menu keys are labeled with the menu.

cross   unitV   norm   dot

The cross Function

cross (cross product) returns the cross product of two real or complex 2-element or 3-element vectors. For example,

cross([a,b,c],[d,e,f]) returns [bf-ce cd-af ae-bd].

The unitV Function

unitV (unit vector) returns the unit vector (each element divided by the norm of the vector) of any real or complex vector. For example,

unitV [a,b,c] returns [a/norm b/norm c/norm].

The norm Function

norm returns the length of any real or complex vector, calculated as $\sqrt{\Sigma(real^2 + imag^2)}$. For example,

norm [a,b,c] returns $\sqrt{(a^2 + b^2 + c^2)}$.

The dot Function

dot (dot product) returns the dot product of any two real or complex vectors. The result is a real number if the vectors are real or a complex number if the vectors are complex. For example,

dot([a,b,c],[d,e,f]) returns ad+be+cf.

The VECTR OPS (Operations) Menu

The VECTR OPS menu displays operations for vectors. Press
[MORE] to move around the menu. When you select an item
from the menu, the name is copied to the cursor location.
Some vector operations are valid only for 2-element or
3-element vectors.

The VECTR OPS Menu

When you select ⟨OPS⟩ from the VECTR menu, the menu
keys are labeled with the vector operations menu.

dim	Fill	►Pol	►Cyl	►Sph
►Rec	li►vc	vc►li		

The dim Function   **dim** (dimension) has three uses:

● To return the length (number of elements) of a vector.

    dim *vector*

    For example, **dim** [-**8,0,1**] returns **3**.

● To create a new vector of specified length (used with
the store instruction). The elements in the new vector
are zeros.

    length→**dim** *vectorname*

    For example, **4**→**dim NEWVECT** creates **NEWVECT** and
    stores [**0 0 0 0**] in it.

● To redimension an existing vector (used with the store
instruction). The elements in the old vector that are
within the new dimensions are not changed. Any
additional elements that are created are zeros.

    length→**dim** *vectorname*

    For example, if **VECT** contains [**2 7 7**], **2**→**dim VECT**
    changes **VECT** in memory to [**2 7**]. Then **3**→**dim VECT**
    changes **VECT** in memory to [**2 7 0**].

Note: The name of a vector followed by an open
parenthesis accesses a specific vector element. It does
not indicate implied multiplication.

The Fill Instruction

Fill stores a value to every element in an existing vector.

Fill(*value,vectorname*)

Conversions

Display conversion instructions in the VECTR OPS menu control how a 2-element or 3-element vector result is displayed, regardless of the MODE setting. They are valid only at the end of a command. The values in the expression are interpreted according to the current MODE setting.

Display Conversion

The 3-element vector conversion equations are:

Cylindrical [r θ z]

$x = r \cos\theta$
$y = r \sin\theta$
$z = z$

Spherical [r θ φ]

$x = r \cos\theta \sin\phi$
$y = r \sin\theta \sin\phi$
$z = r \cos\phi$

The ►Pol Instruction

►Pol (display as polar) displays a 2-element real vector result in polar format, even if the MODE is not **CylV** or **SphereV**.

vector►**Pol** displays [**r** ∠ **θ**]. For example, [**-2,0**]►**Pol** displays [**2** ∠ **3.14159265359**].

The ►Cyl Instruction

►**Cyl** (display as cylindrical) displays a 2-element or 3-element real vector result in cylindrical format, even if the MODE is not **CylV**.

vector►**Cyl** displays [**r** ∠ **θ   0**] or [**r** ∠ **θ   z**]. For example, [**-2,0**]►**Cyl** displays [**2** ∠ **3.14159265359   0**] (a 3-element vector is stored in **Ans**), and [**-2,0,1**]►**Cyl** displays [**2** ∠ **3.14159265359   1**].

The ►Sph Instruction

►**Sph** (display as spherical) displays a 2-element or 3-element real vector result in spherical format, even if the MODE is not **SphereV**.

vector►**Sph** displays [**r** ∠ **θ   0**] or [**r** ∠ **θ** ∠ **φ**]. For example, [**0,0**]►**Sph** displays [**0** ∠ **0** ∠ **0**] (a 3-element vector is stored in **Ans**), and [**0,0,-1**]►**Sph** displays [**1** ∠ **0** ∠ **3.14159265359**].

The ►Rec Instruction

►**Rec** (display as rectangular) displays a 2-element or 3-element real vector result in rectangular format, even if the MODE is not **RectV**.

vector►**Rec** displays [**x   y**] or [**x   y   z**]. For example, [**2** ∠ **π** ∠ **π**]►**Rec** displays [**0   0   -2**].

The li►vc Function

li►vc (convert list to vector) returns a real or complex vector converted from a list.

For example, **li►vc** {**1,2,3**} returns [**1   2   3**].

The vc►li Function

vc►li (convert vector to list) returns a real or complex list converted from a vector.

For example, **vc►li** [**1,2,3**] returns {**1   2   3**}.

The VECTR CPLX (Complex) Menu

The VECTR CPLX menu displays complex functions to use with vectors with complex elements. If a vector has any complex element, all elements in the vector are complex. When you select an item from the menu, the name is copied to the cursor location.

The VECTR CPLX Menu	When you select ⟨CPLX⟩ from the VECTR menu, the menu keys are labeled with the vector complex menu.

conj   **real**   **imag**   **abs**   **angle**

The conj Function	**conj** (conjugate) returns the complex conjugate of a complex vector. The result is a complex vector in which each element is the complex conjugate of the original.

conj *vector*

The real Function	**real** returns a real vector containing the real portion of each element.

real *vector*

The imag Function	**imag** (imaginary) returns a real vector containing the imaginary portion of each element in a complex vector.

imag *vector*

The abs Function	**abs** (absolute value) returns a real vector. If an element is real, **abs** returns the absolute value of the element. If an element is complex, **abs** returns the magnitude (modulus), $\sqrt{(real^2 + imag^2)}$, of the element.

abs *vector*

The angle Function	**angle** returns a real vector (or a real number for 2-element real vectors). If an element is real, **angle** returns **0**. If an element is complex, **angle** returns the polar angle of the complex elements of a vector, calculated as **tan⁻¹** $(imag/real)$ (adjusted by $+\pi$ in the second quadrant, $-\pi$ in the third quadrant).

angle *vector*

Creating a Complex Vector	You can create a complex vector from two real vectors, one containing the real part of each element and one containing the imaginary part of each element.

realvector **+ (0,1)***imagvector*→*cplxvector*

Chapter 14: Equation Solving

This chapter describes three equation-solving features of the TI–85. The SOLVER solves single equations for any variable in the equation. The POLY (Polynomial) Root Finder solves for the real and complex roots of polynomials. The SIMULT (Simultaneous) Equations Solver solves a system of real or complex simultaneous linear equations.

Chapter Contents

Entering an Equation in the SOLVER

The TI-85 SOLVER allows you to solve for any variable in the equation. You first enter the equation, then enter values for each variable in the equation, and then solve for the unknown variable. (Getting Started contains a complete example using the SOLVER.)

Entering the Equation

To display the SOLVER equation entry screen, press [2nd] [SOLVER].

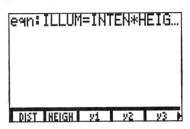

The SOLVER uses the equation in the equation variable **eqn**, which contains the last equation used in the SOLVER, if any. It is displayed on the top line (the example is from Getting Started). You may use or edit the displayed equation, or you may press [CLEAR] to clear the line and enter a new equation. As you enter an equation, it is stored in the variable **eqn**.

The equation can have more than one variable to the left of the equal sign; for example, $A + B = C + \sin\ D$.

You can enter an expression (without an equal sign). The expression is assumed equal to the variable **exp**. For example, if you enter $E + F - \ln\ G$, you will solve the equation $exp = E + F - \ln\ G$.

The menu keys are labeled with the names of previously defined equation variables (for example, the y(x) graphing functions).

- If you select a name from the menu, the name is copied to the cursor location.

- If you press [2nd] [RCL] and then select a name from the menu, the contents are inserted at the cursor location (page 2-9).

If an equation is too long to display in its entirety, ellipsis marks (...) are shown at the left or right. [2nd] [◄] and [2nd] [►] move the cursor to the beginning and end of the equation quickly.

Defining the Variables

All variables except the unknown variable for which you are solving must contain values. The unknown variable may contain a value, which is used as an initial guess. Constants and most system variables are valid in equations. Constants and some system variables cannot be solved for.

Displaying the Variables

To display the SOLVER edit screen, enter the equation and press [ENTER].

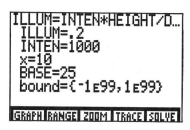

```
ILLUM=INTEN*HEIGHT/D…
  ILLUM=.2
  INTEN=1000
  x=10
  BASE=25
  bound={-1E99,1E99}
```
GRAPH | RANGE | ZOOM | TRACE | SOLVE

The equation is displayed on the top line. To move onto the equation, press [▲] on the first variable; the equation entry screen is displayed.

Variables are listed in the order in which they appear (left to right) in the equation. If any have values, the value is displayed. If you entered an expression (rather than an equation) for **eqn**, **exp** is the first variable listed.

If you used an equation variable in the **eqn** equation, the variables in that equation variable are displayed. For example, if the variable **A** contains **B+C**, the equation **D = 2A** can be solved; the variables **B**, **C**, and **D** are displayed on the SOLVER edit screen.

bound = {lower,upper} defines the bound between which the solution is sought (page 14–7). When you enter the SOLVER, **lower** = -1E99 and **upper** = 1E99. You can edit the list containing **lower** and **upper** (**bound**) in the SOLVER.

Entering Variable Values

You may enter an expression for a variable value. It is evaluated when you move off the variable. If you enter a value or edit an existing value, the value of the variable in memory is changed also.

Expressions must resolve to real numbers at each step during the iteration.

Solving the Equation

You can solve for any user-defined variable located anywhere within an equation or expression.

Initial Guess

You can enter a real value or a real 2-element list (for 2 guesses) as an initial guess (page 14–7) for the unknown variable to be solved for.

Selecting the Variable and Solving the Equation

To solve for the unknown variable, move the cursor to the unknown variable and select ⟨SOLVE⟩.

The solution is displayed on the SOLVER edit screen. A square dot in the first column indicates the variable for which you solved and that the equation is balanced. The value of that variable in memory is changed. If the equation has more variables than can be displayed at one time, use ▼ and ▲ to see all the variables.

```
ILLUM=INTEN*HEIGHT/D…
 ILLUM=.2
 INTEN=1000
■x=3.2022212466712
 BASE=25
 bound={-1E99,1E99}
■left-rt=0
GRAPH RANGE ZOOM TRACE SOLVE
```

A square dot also is displayed next to **left-rt**, which represents the value of the left side minus the value of the right side of the equation (evaluated at the new value of the variable for which you solved).

Equations with Multiple Roots	More than one solution may exist for an equation. You can enter a new initial guess or a new bound to look for additional solutions (page 14–7).
	You also can use the graphing feature to select a new initial guess or set a new bound.
Further Solutions	After solving for a variable, you can continue to explore solutions from this display. Edit the values of any of the variables and solve again.
Editing the Values of Variables	Use the cursor keys to move between and edit the values. The square dots to the left of the variable that you solved for and **left-rt** disappear if you edit any variable. Select 〈SOLVE〉 to solve the equation again.
The Solver Instruction on a Command Line	The instruction **Solver** on the Home screen or in a program, which can be copied from the CATALOG, accesses the SOLVER feature.

Solver(*equation,variablename,guess,bound***)**

equation can be an equation or it can be an expression (which is assumed equal to 0). *variablename* is the name of the variable to solve for. *guess* is a real value or a list of two real values to use as a guess. *bound* is a list of two real values that bound the solution and is optional (-1E99 and 1E99 are used if not specified).

Values must be stored to every variable in the equation, except the one being solved for, before executing the instruction.

When the instruction is executed, the value of the variable for which you are solving is calculated and stored.

For example, **5→A:2→B:Solver(A = B + ln C,C,1)** displays **Done** and stores **20.0855369232** in **C**, but not **Ans**.

Exploring the Solution Graphically

You can examine the equation graphically. On the graph, you can see how many real solutions exist for the equation and use the cursor to select an initial guess.

The Graph

You can display a graph that plots the solutions to the equation. Place the cursor on the unknown variable and select ⟨GRAPH⟩. The unknown variable is plotted on the **x** axis. **left-rt** is plotted on the **y** axis. Solutions exist for the equation where the graph crosses the **x** axis.

Displaying the Graph

SOLVER uses the same RANGE and FORMT settings as the current graphing mode. You may select ⟨RANGE⟩ to display or edit the RANGE variables, which define the current viewing rectangle (Chapter 4); any changes are made in the current graphing mode. The SOLVER does not graph or affect the y(x) or other graphing functions.

Select ⟨GRAPH⟩ to display the graph.

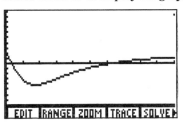

Exploring the Graph

To explore the graph further, you may:

- Use the free-moving cursor (Chapter 4). The coordinate value for the variable and **left-rt** are displayed.

- Select ⟨ZOOM⟩. The menu keys are labeled with the ZOOM features (Chapter 4). Many ZOOM features are available in the SOLVER. After executing a ZOOM operaton, press [EXIT] to display the SOLVER menu.

- Select ⟨TRACE⟩. The panning and QuickZoom features (Chapter 4) are available in the SOLVER. Press [EXIT] to display the SOLVER menu.

Controlling the Solution

You can enter an initial guess and set the upper and lower bound of the solution to help the SOLVER find the solution, whether from the SOLVER edit screen, the SOLVER graph, or the Solver instruction. The ROOT and ISECT operations on the GRAPH MATH menu also use the SOLVER to find solutions.

Using the SOLVER

By selecting a bound and/or an initial guess, you can control the iterative SOLVER process to:

- Find a solution.

- Define which solution you want for equations with multiple solutions. (Use a close bound, in addition to initial guess, for best results when solving for a particular root.)

- Find the solution more quickly.

Bounding the Solution

The SOLVER seeks a solution only within a bound. On the SOLVER edit screen, the bound is displayed as **bound = {lower,upper}** and can be edited. On a graph, **lower** and **upper** are displayed as triangular indicators at the top of the screen and can be set. You can store values to **lower** and **upper** with $\boxed{\text{STO}\blacktriangleright}$. The **Solver** instruction uses -1E99 and 1E99 unless the optional fourth argument is specified, which does not change **lower** and **upper** in memory.

Setting the Lower and Upper Bounds from a SOLVER Graph

When you select ⟨GRAPH⟩ from the SOLVER menu, the variables **lower** and **upper** (*bound*) are changed immediately to the values of **xMin** and **xMax**, if they are outside of **xMin** and **xMax**. If you zoom on a graph, **lower** and **upper** are changed to **xMin** and **xMax**.

To set the value of **lower** or **upper**, press $\boxed{\text{MORE}}$ from the SOLVER graph and then select ⟨LOWER⟩ or ⟨UPPER⟩. Move the cursor to the position you want for the bound. Press $\boxed{\text{ENTER}}$ to change the value in memory. A triangular indicator at the top of the screen shows the point.

Initial Guess

You may enter one or two initial guesses on the SOLVER edit screen. If no guess is given, (**upper-lower**)/2 is used as the initial guess. On the SOLVER graph, you can move the cursor to set the initial guess. The third argument for the **Solver** instruction sets one or two initial guesses. The guess(es) must be within the bound.

Selecting a New Guess from a SOLVER Graph

Position the free-moving or TRACE cursor at the value you want to use as a new initial guess and select ⟨SOLVE⟩. The result is displayed on the SOLVER edit screen.

Entering the POLY (Polynomial) Equation

2nd [POLY] **accesses the POLY (polynomial) Root-Finding capabilities of the calculator. You can solve real or complex polynomials of up to 30th order.**

Entering the Polynomial

1. Press 2nd [POLY]. The POLY order screen appears.

2. Enter an integer between 2 and 30 (which can be an expression). Press ENTER. The coefficient entry screen is displayed. An example for a fourth-order polynomial is shown.

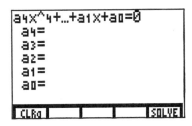

The equation is displayed on the top line for reference; you cannot edit it. The coefficients are used for POLY entry only; they do not update variables a0, a1, a2, etc.

3. Enter a real or complex value (which can be an expression) for the coefficient. Press ENTER.

4. Continue entering the coefficients.

Note: Select ⟨CLRa⟩ from the POLY editor menu to clear all of the coefficients. CLEAR clears only the line on which the cursor is located.

Note: If you press a key that accesses a menu, the POLY editor menu moves to the seventh line (if it is not already there), and the selected menu is displayed on the eighth line.

Solving the Polynomial

You can solve for all roots of the polynomial, real and complex.

Solving the Polynomial

Once you have entered all of the coefficients, select ⟨SOLVE⟩. The roots of the polynomial are calculated and displayed. Results can be scrolled, if necessary. Results cannot be edited and they are not stored in variables.

```
a4x^4+...+a1x+a0=0
 x1=(.287815479558,1...
 x2=(.287815479558,-...
 x3=(-1.28781547956,...
 x4=(-1.28781547956,...


 COEFS STOa
```

Storing Values

You can store any value on the polynomial entry or results screen to a variable. Position the cursor on the variable you wish to store. Press STO► and enter the variable name after the Name= prompt on the seventh line.

To store the coefficients of the polynomial in a list, select ⟨STOa⟩, and then enter the name of the list.

Editing the Coefficients

You can edit the coefficients and calculate new solutions. Select ⟨COEFS⟩ to return to the coefficient entry screen.

The poly Function in an Expression

The **poly** function on the Home screen or in a program, which can be copied from the CATALOG, accesses the POLY (polynomial) root-finder feature.

poly a_list

a_list is a real or complex list containing the coefficients of the polynomial. When the expression is evaluated, the result is a list containing the solutions to the polynomial.

Entering SIMULT (Simultaneous) Equations

2nd [SIMULT] accesses the Simult (simultaneous) Equations
solving capabilities of the calculator. You can solve systems
of up to 30 linear equations with 30 unknowns.

**Entering the
Equations**

1. Press 2nd [SIMULT]. The SIMULT screen appears.

```
SIMULT
Number=
```

2. Enter an integer between 2 and 30 (which can be an
   expression) for the number of simultaneous
   equations. Press ENTER. The coefficient entry screen
   for the first equation appears. An example for a
   system of four equations and four unknowns is
   shown. The equation is displayed on the top line for
   reference; you cannot edit it.

```
a1,1X1...a1,4X4=b1
  a1,1=
  a1,2=
  a1,3=
  a1,4=
  b1=

PREV  NEXT  CLRa       SOLVE
```

3. Enter a real or complex value (which can be an
   expression) for the first coefficient, $a_{1,1}$. Press ENTER.

4. Enter all coefficients for the first equation. If you
   press ENTER after entering the last coefficient or
   select ⟨NEXT⟩, the second equation is displayed. Enter
   the remaining coefficients.

⟨PREV⟩ and ⟨NEXT⟩ move between equations. ▲, ▼,
and ENTER move between coefficients and equations.
CLEAR clears only the line on which the cursor is
located. ⟨CLRa⟩ clears the coefficients for the current
equation.

Note: If you press a key that accesses a menu, the SIMULT
editor menu moves to the seventh line (if it is not already
there), and the selected menu is displayed on the eighth
line.

Solving Simultaneous Equations

After you find the solutions to the simultaneous equations, you can store the results.

Solving the Equations

After entering the coefficients, select <SOLVE>.

```
x1=-.763555883438
x2=-2.08779048322
x3=.758391737366
x4=1.52342309111



COEFS  STOa   STOb   STOx
```

Storing the Coefficients or Results

The results are displayed only; they cannot be edited and they are not stored in memory. The coefficients are used for SIMULT entry only; they do not update variables a11, b1, x1, etc.

- To store coefficients $a_{1,1}$, $a_{1,2}$, ..., $a_{n,n}$ into an $n \times n$ matrix, select <STOa>.

- To store coefficients b_1, b_2, ..., b_n into a vector of dimension n, select <STOb>.

- To store the results x_1, x_2, ..., x_3 into a vector of dimension n, select <STOx>.

Storing a Single Value

You can store any value on the coefficients entry or results screen to a variable. Press [STO▶] and enter the variable name after the Name= prompt.

Editing the Equation

You can edit the coefficients and calculate new solutions. Select <COEFS> to return to the first coefficient entry screen.

The simult Function in an Expression

The **simult** function on the Home screen or in a program, which can be copied from the CATALOG, accesses the SIMULT equation-solver feature.

simult(a_matrix**,**b_vector**)**

a_matrix is an n×n real or complex matrix containing the a coefficients. b_vector is an n-dimension real or complex vector containing the b coefficients. When the expression is evaluated, the result is an n-dimension vector containing the values of x.

Example: Simultaneous Equations

The SIMULT feature of the TI–85 can solve large systems of linear equations. Solve the 10 by 10 system below.

Problem

$$4x_1 + 9x_2 + 7x_3 + 8x_4 + 3x_5 + 5x_6 + 3x_7 + 5x_8 + 8x_9 + 6x_{10} = 3$$
$$8x_1 + 3x_2 + 8x_3 + 9x_4 + 9x_5 + 5x_6 + 4x_7 + 7x_8 + 0x_9 + 0x_{10} = 7$$
$$1x_1 + 2x_2 + 6x_3 + 7x_4 + 7x_5 + 0x_6 + 3x_7 + 4x_8 + 1x_9 + 5x_{10} = 9$$
$$4x_1 + 4x_2 + 0x_3 + 3x_4 + 0x_5 + 5x_6 + 7x_7 + 7x_8 + 2x_9 + 4x_{10} = 6$$
$$7x_1 + 5x_2 + 0x_3 + 7x_4 + 0x_5 + 9x_6 + 3x_7 + 6x_8 + 1x_9 + 0x_{10} = 5$$
$$2x_1 + 7x_2 + 0x_3 + 3x_4 + 4x_5 + 7x_6 + 8x_7 + 8x_8 + 3x_9 + 9x_{10} = 1$$
$$2x_1 + 6x_2 + 1x_3 + 5x_4 + 2x_5 + 4x_6 + 7x_7 + 8x_8 + 4x_9 + 7x_{10} = 5$$
$$4x_1 + 3x_2 + 6x_3 + 7x_4 + 0x_5 + 7x_6 + 9x_7 + 1x_8 + 6x_9 + 4x_{10} = 0$$
$$2x_1 + 1x_2 + 9x_3 + 3x_4 + 8x_5 + 6x_6 + 9x_7 + 5x_8 + 7x_9 + 5x_{10} = 0$$
$$9x_1 + 4x_2 + 3x_3 + 0x_4 + 9x_5 + 3x_6 + 8x_7 + 0x_8 + 1x_9 + 1x_{10} = 0$$

Procedure

1. Press [2nd] [SIMULT]. Enter **10** for the number of equations.

2. Enter the coefficients for each of the equations in the coefficient editor.

```
a1,1X1…a1,10X10=b1
  a1,1=
  a1,2=
  a1,3=
  a1,4=
  a1,5=
↓a1,6=
 PREV  NEXT  CLRa        SOLVE
```

3. Select ⟨SOLVE⟩. The results are displayed.

4. Select ⟨STOa⟩, ⟨STOb⟩, and ⟨STOx⟩ to store the coefficients and results to **SA**, **SB**, and **SX**.

```
x1=4.68371492704
x2=-4.56462355238
x3=-1.46983158834
x4=.800986449893
x5=-.27045916741
x6=-1.04111950523
↓x7=-2.48139301021
 COEFS  STOa  STOb  STOx
```

Chapter 15: Statistical Calculations

This chapter describes the TI–85 tools for entering and analyzing statistical data. These include entering data points in the STAT editor, calculating statistical results, performing regression analyses, and displaying statistical data graphically.

Statistical Analysis

The TI–85 analyzes one-variable and two-variable statistical data. Statistical data is stored in lists. Seven types of regression analyses are available to analyze statistical data.

One-Variable Statistics

One-variable statistics is used to analyze data with one measured variable. The optional y element is the frequency of occurrence of the associated x element. The y value must be an integer greater than or equal to zero or an error will result during the statistical results calculation.

Two-Variable Statistics

Two-variable statistics is used to analyze paired results between which there is a relationship. The x element is the value of the independent variable; the y element is the value of the dependent variable.

Statistical Data

A statistical analysis requires a set of data points (x, y pairs), each with an x value and a y value.

The data sets are stored in memory as two lists that can have user-assigned names. One list contains x values and the other contains y values.

- A pair of lists can be entered or edited as data points in the STAT editor (pages 15–4 through 15–7).

- A list can be entered, stored, and used from a command line (Chapter 12).

- A single list can be entered, stored, and edited element by element in the LIST editor (Chapter 12).

Statistical Analysis

When you perform a statistical analysis:

- The statistical results are calculated and stored in the result variables. You can display and use the contents of the current result variables, but you cannot store to them.

- The regression equation or the polynomial regression coefficients are calculated and stored for two-variable data.

- The list variables **xStat** and **yStat** are updated with the data from the lists used in the analysis.

Result variables always match the data in **xStat** and **yStat**. If you change **xStat** or **yStat** or edit any lists in the STAT editor, the result variables are cleared.

The STAT (Statistical) Menu

The STAT menu accesses the statistical editor, where you enter or edit lists, and commands to calculate and display statistical results, calculate regressions, draw (plot) statistical data, and forecast values based on the current regression equation.

The STAT Menu

When you press $\boxed{\text{STAT}}$, the menu keys are labeled with the statistical menu.

CALC	EDIT	DRAW	FCST	VARS

Item	Accesses
CALC	STAT list selection screen and menu of calculation instructions (page 15–8).

1-VAR	LINR	LNR	EXPR	PWRR
P2REG	P3REG	P4REG	STREG	

EDIT	STAT list selection screen and editor, where you enter and edit data (page 15–4).
DRAW	Menu of STAT drawing instructions (page 15–12).

HIST	SCAT	xyLINE	DRREG	CLDRW
DrawF	STPIC	RCPIC		

FCST	The forecast editor (page 15–14).
VARS	Menu of statistical result variables (page 15–10).

$\bar{x}$	σx	Sx	$\bar{y}$	σy
Sy	Σx	Σx^2	Σy	Σy^2
Σxy	RegEq	corr	a	b
n	PRegC			

Selecting and Loading Lists

To define new lists, edit existing lists, or calculate statistical results, you first must select the lists.

Selecting the List Names

1. From the STAT menu, either:

   - Select ⟨EDIT⟩ to enter or edit lists.

   - Select ⟨CALC⟩ to calculate statistical results.

   The list selection screen is displayed. The names of the lists most recently entered on the list selection screen are displayed. **xStat** and **yStat** are the first two menu items. The other menu keys are labeled with the names of existing lists in alphabetical order.

2. Enter the name of the list of x values and then press [ENTER]. You can:

   - Use the displayed name.

   - Select an existing name from the menu, which replaces the name that is displayed.

   - Type the name of a new or existing list of up to eight characters (case-sensitive). The keyboard is set in ALPHA-lock.

3. Enter the name of the list of y values and then press [ENTER]. Either:

   - The STAT editor is displayed (page 15–5).

   - The CALC menu is displayed (page 15–8).

Loading Lists in the Editor

Data points for statistical analysis can be entered in the STAT editor. You can select the names of existing lists to edit. You can enter data points to define new lists.

Loading the Lists

After you have selected the names of the lists, they are displayed in the STAT editor.

- If the lists are new, only the first data point is displayed. The x element is blank and the y element has a default value of 1.

- If the lists already exist, the contents are displayed.

If you load lists of unequal lengths, a warning message **list length mismatch** is displayed.

- To load the lists in the STAT editor, select ⟨CONT⟩. The x elements are filled with 0's or the y elements are filled with 1's in the shorter list.

- To leave the STAT application and return to the Home screen, select ⟨EXIT⟩.

Entering and Editing Data

After you have selected the names of the lists, you enter new data points and edit existing data points in the STAT editor. As you edit the data points, the lists that you are editing are changed in memory.

Editing Data Points with the STAT Editor

In the STAT editor, you enter or edit a pair of lists on a point-by-point basis. ↓ is displayed at the left of the fifth line if there are more than two data points. An example for two new lists is shown.

Enter new real values (which can be expressions) for the data points, as appropriate. The expression is evaluated when you move off the element or leave the editor.

For one-variable data, the y values represent the frequencies of occurrence and must be integers.

If you change any data point in the editor, the current statistical results are cleared.

Note: If you press a key that accesses a menu, the STAT editor menu moves to the seventh line (if it is not already there), and the selected menu is displayed on the eighth line.

Moving around the STAT Editor	Key	Action
	▶ ◀	Moves the cursor within a list element.
	▲ ▼	Moves the cursor between list elements.
	ENTER	Moves the cursor to the next list element.
	⟨INSi⟩	Inserts new data point (x, y pair) above the data point where the cursor is located.
	⟨DELi⟩	Deletes both the x and y values of the data point where cursor is located.

Note: To move quickly to the final data point, press ▲ from the first x value.

Sorting Lists

The TI–85 can sort the current data points into numerical order, from smallest to largest, based on either the x values or the y values.

- Select ⟨SORTX⟩ to sort based on the x values.

- Select ⟨SORTY⟩ to sort based on the y values.

The data points in the STAT editor are sorted and the elements in both the x list and the y list in memory are reordered correspondingly.

Note: To sort one of the lists without affecting the other list, use the LIST **sortA** or **sortD** instruction from the Home screen or from a program.

Clearing Lists

To clear all data points in both lists, select ⟨CLRxy⟩ from the STAT editor menu.

- The data points in the STAT editor are cleared and only the first data point is displayed. The x value is blank and y has a default value of 1.

- The lists in memory are cleared.

Calculating Statistical Results

To calculate statistical results or to perform a **regression** analysis, first select the lists to use and then select the type of calculation using the STAT CALC instructions. Press ⌜MORE⌝ to move around the menu.

The STAT CALC Menu

After you select the lists to use in the calculation (page 15–4), the menu keys are labeled with the first five items of the statistical calculation menu.

1-VAR	**LINR**	**LNR**	**EXPR**	**PWRR**
P2REG	**P3REG**	**P4REG**	**STREG**	

Analysis	Regression Equation
One-variable results	for y=integers ≥ 0
Linear regression	$y=a+bx$
Logarithmic regression	$y=a+b\ln(x)$, for x>0
Exponential regression	$y=a\,b^x$, for y>0
Power regression	$y=a\,x^b$, for x >0 and y>0
2nd-order polynomial regression	$y=a_2x^2+a_1x+a_0$ *
3rd-order polynomial regression	$y=a_3x^3+...+a_1x+a_0$ *
4th-order polynomial regression	$y=a_4x^4+...+a_1x+a_0$ *

*The coefficients $a_4,...,a_0$ are returned in the list **PRegC**; they do not update variables a0, a1, etc.

Notes about Statistical Calculations

For regression analysis, the statistical results are calculated using a least-squares fit. The transformed values used are:

- The linear model uses x and y.

- The logarithmic model uses $\ln(x)$ and y.

- The exponential model uses x and $\ln(y)$.

- The power model uses $\ln(x)$ and $\ln(y)$.

The polynomial models **P2REG**, **P3REG**, and **P4REG** use quadratic, cubic, and quartic polynomial least-squares regression (page 15–11).

Statistical Results Display

When you select the type of statistical calculation, it is calculated, the results are stored in the statistical result variables, and the most commonly referenced statistical result variables are displayed.

Calculating the Results

The results screens for **1-VAR**, **LINR**, and **P2REG** for the lists {12,236,99,63,87} and {1,3,2,3,1} are shown below.

One-Variable Analysis

Regression

Polynomial Regression

Continuing Calculations

To perform another type of statistical calculation on the same lists, select the type from the menu. The new calculation is performed immediately and the results are displayed.

Statistical Results

The TI-85 updates the statistical result variables when a one-variable or two-variable (but not polynomial) analysis is performed; you cannot store to them. These variables can be recalled using the STAT VARS menu (order shown below) or the VARS STAT (alphabetical order) screen.

The Statistical Result Variables

Variable Name	Meaning
$\bar{x}$	Mean of x values
σx	Population standard deviation of x
Sx	Sample standard deviation of x
$\bar{y}$	Mean of y values
σy	Population standard deviation of y
Sy	Sample standard deviation of y
Σx	Sum of x values
Σx^2	Sum of the squares of x values
Σy	Sum of y values
Σy^2	Sum of the squares of y values
Σxy	Sum of the product of x and y values
RegEq	Regression equation
corr	Correlation coefficient
a	y intercept of regression equation
b	Slope of regression equation
n	Number of data points
PRegC	Polynomial regression coefficients

One-Variable Results

After the **1-VAR** instruction is executed, only the result variables $\bar{x}$, Σx, Σx^2, **Sx**, σx, and **n** have a calculated value and are valid in expressions. The other result variables are not valid and cause an error if used.

Two-Variable Results

After a two-variable regression model (other than a polynomial regression) is executed, all result variables are calculated and are valid in expressions. The regression equation is stored in **RegEq**.

corr, the correlation coefficient, measures the goodness of fit of the equation with the data points. In general, the closer **corr** is to 1 or -1, the better the fit. If **corr** is zero, then x and y are completely independent.

Storing Results

To store results, return to the Home screen and store from the command line. You can access the names of the statistical result variables from the STAT VARS menu or from the VARS STAT screen. For example, $\bar{x} \rightarrow$ **A** stores the mean of the x values in the variable **A**.

Using a Statistical Result Variable in an Expression	All statistical result variables, including **RegEq** (regression equation) and **PRegC** (polynomial regression coefficients), can be used in expressions. To use a statistical result variable in an expression, type in the name or use the STAT VARS menu or the VARS STAT screen to copy the name, or RCL the contents into the expression.
Displaying the Value of a Statistical Result Variable	To display the value of a statistical result variable, enter the name of the variable on a blank line on the Home screen and press ENTER. The value is displayed.
The Regression Equation	**RegEq**, the regression equation, has numeric values for all coefficients, not the variable names; for example, **3 + 5x**. The coefficients have up to 14 digits. When **RegEq** is evaluated, the current value of x is used.
Storing the Regression Equation	**STREG** (store regression) stores the current regression equation to a variable. When you select ⟨STREG⟩, the cursor is positioned after **Name =** on the prompt line. Enter the name to which to store the regression equation. Press ENTER. For example, select ⟨STREG⟩ and then type **y1** ENTER to store the regression equation for graphing.
Polynomial Regressions	**P2REG**, **P3REG**, and **P4REG** (second, third, and fourth order polynomial regressions) perform a polynomial regression or a polynomial fit depending on the number of data points in the STAT lists. For example, **P3REG** performs a regression for 5 or more data points and a fit for 4 data points. The result for a polynomial regression is stored in **PRegC** (polynomial regression coefficients), a list containing the coefficients for the polynomial regression equation. For example, for **P3REG**, the result **PRegC = {3 5 -2 7}** would represent $y = 3x^3 + 5x^2 - 2x + 7$. **PRegC** is the only statistical result variable calculated for a polynomial regression.

The DRAW Menu

A STAT DRAW operation can be selected to display statistical data graphically. Lists xStat and yStat are used if current; otherwise, the lists most recently selected for editing or calculating are used. Press [MORE] to move around the menu. See Chapter 4 for information about graphing and drawing.

The STAT DRAW Menu

When you select ⟨DRAW⟩ from the STAT menu, the current graph is displayed and the menu keys are labeled with the statistical drawing menu.

HIST	SCAT	xyLINE	DRREG	CLDRW
DrawF	STPIC	RCPIC		

Item	Action
HIST	Draws a histogram of one-variable data.
SCAT	Draws a scatter plot of the data points.
xyLINE	Plots and connects data points with lines.
DRREG	Draws the regression equation (page 15–13).
CLDRW	Clears all drawings on current graph.
DrawF	Instruction that draws a function.
STPIC	Stores the current picture (page 15–13).
RCPIC	Superimposes picture on graph (page 15–13).

Histogram

HIST draws one-variable data as bar charts. The RANGE variable **xScl** defines the width of the bars (up to 63 bars). A data value on the edge of a bar is counted in the bar to the right.

Scatter Plot

SCAT draws each data point as a coordinate.

Line Drawing

xyLINE draws each data point as a coordinate in the order they are in the data lists and connects the points with a line. You may want to use SORTX to sort the data first.

Clearing a Drawing

CLDRW displays the current graph with no drawn elements.

The DrawF Function

When you select ⟨DrawF⟩, the instruction **DrawF** is copied to the Home screen. It draws a function in the current graphing MODE (Chapter 4).

Drawing Statistical Data

Three instructions, HIST, SCAT, and xyLINE draw statistical data on the current graph. The regression equation resulting from a statistical regression analysis can be drawn on the current graph.

Before Drawing

The STAT DRAW instructions are tied closely to the GRAPH operations (Chapter 4).

• The current RANGE variables define the viewing rectangle. You may want to check and change the RANGE variables.

• Any currently selected functions will be plotted. You may want to edit, select, or unselect functions in the GRAPH editor.

• Any drawings on the current graph will display. You may want to select ⟨CLDRW⟩ to clear any existing drawings and display the graph.

Drawing Statistical Data

To plot a graph of statistical data you have entered, select the type of drawing (HIST, SCAT, or xyLINE) from the STAT DRAW menu. If you have calculated a regression (or 1-VAR), **xStat** and **yStat** are used; otherwise, the last lists edited are used.

Plotting Statistical Data and Regression Equations

DRREG (draw regression) draws the current regression equation on the current graph.

To compare statistical data graphically to more than one regression:

1. After you calculate each regression, in **Func** MODE, select ⟨STREG⟩ from the STAT CALC menu. Enter **y**n at the **Name=** prompt. The contents of the current regression equation are copied to the y(x) function.

2. Select SCAT from the STAT DRAW menu. The regressions will be plotted and then the points will be drawn on the same graph.

Storing and Recalling a Stat Drawing

The **STPIC** instruction stores the current picture as a named item. The **RCPIC** instruction superimposes the stored picture on the current graph. When you select ⟨STPIC⟩ or ⟨RCPIC⟩, the cursor is positioned after **Name=** on the prompt line. The menu keys are labeled with the names of existing pictures. Enter the name. Press ENTER.

Forecasting a Statistical Data Value

The forecasting screen provides an easy method to forecast either an x or a y value based on the current regression equation. An error is returned and you cannot enter FCST if there is not a current regression equation.

The Forecasting Screen

When you select ⟨FCST⟩ from the STAT menu, the forecasting screen is displayed. The current regression equation model is on the top line. You cannot move the cursor onto the equation.

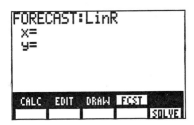

Entering the x or y Value

1. You must enter a real value (which can be an expression) for either x or y.

2. Position the cursor on the variable for which you want to solve and select ⟨SOLVE⟩. The value, if any, in the variable is ignored; you need not clear it.

The solution is displayed on the same screen. A square dot in the first column indicates the variable for which you solved. **FCST** does not update the variables **x, y**, and **Ans**.

Further Solutions

You can continue to enter and forecast x and y values from this display.

Storing x and y

You can store either value in the **FCST** editor to a variable. With the cursor on the value to store, press [STO▸], type the variable name after the **Sto** prompt on the line above the menu. Press [ENTER].

Polynomial Regression

If the most recent calculation was a polynomial regression, then only y values can be forecast.

Using STAT Operations on a Command Line

You can access the statistical analysis capabilities of the TI–85 on the Home screen and in the program editor. Names of functions and instructions can be typed, selected from the CATALOG, or selected from the STAT menu in the program editor.

Using STAT Operations on the Home Screen or from a Program

To use a STAT operation on the Home screen or from a program, enter the name of the instruction or function:

- Type the name.

- Select the name from the CATALOG.

- In the program editor, you can select the name from a STAT menu.

Specifying the Lists

Sortx, **Sorty**, and the CALC and DRAW instructions can be entered with or without list arguments.

- If there are no arguments, **xStat** and **yStat** are used as the lists of x and y values.

- If the second argument is omitted, frequencies of 1 are assumed for **OneVar** and **Hist**.

- If you enter arguments to the instruction, they specify the x list and y list to use. You can enter the names of lists, or copy the names from the STAT NAME or LIST NAME menus.

- You may type a list directly in the form {**1,2,3**}. This is a temporary list; however, when a statistical analysis is performed, the list is stored as **xStat** or **yStat**.

Note: STAT lists must be real, not complex. The lists must be the same length.

The STAT Menu in the Program Editor

When you press [STAT] in the program editor, the menu keys are labeled with the program STAT menu.

CALC	VARS	DRAW	fcstx	fcsty
Sortx	Sorty			

The STAT CALC Instructions

The **OneVar** instruction can have 0, 1, or 2 arguments:

OneVar, **OneVar** *x_list*, or **OneVar** *x_list,freq_list*

The **LinR, LnR, ExpR, PwrR, P2Reg, P3Reg**, and **P4Reg** instructions can have 0 or 2 arguments:

LinR or **LinR** *x_list,y_list*

If a statistical calculation is performed from the Home screen or from a program, the results screen is not displayed automatically; you must use the **ShwSt** instruction to display it.

The **ShwSt** instruction displays the current **OneVar** results or the most frequently used current regression results. **ShwSt** has no arguments.

When the instruction is executed, the results screen is displayed. In a program, if **Pause** (Chapter 16) is the next program command, the program halts temporarily for you to examine the screen. Execution resumes when you press ENTER.

The STAT CALC Menu in the Program Editor

The STAT CALC menu in the program editor is:

OneVar	LinR	LnR	ExpR	PwrR
P2Reg	P3Reg	P4Reg	ShwSt	

The STAT VARS Menu in the Program Editor

The STAT VARS menu lists the statistical result variables for use in expressions.

The STAT Forecast Functions

fcstx or **fcsty** returns a forecasted value for x or y based on the current regression equation. One argument, the known value, is required:

fcstx *y_value* and **fcsty** *x_value*

The STAT DRAW Instructions

Hist displays the current graph with the histogram. **Hist** can have 0, 1, or 2 arguments:

Hist, **Hist** x_list or **Hist** $x\_list,freq\_list$

Scatter displays the current graph with a scatter drawing. **xyline** displays the current graph with a drawing of connected data points. **Scatter** and **xyline** can have 0 or 2 arguments:

Scatter or **Scatter** x_list,y_list

DrawF draws a function on the current graph. It requires one argument, an expression in terms of **x**:

DrawF $expression$

ClDrw clears all drawings on the current graph, but does not display the graph.

ClDrw has no arguments.

StPic stores the current graph picture as a named item. **RcPic** superimposes the stored picture on the current graph.

StPic $picname$ or **RcPic** $picname$

The STAT DRAW Menu in the Program Editor

The STAT DRAW menu in the program editor is:

Hist	**Scatter**	**xyline**	**DrawF**	**ClDrw**
StPic	**RcPic**			

The STAT Sort Instructions

Sortx sorts the elements in the specified existing lists as data-point pairs in ascending order based on the x values. **Sorty** sorts based on the y values. The lists are changed in memory. If **xStat** or **yStat** are used for either list, the result variables are cleared.

Sortx $x\_listname,y\_listname$

Example: Analyzing Two-Variable Statistics

Find the best regression to fit the observed data by displaying the data graphically and then determining the best fit visually.

Problem

x	y	x	y
4.4	6.5	4.7	8.0
.4	-.9	-.8	3.5
-1.7	8.4	3.5	1.5
1.9	-1.9		

Procedure

1. Press [STAT]. Select ⟨EDIT⟩. Enter the names of the lists, **XLIST** and **YLIST**. Enter the data points. Select ⟨SORTX⟩ to order the points.

2. Return to the Home screen. Use the **min** and **max** functions from the MATH NUM menu to set meaningful RANGE values.

   min(XLIST)→xMin
   max(XLIST)→xMax
   min(YLIST)→yMin
   max(YLIST)→yMax

4. Press [2nd] [CATALOG] **F** (the keyboard is already in ALPHA-LOCK; this moves the cursor to the first command beginning with F). Press ⟨PAGE↓⟩ and copy **FnOff** to the Home screen and press [ENTER] to turn off all y(x) equations.

5. Press [STAT] ⟨DRAW⟩ ⟨xyLINE⟩. The seven observed points are plotted. Press [CLEAR] to clear the menus.

6. Press [STAT] ⟨CALC⟩. Press [ENTER] [ENTER] to accept the lists **XLIST** and **YLIST**.

7. Based on the scatter plot, select ⟨P2REG⟩, which is the best regression to fit the data.

8. The regression equation is calculated and the polynomial coefficients stored in **PRegC**. Select ⟨STREG⟩ and store the regression equation in **y1**.

9. Press [STAT] ⟨DRAW⟩ ⟨xyLINE⟩ to plot the regression equation on top of the points. Press [CLEAR] to view the entire graph.

Chapter 16: Programming

This chapter describes specific programming commands and how to enter and execute programs on the TI-85.

Chapter Contents

Using Programs

Most features of the TI-85 are accessible from programs.
Programs can access all variables and named items. The
number and size of programs that you can store are limited
only by available memory.

Notes about Using Programs

On the TI-85, programs are identified in memory by
names. Program names are governed by the same rules as
variable names (Chapter 2).

A program consists of a series of program commands,
which begin with a **:** (colon). A program command can be
an expression or an instruction.

The TI-85 checks for errors during program execution,
not as you enter or edit the program.

Variables are global. All variables can be accessed from
all programs. Storing a value to a variable from a program
changes the value in memory during program execution.

Programs update the variable **Ans** during program
execution, just as expressions do on the Home screen.

Programs do not update Last Entry as each command is
executed.

Menus in the Program Editor

When you display an application menu from the program
editor (page 16-20), the menu may be reorganized. You
see only the menu items that are allowed in programming
(characters or the names of variables and functions or
instructions).

Memory Management

The number of programs that you can store is limited
only by available memory. Memory status is displayed on
the MEM RAM screen. To increase available memory,
delete variables and named items, including other
programs, from the MEM DELET screen (Chapter 18).

To access the memory management menu, press [2nd]
[MEM] from the Home screen.

Executing a Program

To execute a program, begin on a blank line on the Home screen.

1. Enter the program name in one of the following ways:

   • Type the name (case-sensitive).

   • Copy the name from the VARS PRGM screen.

   • Copy the name from the PRGM NAMES menu.

2. Press [ENTER] and begin execution of the program.

While the program is executing, the busy indicator is displayed.

Note: There may be a brief pause the first time a program is executed while the TI–85 prepares to run the program.

"Breaking" a Program

[ON] acts as a break during program execution. When you press [ON] to stop program execution, **ERROR 06 BREAK** is displayed on the error screen.

• To go to where the interrupt occurred, select ⟨GOTO⟩.

• To return to the Home screen, select ⟨QUIT⟩.

Erasing a Program

1. If you are in the program editor, press [2nd] [QUIT] to return to the Home screen.

2. Press [2nd] [MEM] and then select ⟨DELET⟩ to display the data types menu.

3. Select ⟨PRGM⟩.

4. Move the cursor to the name of the program you want to delete and press [ENTER].

Sample Program

A program is a set of commands that can be executed sequentially, as if the commands had been entered one at a time on the Home screen. The sample program below shows how a TI-85 program appears. The program instructions are explained in this chapter.

Sample Program   The program below creates a table by evaluating a function, its first derivative, and its second derivative, at intervals in the graphing range, stores the results in a matrix and displays them. Then the function, its derivative, and its integral are graphed and displayed for the user to trace.

The program I/O (Input/Output) instructions allow you to enter values and display results during program execution (page 16-9).

The program CTL (control) instructions make it easy to repeat or skip a group of commands during program execution (page 16-14).

`PROGRAM:FUNCTABL`	Name of program
`:Func:Fix 2:FnOff`	Set MODE, turn off functions (GRAPH)
`:ZDecm`	Set viewing rectangle (GRAPH)
`:FUNCTION=.6x cos x`	Define the function (assignment statement)
`:ClLCD`	Clear the display (I/O menu)
`:Eq▶St(FUNCTION,STRIN G)`	Convert equation to string (STRNG)
`:Disp "FUNCTION=",STR ING`	Display the function (I/O menu)
`:{13,4}→dim MVALUES`	Create matrix to contain table (MATRX)
`:For(y,1,13)`	Begin **For** loop (CTL menu)
`:xMin+y*10*Δx→POINT`	Evaluate at every 10th **x** value
`:POINT→MVALUES(y,1)`	Store **x** value in column 1 of table
`:evalF(FUNCTION,x,POI NT)→MVALUES(y,2)`	Store evaluated function in column 2 of table
`:der1(FUNCTION,x,POIN T)→MVALUES(y,3)`	Store value of first derivative in column 3 of table
`:der2(FUNCTION,x,POIN T)→MVALUES(y,4)`	Store value of second derivative in column 4 of table
`:End`	End of **For** loop (CTL menu)
`:Pause MVALUES`	Display table
`:y1=FUNCTION`	Graph the function
`:y2=der1(FUNCTION,x)`	Graph the first derivative
`:y3=der2(FUNCTION,x)`	Graph the second derivative
`:Trace`	Display the graph to trace

The PRGM (Program) Menu

The PRGM menu accesses the names of all existing programs and the program editor, where you enter and edit programs.

The PRGM Menu

When you press [PRGM], the menu keys are labeled with the program menu.

NAMES   EDIT

Item	Accesses
NAMES	Menu of existing programs.
EDIT	The program editor, where you enter and edit program commands (page 16-6).

Names of Programs

The PRGM NAMES menu displays the names of existing programs in alphabetical order. Press [MORE] to move around the menu. When you select an item, the name of the program is copied to the cursor location.

Entering and Editing a Program

In general, any command that can be executed from the Home screen can be included in a program, and vice versa. A program command always begins with a colon.

Selecting a Program

To enter a new program or edit an existing one, you first must select the program name. Program names follow the rules for variable names.

1. Select ⟨EDIT⟩ to display the program selection screen.

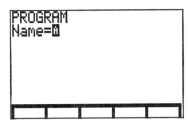

```
PROGRAM
Name=▓
```

2. Enter the name of the program to edit. The keyboard is set in ALPHA-lock. The menu keys are labeled with the names of existing programs in alphabetical order.

   • Type the name of the program, new or existing, up to eight characters (case-sensitive).

   • Select the name from the menu.

3. Press ENTER to display the program editor.

   • For a new program, the name of the program and the colon at the beginning of the first command line are displayed.

   • For an existing program, the instructions in that program are displayed.

Entering Program Commands   The program editor displays the name of the program and the editor menu.

```
PROGRAM:FUNCTABL
:Func:Fix 2:FnOff
:ZDecm
:FUNCTION=.6x cos x
:ClLCD
:Eq▸St(FUNCTION,STRIN
G)
PAGE↓ PAGE↑  I/O   CTL  INSc ▸
```

A colon indicates the beginning of each program command. Press [ENTER] to indicate the end of a command line. A command may be longer than one line on the screen; if so, it will wrap to the next screen line. [2nd] [◄] and [2nd] [►] move the cursor to the beginning and end of the command line.

To enter more than one command on a command line, separate them with a colon (Chapter 1).

You can use the RCL feature (Chapter 2) to copy (insert) the contents of a variable into a program, and then edit the characters.

You can use the RCL feature to copy (insert) all of the commands of one program into another, and then edit the commands. You can use this feature to create templates for frequently used groups of instructions, such as setting RANGE variables.

In the program editor, if you press a key that accesses a menu, the program editor menu moves to the seventh line (if it is not already there), and the selected menu is displayed on the eighth line.

To enter comments in a program, enter the comments as a string, for example: **"Test for change<.01"**

Entering and Editing a Program (Continued)

Changing a Program Command

To change a program command, move the cursor to the command.

- Position the cursor and then make the changes.

- Press [CLEAR] to clear (blank) the entire command line (the leading colon is not deleted), and then enter a new program command.

Inserting a Program Command

INSc (insert a command) inserts a blank command line above the command line where the cursor is positioned.

Deleting a Program Command

DELc (delete a command) is in the second set of menu items in the program editor menu.

To delete a command line, move the cursor to anywhere on the line and select ⟨DELc⟩. The entire command line (up to 100 characters), including any colons, is deleted.

"Undeleting" a Program Command

You can use DELc and UNDEL to "cut and paste" a program command line.

UNDEL (undelete) is in the second set of menu items in the program editor menu.

You can "undelete" the last command line (up to 100 characters) that you deleted. Position the cursor where you want the command and select ⟨UNDEL⟩. The command line, including the beginning colon, is inserted at the cursor position.

Copying a Program Command

You can "undelete" the last deleted command (up to 100 characters) more than once to copy it to other locations in the program, where you can edit it. You can "undelete" it into other programs, also.

Leaving the Program Editor

When you finish entering or editing a program, press [2nd] [QUIT] to leave the program editor and return to the Home screen in order to execute the program.

The I/O (Input/Output) Menu

The PRGM I/O menu displays the program input/output instructions. Press MORE to move around the menu. When you select an item from the menu, the name is copied to the cursor location.

The PRGM I/O Menu

When you select ⟨I/O⟩ from the program editor menu, the menu keys are labeled with the first five items of the PRGM I/O menu.

Input	Promp	Disp	DispG	Outpt
InpSt	getKy	ClLCD	PrtSc	"

Item	Accesses
Input	Instruction to enter and store values during execution or to use the free-moving cursor on a graph (page 16–10).
Prompt	Instruction to prompt for entry of values for one or more variables (page 16–10).
Disp	Instruction to display text, a value or the Home screen (page 16–11).
DispG	Instruction to display the current graph (page 16–12).
Outpt	Instruction to display text at a specified position on the display (page 16–12).
InpSt	Instruction to enter and store a string during execution (page 16–12).
getKy	Instruction to check the keyboard for a keystroke (page 16–13).
ClLCD	Instruction to clear the display (page 16–13).
PrtScrn	Instruction to print the current screen on a printer connected to an IBM®-compatible or Macintosh® computer (page 16–13).
"	" character for entering display text.

The Input/Output Instructions

The I/O instructions control input to and output from a program during execution. These instructions are on the PRGM EDIT I/O menu, which you access in the program editor.

The Input Instruction

- If the **Input** instruction has no arguments, it is used to explore a graph.

- If the **Input** instruction has one or two arguments, it is used to store a value to a variable.

The Input Instruction with Graphing

Input with no arguments displays the current graph. You can move the free-moving cursor, which updates **x** and **y** (and **r** and θ in **PolarGC** graph format). The dotted bar busy indicator displays. Press ENTER to resume execution.

The Input Instruction with Variables

Input with one argument (a variable name) displays a **?** during execution. Enter a value and press ENTER. The value is stored to that variable, and the program resumes execution.

Input *variablename*

Input with two arguments (a string of up to 21 characters to display as a prompt and a variable name) displays the string. Enter a value and press ENTER. The value is stored to that variable, and the program resumes execution.

Input *"string",variablename*

The Prompt Instruction

Prompt has one or more variable names as arguments. During execution the TI–85 displays each variable name, one at a time, followed by **=?**. Enter a value and then press ENTER for each variable. The values are stored, and the program resumes execution.

Prompt *variable1name,variable2name,* . . .

Notes

If an expression is entered in response to **Input** or **Prompt**, the expression is evaluated and then stored.

y*n* and other graphing variables are not valid arguments for **Input** or **Prompt**.

The Disp Instruction	• If **Disp** (display) has no arguments, it displays the Home screen.
	• If **Disp** has one or more arguments, it displays text and values.
Displaying the Home Screen	**Disp** with no arguments displays the Home screen.
Displaying Messages and Values	**Disp** with one or more arguments displays the value of each argument.

Disp *value1,value2,* . . .

If an expression is entered for the value, it is evaluated and then displayed according to the current MODE settings. String arguments display on the left of the current display line. Numerical values are displayed on the right of the following line.

For example, **Disp "The result is",** π**/2** displays

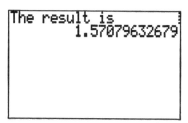

```
The result is
          1.57079632679
```

If **Pause** (page 16–18) is the next program command, the program halts temporarily so you can examine the screen. Press [ENTER] to resume execution.

Note: If a value or string is too large to display in its entirety, ... is displayed in the rightmost column, but the value cannot be scrolled. (To scroll the value, use **Pause** *value* instead.)

The Input/Output Instructions (Continued)

The DispG Instruction	**DispG** (display graph) displays the current graph. If **Pause** (page 16–18) is the next program command, the program halts temporarily so you can examine the screen. Press ENTER to resume execution.
	DispG has no arguments.
The Outpt Instruction	**Outpt** (output) displays text or values beginning at a specific position on the display and typing over any existing characters.
	Outpt requires three arguments. The first argument is the line (1 through 8), the second argument is the column (1 through 21), and the third argument is a string or a value. Expressions are evaluated and values are displayed according to the current MODE settings. Matrices are displayed in entry format and wrap to the next line.
	Outpt(_line,col,string_**)** or **Outpt(**_line,col,value_**)**
The InpSt Instruction	**InpSt** (input string) is used to enter strings during execution.
	InpSt with one argument (a variable name) prompts with a **?**. Enter the characters to be stored in a string and press ENTER. Do not enter the quotation marks. The string is stored to that variable, and the program resumes execution.
	InpSt _variablename_
	InpSt with two arguments (a string of up to 21 characters and a variable name) displays the string. Enter the characters to be stored in the string variable and press ENTER. Do not enter the quotation marks. The string is stored to that variable, and the program resumes execution.
	InpSt _string,variablename_
	Note: **InpSt** is used with the **St►Eq** instruction to input equations for graphing or solving. For example, replacing the third command in the sample program (page 16–4) with **InpSt "Enter function ",STRING:St►Eq(STRING,FUNCTION)** lets the user enter the function.

The getKy Function

getKy (get key) returns a number corresponding to the last key pressed, according to the diagram below. If no key has been pressed, it returns 0. **getKy** can be used inside loops to transfer control. **getKy** has no arguments.

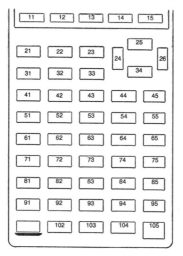

Note: You can press ⟨ON⟩ at any time to act as a break during execution (page 16–3).

The ClLCD Instruction

ClLCD (clear LCD) clears the Home screen during execution and places the cursor in the upper left corner, but program execution does not pause unless **Pause** is the next command. **ClLCD** has no arguments.

The PrtScrn Instruction

PrtScrn (print screen) prints the current screen on a printer attached to an IBM®-compatible or Macintosh® computer if you are using LINK-85 software (Chapter 19). The dotted bar busy indicator displays. Press ⟨ENTER⟩ to resume execution. **PrtScrn** has no arguments.

PrtScrn acts like **Pause** if you are not using LINK-85.

The CTL (Control) Menu

The PRGM CTL menu displays the program control
instructions. Press $\boxed{\text{MORE}}$ to move around the menu. When
you select an item from the menu, the name is copied to the
cursor location.

**The PRGM CTL
Menu**

When you select ⟨CTL⟩, the menu keys are labeled with
the first five items of the menu.

If	Then	Else	For	End
While	Repea	Menu	Lbl	Goto
IS>	DS<	Pause	Retur	Stop

Item	Accesses
If	Instruction to create conditional test (page 16–15).
Then	Instruction used with **If** instruction (page 16–15).
Else	Instruction used with **If-Then** instructions (page 16–15).
For	Instruction to create incrementing loop (page 16–16).
While	Instruction to create conditional loop (page 16–16).
Repeat	Instruction to create conditional loop (page 16–16).
End	Instruction to signify end of a loop, **If-Then**, or **Else** (page 16–15).
Menu	Instruction to define menu items and branches (page 16–17).
Lbl	Instruction to define a label (page 16–17).
Goto	Instruction to branch to a label (page 16–17).
IS>(	Instruction to increment and skip if greater than (page 16–18).
DS<(	Instruction to decrement and skip if less than (page 16–18).
Pause	Instruction to pause program execution (page 16–18).
Return	Instruction to return from a subroutine (page 16–18).
Stop	Instruction to stop execution (page 16–18).

The Control Instructions

The PRGM CTL (control) instructions direct the flow within an executing program. These instructions are on the PRGM EDIT CTL menu, which you access in the program editor.

The If Instruction

If is used for testing and branching. It has one argument: an expression defining a condition, frequently a relational test (Chapter 3).

If the condition is false (the argument evaluates to zero), the next program command is skipped. If the condition is true (the argument is nonzero), execution continues with the next program command. **If** instructions can be nested.

:**If** *condition*
:*command if true*
:*command*

The If-Then Instructions

Then following an **If** instruction executes a group of commands if the argument is true. An **End** instruction identifies the end of the loop.

:**If** *condition*
:**Then**
:*command if true*
:*command if true*
:**End**
:*command*

The If-Then-Else Instructions

Else following **If-Then** instructions executes a group of commands if the argument is false. An **End** instruction identifies the end of the loop.

:**If** *condition*
:**Then**
:*command if true*
:*command if true*
:**Else**
:*command if false*
:*command if false*
:**End**
:*command*

The End Instruction

End identifies the end of a group of program commands. Each **For**, **While**, **Repeat**, or **Else** loop must have an **End** instruction at the "bottom," as must a **Then** loop without an associated **Else**.

The Control Instructions (Continued)

The For Instruction

For is used for looping and incrementing. It has four arguments: the name of the variable to be incremented, a beginning value, a maximum or minimum value not to be exceeded, and a real increment (optional; the default is 1). An **End** instruction identifies the end of the loop. **For** loops can be nested.

:For(*variablename,begin,end,increment*)
:*command while end not exceeded*
:*command while end not exceeded*
:End
:*command*

The While Instruction

While performs a group of commands while a condition is true. It has one argument: an expression defining a condition, frequently a relational test (Chapter 3). An **End** instruction identifies the end of the loop.

The condition is tested when the **While** instruction is encountered. If the condition is true (the argument is nonzero), the program executes the next commands until an **End** instruction is encountered. If the condition is false (the argument evaluates to zero), the program executes the commands following the **End** instruction. **While** instructions can be nested.

:While *condition*
:*command while condition is true*
:*command while condition is true*
:End
:*command*

The Repeat Instruction

Repeat repeats a group of commands until a condition is true. It is similar to the **While** instruction, but the condition is tested when the **End** instruction is encountered; thus the commands will always be executed at least once. **Repeat** instructions can be nested.

:Repeat *condition*
:*command until condition is true*
:*command until condition is true*
:End
:*command*

The Menu Instruction

Menu sets up branching within a program as selected from menu keys. If the **Menu** instruction is encountered during execution, the eighth line of the display shows the specified menu items, the dotted bar busy indicator is displayed, and execution pauses until a menu key is pressed.

Menu can have up to 15 arguments: up to five sets of three arguments. The first argument in each set is the number of the menu key (1 through 5). The second argument is a string to display as the menu item, either the name of a string or text enclosed between " marks. The third argument is the label to branch to if that key is pressed. Undefined menu items are blank.

Menu(*n,string,label,...,n,string,label***)**

For example, during execution the instruction
Menu(1,"a=1",A1,2,"a>1",A2,5,"a=0",A5) displays

a=1	a>1			a=0

Then the program pauses until you press F1 , F2 , or F5 . If you press F1 , for example, the menu disappears and the program continues execution at the **Lbl A1** command.

The Lbl and Goto Instructions

Lbl (label) and **Goto** (go to) are used together for branching.

Lbl has one argument, which assigns a label to a program command. A label can be up to eight characters, following the rules for variable names.

Lbl *label*

Goto has one argument, a label to which to branch. The instruction transfers control to that label.

Goto *label*

The Control Instructions (Continued)

**The IS>
Instruction**

IS> (increment-and-skip) has two arguments: the name of a nonsystem variable and a real value not to be exceeded (which can be an expression). The instruction adds 1 to the variable; if the result is greater than the second argument, the next program command is skipped.

:**IS>**(*variablename,value*)
:*command if variable ≤ value*
:*command if variable > value*

**The DS<
Instruction**

DS< (decrement-and-skip) has two arguments: the name of a nonsystem variable and a real value (which can be an expression). The instruction subtracts 1 from the variable; if the result is less than the second argument, the next program command is skipped.

:**DS<**(*variablename,value*)
:*command if variable ≥ value*
:*command if variable < value*

**The Pause
Instruction**

Pause suspends execution of the program so you can see results or graphs. **Pause** can be used with no arguments or with one argument. The value of the argument is displayed and can be scrolled. While the program is paused, the dotted bar busy indicator displays. Press [ENTER] to resume execution.

Pause or **Pause** *value*

**The Return
Instruction**

Return exits a subroutine and returns to the calling program (page 16–19), even if encountered within nested loops. Any loops are ended. There is an implied **Return** at the end of any program called as a subroutine. Within the main program, it stops execution and returns to the Home screen.

Return has no arguments.

**The Stop
Instruction**

Stop stops execution of a program and returns you to the Home screen.

Stop has no arguments.

Calling Other Programs

On the TI-85, any program can be executed as a program or called from another program as a subroutine. Enter the name of the program to use as a subroutine on a line by itself (as a command).

Calling a Program from Another Program

To call one program from another, enter the name of the program as a command:

- Type the name of the program (case-sensitive).

- Select the name from the VARS PRGM screen.

- Press [PRGM] and select the name from the menu.

When this command is encountered during execution, the next command that the program executes is the first command in the second program. It returns to the subsequent command in the first program when it encounters either a **Return** instruction or the implied **Return** at the end.

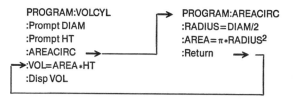

```
PROGRAM:VOLCYL              PROGRAM:AREACIRC
:Prompt DIAM               :RADIUS=DIAM/2
:Prompt HT                 :AREA=π∗RADIUS²
:AREACIRC →                :Return  →
:VOL=AREA∗HT
:Disp VOL
```

Notes about Calling Programs

Variables are global. The same variable name in two programs or on the Home screen accesses the same location in memory. If you store a new value to a variable from a program, it is changed in memory. Any future references to that variable use the new value.

The **Goto** and **Lbl** arguments are local to the program in which they are located. A label in one program is not "known" by another program. You cannot use a **Goto** instruction to branch to a label in another program.

The **Return** instruction exits a subroutine and returns to the calling program, even if encountered within nested loops. There is an implied **Return** at the end of any program called as a subroutine.

Using Application Operations in Programs

In the program editor, you can access application menus to copy instructions, functions, and names to program commands. Some may require arguments.

Accessing Application Operations in the Program Editor

To enter the name of an instruction or function from an application in a program command:

- Type the name (not case-sensitive).

- Select the name from the CATALOG.

- Select the name from the application menu.

In the program editor, you can access items on application menus using keystrokes similar to those you used in the application. For example, in the program editor you can press [2nd] [MATRX] ⟨MATH⟩ ⟨det⟩ to access **det** on the MATRX MATH menu. Menu items that are not appropriate as instructions or functions (EDIT, for example) do not appear. Therefore, items may be arranged slightly differently.

Applications using full-screen editors, such as SOLVER, SIMULT, POLY and MATH INTER, can be accessed from programs as instructions or functions with arguments. Appendix A lists instructions, functions, and their arguments.

When you select the item, the name is copied to the cursor location.

Setting Modes and Formats from Programs

To set modes or graph formats in a program, enter the name of the mode or format as an instruction, preceded by a colon. You can type in the name, select it from the CATALOG, or select it from the MODE or GRAPH FORMT screen.

To select the name from the MODE or GRAPH FORMT screen, from the program editor press [2nd] [MODE] or [GRAPH] ⟨FORMT⟩, place the cursor on the mode or format that you want to set, and press [ENTER]. The name is copied to the cursor location.

Note: If you select the number of digits for fixed mode, the instruction **Fix** n is copied to the cursor location.

Chapter 17: Applications

This chapter contains application examples that incorporate features described in the preceding chapters. Two of the examples use a program.

Chapter Contents

Characteristic Polynomial and Eigenvalues

Use the matrix and graphing features of the TI-85 to explore the relationship between the characteristic polynomial and eigenvalues of a matrix.

Procedure

1. On the Home screen or using the matrix editor, enter matrix **A**:

   ```
   [[-2  2  1  4]
    [ 3 -2  3  6]
    [ 7 -2  6  0]
    [-5  2  6 -2]]
   ```

2. The characteristic polynomial is defined as det(A − X∗I). To graph the polynomial, in **Func** MODE press GRAPH , select ⟨y(x)=⟩, select ⟨ALL-⟩ to turn off all functions, and then enter:

   y1 = det (A − x∗ident 4)

3. Select ⟨RANGE⟩. For exploration with TRACE and the free-moving cursor, you can enter expressions for **xMax** and **yMax** to set nice values of Δ**x** (.2) and Δ**y** (100) directly from the RANGE screen.

xMin = -10	**yMin = -2500**
xMax = -10 + .2∗126	**yMax = -2500 + 100∗62**
xScl = 10	**yScl = 500**

4. Select ⟨ROOT⟩ from the GRAPH MATH menu and find both real roots.

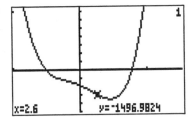

**Procedure
(Continued)**

5. Return to the Home screen and solve for the
   eigenvalues directly:

   eigVl A

   There are two real and two complex eigenvalues.
   Compare the real eigenvalues with the real roots
   found in step 4.

6. Press GRAPH and select ⟨TRACE⟩. Choose five
   integer points on the function; for example:

-2	-672
0	-940
2	-1360
4	-1740
5	-1750

7. Press STAT and enter the coordinates into lists **AX**
   and **AY** in the STAT editor.

8. Select ⟨CALC⟩, specify lists **AX** and **AY**, and then
   select ⟨P4REG⟩. This gives the unique fourth-order
   polynomial that contains these points.

9. Press GRAPH. Select ⟨y(x)=⟩ and enter:

   y2 = pEval(PRegC,x)

10. Select ⟨TRACE⟩ and compare **y1** and **y2**.

11. Return to the Home screen and find the roots of the
    PRegC polynomial:

    poly PRegC

12. Compare the results to the values found in steps 4
    and 5.

The Fundamental Theorem of Calculus

The TI–85 can graph functions that are defined by integrals or derivatives.

Problem 1

Demonstrate graphically that

$$F(x) = \int_1^x 1/t \, dt = \ln(x), \, x > 0 \text{ and that}$$

$$D_x \left[\int_1^x 1/t \, dt \right] = 1/x$$

Procedure 1

1. Press [2nd] [TOLER] and set **tol=1** and δ **=.01**.

2. In **Func** MODE, press [GRAPH]. Select ⟨RANGE⟩. Set the RANGE variables.

xMin=.01	**yMin=-1.5**
xMax=10	**yMax=2.5**
xScl=1	**yScl=1**

3. Select ⟨FORMT⟩. Select **SimulG**.

4. Select ⟨y(x)=⟩, select ⟨ALL-⟩ to turn off all functions, and then enter:

   y3=fnInt(1/t,t,1,x)
   y4=ln x

5. Select ⟨TRACE⟩. The busy indicator displays while the graph is being plotted. Use the cursor keys to compare the values of the two graphed functions, **y3** and **y4**.

6. Select ⟨y(x)=⟩, select ⟨ALL-⟩ to turn off **y3** and **y4**, and then enter:

   y5=nDer(y3,x)
   y6=1/x

7. Select ⟨TRACE⟩. The busy indicator displays while the graph is being plotted. Again, use the cursor keys to compare the values of the two graphed functions, **y5** and **y6**.

Problem 2

Explore the functions defined by

$$y = \int_{-2}^{x} t^2 \, dt, \quad \int_{0}^{x} t^2 \, dt, \quad \text{and} \quad \int_{2}^{x} t^2 \, dt$$

Procedure 2

1. Press $\boxed{\text{GRAPH}}$, select ⟨y(x)=⟩, and select ⟨ALL-⟩ to turn off all functions. On the TI–85, the three functions above can be defined simultaneously by:

   y7 = fnInt(t², t, {-2,0,2}, x)

2. Select ⟨FORMT⟩. Select **SeqG**.

3. Select ⟨ZSTD⟩ from the GRAPH ZOOM menu.

4. Select ⟨TRACE⟩. Notice that the functions appear identical, but shifted vertically by a constant.

5. Select ⟨y(x)=⟩, select ⟨ALL-⟩ to turn off **y7**, and then enter:

   y8 = nDer(y7, x)

6. Select ⟨TRACE⟩. Notice that although the three graphs defined by **y7** are unique, they share the same derivative.

Symmetry of the Roots of a Complex Number

Find the cube roots of (1,2). The nth roots of a complex number (a,b) are evenly spaced on a circle of radius abs(a,b) $\wedge$ (1/n), centered at the origin. In fact, all roots of a complex number are defined for k=0,1,...,n−1 by
(a,b) $\wedge$ (1/n)=abs(a,b)^(1/n) $*$ e $\wedge$ ((0,angle(a,b)+2kπ)/n)

Procedure

1. In **Func** MODE, press [GRAPH]. Select ⟨y(x)=⟩ and select ⟨ALL-⟩ to turn off all functions.

2. Select ⟨RANGE⟩, set **xMin = -2**, **xMax = 2**, **yMin = -2**, and **yMax = 2**, and then select ⟨ZOOM⟩ ⟨ZSQR⟩ to set the aspect ratio.

3. On the Home screen, enter and execute these instructions.

   ```
   1→K:3→N:1→A:2→B:P1=ab
   s (A,B)^(1/N)*e^((0,a
   ngle (A,B)+2*K*π)/N):
   PtOn(real P1,imag P1)
   :K+1→K
   ```

   The first four instructions initialize values to set up the problem. The next instruction stores the expression that defines the first root, which is a complex number when it is evaluated.

   The sixth instruction draws the root as a point.

4. On the Home screen, press [2nd] [ENTRY] to recall Last Entry. Delete the first instruction **1→K:**.

5. Press [ENTER] to execute all the commands again. The second point is drawn.

6. Return to the Home screen. Press [ENTER] to execute all the commands again. Repeat until all **N** points are drawn.

7. Press [GRAPH] ⟨DRAW⟩ ⟨CIRCL⟩.

8. Press [ENTER] to set the center of the circle at the origin, then move the cursor to one of the points. Press [ENTER] again. The circle is drawn, intersecting all points.

9. Select ⟨CLDRW⟩ from the DRAW menu. Return to the Home screen. Recall Last Entry. Insert the instruction **1→K:** at the beginning. Change **N** (number of roots) to **10**. Press [ENTER]. Repeat steps 4 through 8.

Fractions and Matrices

The TI-85 has the capability to compute and display fractions.

Procedure

1. In the MATRX editor, enter matrix **A**:

$$\begin{bmatrix} 0 & 4 & 5 & 7 \\ 9 & 7 & 0 & 7 \\ 1 & 2 & 1 & 3 \\ 7 & 4 & 0 & 0 \end{bmatrix}$$

2. On the Home screen, augment the identity matrix to **A** and find **A**⁻¹ using the **rref** function.

   rref aug(A,ident 4)

3. Display the solution portion of the result matrix as a fraction using the **►Frac** instruction.

   Ans(1,5,4,8)►Frac

   ```
   [[14/25    16/25   -14/5    -7/25  ]
    [-49/50  -28/25   49/10    37/50  ]
    [31/50    7/25    -21/10   -3/50  ]
    [13/50    11/25   -13/10  -19/50]]
   ```

4. Check the result by computing A⁻¹ ∗ A.

   round(Ans∗A,0)

   ```
   [[1  0  0  0]
    [0  1  0  0]
    [0  0  1  0]
    [0  0  0  1]]
   ```

Finding the Area between Curves

Find the area of the region bounded by
$f(x) = 300 \, x/(x^2 + 625)$
$g(x) = 3 \cos 0.1x$
$x = 75$

Procedure

1. In **Func** MODE, press $\boxed{\text{GRAPH}}$, select ⟨y(x)=⟩, select ⟨ALL-⟩ to turn off all functions, and enter:

   y9 = 300 x/(x² + 625)
   y10 = 3 cos .1 x

2. Select ⟨RANGE⟩. Set the RANGE variables.

   xMin = 0   **yMin = -5**
   xMax = 100   **yMax = 10**
   xScl = 10   **yScl = 1**

3. Select ⟨GRAPH⟩.

4. Select ⟨MATH⟩ ⟨ISECT⟩. Move the TRACE cursor near the intersection of the functions. Press $\boxed{\text{ENTER}}$ to select **y9**. The cursor moves to **y10**. Press $\boxed{\text{ENTER}}$. The solution uses the SOLVER. The cursor location is used as an initial guess. The value of **x** at the intersection, which is the lower limit of the integral, is stored in **Ans** and **x**.

5. Return to the Home screen. To see graphically the area you are going to integrate, enter:

   Shade(y10,y9,Ans,75)

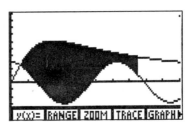

6. Press $\boxed{\text{2nd}}$ [TOLER] and set **tol**=1E-5. Return to the Home screen and compute the integral.

   fnInt(y9 – y10,x,Ans,75)

   The area is **325.839961998**.

Minimizing the Solid of Revolution

Consider the solid of revolution determined by revolving the regions bounded by the line $y=c$ for $0 \leq c \leq 1$ and the curve $y=\sin x$ for $0 \leq x \leq \pi$ about the line $y=c$. Find the value of c that minimizes this volume and the minimum volume.

Problem

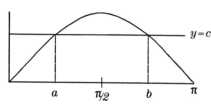

Procedure

1. Let $a=\sin^{-1} c$ and $b=\pi-\sin^{-1} c$. From visual inspection, the problem can be divided into three intervals: 0 to a, a to b, b to π. For any value of c, $0 \leq c \leq 1$, the volume of the solid of revolution is given by
   $$V = \int_0^a \pi(c - \sin x)2 \, dx$$
   $$+ \int_b^a \pi(c - \sin x)2 \, dx$$
   $$+ \int_b^\pi \pi(c - \sin x)2 \, dx.$$

2. By symmetry around π/2, the volume simplifies to
   $$V = 2*(\int_0^a \pi(c - \sin x)^2 \, dx$$
   $$+ \int_a^{\pi/2} \pi(c - \sin x)^2 \, dx)$$
   $$= 2\pi * \int_0^{\pi/2} (c - \sin x)^2 \, dx.$$

3. Press [2nd] [TOLER] and set **tol=1E-5**.

4. Press [GRAPH]. Select ⟨y(x)=⟩ and select ⟨ALL-⟩ to turn off all functions. On the TI–85, **x** is the independent variable for function graphing, so substitute **t** for x and **x** for c:

   y11 = 2πfnInt((x − sin t)², t, 0, π/2)

5. Select ⟨RANGE⟩. Set the RANGE variables.

xMin = 0	**yMin = 0**
xMax = 1	**yMax = 5**
xScl = .5	**yScl = 1**

6. Select ⟨FMIN⟩ from the GRAPH MATH menu. The busy indicator displays while the function is plotted.

7. Press [ENTER] to select **y11**. The busy indicator displays and the solutions are displayed at the bottom. The minimum volume occurs at **x = .63662089163** ($c=2/\pi$). It is **y = .93480220056** ($V(c)=\pi^2/2-4$).

Electrical Circuits

Use the list and statistical drawing features of the TI–85 to analyze an unknown electrical circuit.

Problem

The d.c. current in milliamps (CURR) and voltage in volts (VOLT) data shown was measured on an unknown circuit in a "black box." Calculate power in milliwatts.

What is the average of the measured power?

Estimate the power in milliwatts at a current of 125 ma using three TI–85 features: free-moving cursor, interpolate, and regression forecast.

CURR (ma)	VOLT (volts)
10	2
20	4.2
40	10
60	18
80	32.8
100	56
120	73.2
140	98
160	136

Procedure

1. Press [2nd] [LIST]. Use the list editor to enter list **CURR**.

2. Press [2nd] [LIST]. Use the list editor to enter list **VOLT**.

3. Press [2nd] [QUIT] to return to the Home screen.

4. Calculate and store values for power. To see the results, use the LIST editor or the STAT editor, or display the lists on the Home screen.

   CURR∗VOLT→POWER

5. Press [GRAPH] ⟨RANGE⟩. Set the RANGE variables.

   xMin = 0   yMin = 0
   xMax = max(POWER) yMax = max(CURR)
   xScl = 1000   yScl = 10

Procedure (Continued)

6. Return to the Home screen. Plot the pairs.

FnOff
xyLine POWER,CURR

7. Use the free-moving cursor to estimate **POWER** at **CURR=125**.

8. Press [2nd] [MATH] and select ⟨INTER⟩. To interpolate **POWER** at **CURR=125** enter the nearest pairs: **x1=POWER(7)**, **y1=CURR(7)**, **x2=POWER(8)**, and **y2=CURR(8)**. Enter **y=125** and solve for **x**.

9. Press [STAT], select ⟨CALC⟩ and specify lists **POWER** and **CURR**. Calculate each of the regression types in turn to determine which gives the best value of **corr** (PWRR).

10. Execute the best regression again. Select ⟨FCST⟩. To forecast **POWER** at **CURR=125**, enter **y=125** and solve for **x**. Compare to your answers from steps 7 and 8.

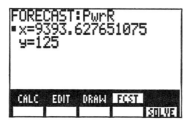

Unusual Equation

Using the SOLVER or GRAPH MATH operations, you can easily solve problems that are difficult or impossible to solve analytically.

Problem

Solve for x: $\int_0^x \frac{\sin t}{t} dt = 1.8$

Procedure

1. On the Home screen, enter:

   y12 = fnInt(sin t/t,t,0,x)

2. On the TOLERANCES editor, set **tol = 1**.

3. On the SOLVER editor, define **eqn** as:

   y12 = 1.8

4. On the SOLVER variables screen, enter **0** as your initial guess for **x**, and select 〈SOLVE〉. (**t** is a dummy variable of integration and may be any value; use 1.) The busy indicator displays while the solution is calculated.

5. Select 〈RANGE〉. Change the RANGE variables.

xMin = 0	**yMin = -.5**
xMax = 10	**yMax = .5**
xScl = 1	**yScl = .1**

6. Select 〈GRAPH〉. The value of **left-rt** for each value of **x** is plotted. Notice that the problem has at least two solutions.

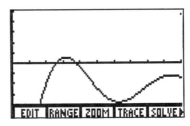

7. Move the cursor near the solution that you did not find in step 4. Press 〈SOLVE〉 to calculate the second solution using the cursor location as your initial guess.

8. Press [GRAPH] ⟨y(x)=⟩. Notice that **yl2** contains the expression stored from the Home screen in step 1. Enter **yl3 = 1.8**.

9. Select ⟨RANGE⟩. Set the RANGE variables.

xMin = 0   **yMin = 0**
xMax = 10 **yMax = 2**
xScl = 1   **yScl = .1**

10. Select ⟨FORMT⟩. Select **SimulG**.

11. Select ⟨ISECT⟩ from the GRAPH MATH menu.

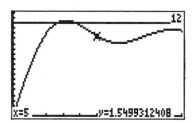

12. Move the cursor to one of the intersection points and press [ENTER] to select the function.

    Hint: You can TRACE more quickly by placing the cursor on function **yl3**, because the function evaluation for each **x** is faster.

13. Press [ENTER] to select the other function. The busy indicator displays as the intersection is calculated.

14. Repeat for the other intersection. Compare the solutions.

Program: Taylor Series

This program lets the user enter a function and specify the order and center point, calculates the Taylor series approximation for the function, and plots them both. It demonstrates several CTL and I/O instructions.

Procedure

1. Enter the program to store the Mobius series. This program will be executed from the TAYLOR program as a subroutine.

```
PROGRAM:MOBIUS
:{1,-1,-1,0,-1,1,-1,0
,0,1,-1,0,-1,1,1,0,-1
,0,-1,0}→MSERIES
:Return
```

2. Enter the program to calculate the Taylor series.

```
PROGRAM:TAYLOR
:Func:FnOff
:y14=pEval(TPOLY,x-ce
nter)
:1E-9→ε:.1→r r              ε is on CHARS GREEK menu
:CILCD
:InpSt "FUNCTION: ",E       User enters y(x) function
Q
:St▸Eq(EQ,y13)
:Input "ORDER: ",orde       User enters order
r
:order+1→dimL TPOLY
:Fill(0,TPOLY)
:Input "CENTER: ",cen       User enters center
ter
:evalF(y13,x,center)→
f0
:f0→TPOLY(order+1)
:If order≥1
:der1(y13,x,center)→T
POLY(order)
:If order≥2
:der2(y13,x,center)/2
→TPOLY(order-1)
:If order≥3
:Then                       Begin **Then** group
:MOBIUS                     Call as subroutine
:For(N,3,order,1)           Begin **For** group
:abs f0→gmax:gmax→bml
:1→m:0→ssum
```

`:While abs bmi≥ε*gmax`	Begin **While** group
`:While MSERIES(m)==0`	Begin **While** group
`:m+1→m`	
`:End`	End **While** group
`:0→bsum`	
`:For(J,1,m*N,1)`	Begin **For** group
`:rr*e^(2π(J/(m*N))*(0`	
`,1))+(center,0)→x`	
`:real y13→gval`	
`:bsum+gval→bsum`	
`:max(abs gval,gmax)→g`	
`max`	
`:End`	End **For** group
`:bsum/(m*N)-f0→bmi`	
`:ssum+MSERIES(m)*bmi→`	
`ssum`	
`:m+1→m`	
`:End`	End **While** group
`:ssum/(rr^N)→TPOLY(or`	
`der+1-N)`	
`:End`	End **For** group
`:End`	End **Then** group
`:ZStd`	

3. Return to Home screen, execute program TAYLOR.

4. When prompted, enter the function, order, and center of the series approximation.

Note: The higher-order derivative values necessary for this program are calculated numerically based on the methods in J. N. Lyness and C. B. Moler, "Numerical Differentiation of Analytic Functions," *SIAM Journal of Numerical Analysis* 4 (1967): 202–210.

Convergence of the Power Series

Use the TI-85 sum and seq functions to plot partial sums of infinite power series.

Problem

Although the analytic antiderivative of (sin x)/x does not exist, an infinite series analytic solution can be found by taking the series definition of sin x, dividing each term of the series by x, and integrating term by term to yield:

$$\sum_{n=1}^{\infty} -1^{n+1} t^{2n-1} / ((2n-1) (2n-1)!)$$

Finite approximations of this power series solution can be plotted on the TI-85 using the **sum** and **seq** functions.

Procedure

1. Press [2nd] TOLER. Set **tol=1**.

2. Press [2nd] MODE. Select **Param** and **Radian**.

3. Press [GRAPH]. Select ⟨E(t)=⟩, select ⟨ALL–⟩ to turn off all functions.

4. Enter the parametric equations for the power series approximation:

   xt1=t
   yt1=sum seq((-1)^(j+1)t^(2j–1)/((2j–1)(2j–1)!),j,1,10,1)

5. Use **fnInt** to plot the antiderivative of (sin x)/x to compare to the plot of the power series approximation Enter the parametric equations:

   xt2=t
   yt2=fnInt(sin w/w,w,0,t)

6. Select ⟨RANGE⟩. Set the RANGE variables:

tMin = -15	xMin = -15	yMin = -3
tMax = 15	xMax = 15	yMax = 3
tStep = 0.5	xScl = 1	yScl = 1

7. Select ⟨FORMT⟩. Select **SimulG**.

**Procedure
(Continued)**

8. Select ⟨GRAPH⟩ to plot the parametric equations. (Use CLEAR to see the graph without the menu.)

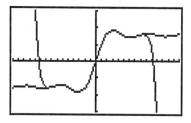

9. Modify **yt1** to compute the first 16 terms of the power series by changing **10** to **16.** Plot the equations again.

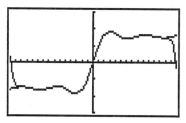

10. Note that in this example **tStep** controls the plotting speed. Change **tStep** to **1.0** and observe the differences in plotting speed and smoothness of the curves.

Linear Circuits

Use the simultaneous equation feature of the TI-85 to solve a linear circuit, which requires complex coefficients. On the TI-85 you can display complex elements in either rectangular or polar format.

Problem

Systems of equations with complex coefficients are very common in engineering applications. The solution to the system is a vector with complex elements. Consider the following circuit:

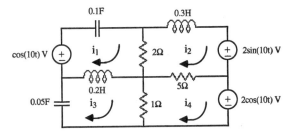

In the phasor domain the circuit becomes:

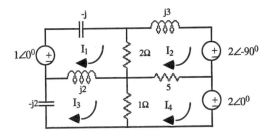

Impedance is in ohms and voltage source is in volts. Using the diagram, the simultaneous equations for the phasor currents I_1 though I_4 are, where j is the notation commonly interchanged with $i = \sqrt{(-1)}$:

$$
\begin{array}{rcl}
(2+j)\,I_1 \quad -2\,I_2 -j2\,I_3 & = & 1 \\
-2\,I_1 + (7+j3)\,I_2 \quad\quad -5\,I_4 & = & j2 \\
-j2\,I_1 \quad\quad +I_3 \;-I_4 & = & 0 \\
-5\,I_2 \;-I_3 +6\,I_4 & = & \text{-2}
\end{array}
$$

Procedure

1. Press [2nd] [SIMULT]. Enter **4** for the number of equations.

2. Enter the coefficients for each equation:

   $a_{1,1} = $ **(2,1)**
   $a_{1,2} = $ **-2**
   $a_{1,3} = $ **(0,-2)**
   $a_{1,4} = $ **0**
   $b_1 = $ **1**

   $a_{2,1} = $ **-2**
   $a_{2,2} = $ **(7,3)**
   $a_{2,3} = $ **0**
   $a_{2,4} = $ **-5**
   $b_2 = $ **(0,2)**

   $a_{3,1} = $ **(0,-2)**
   $a_{3,2} = $ **0**
   $a_{3,3} = $ **1**
   $a_{3,4} = $ **-1**
   $b_3 = $ **0**

   $a_{4,1} = $ **0**
   $a_{4,2} = $ **-5**
   $a_{4,3} = $ **-1**
   $a_{4,4} = $ **6**
   $b_4 = $ **-2**

3. Select ⟨SOLVE⟩ to solve the system of equations.

   $x_1 = $ **(-.056299261854,.208557487802)**
   $x_2 = $ **(.142624796697,.938321030902)**
   $x_3 = $ **(-.757913174027,.803202802452)**
   $x_4 = $ **(-.340798198424,.91580132616)**

4. Select ⟨STOx⟩, enter **SOL**, and then press [ENTER] to store the solution vector to a variable.

5. To see the results in Polar format, press [2nd] [MODE] and select **PolarC**. On the Home screen, display the vector **SOL**. Each element is displayed in polar format, which is appropriate for phasor quantities.

Reservoir Problem

Use parametric graphing on the TI-85 to simulate water flow out of a hole in a reservoir.

Problem

Many transient phenomena can be best understood through the use of animation. On the TI-85, parametric graphing can be used to visualize a process over time, providing valuable insight into dynamic problems.

Suppose we have a water reservoir with a relatively small hole in its side. We are interested in the general problem of the distance from the reservoir where the water jet will hit the ground. Specifically, we want to know at what height on the reservoir should the hole be placed to get the maximum distance for the water jet.

Assume that the height of the reservoir is 2 meters and that the diameter of the hole is small in comparison to the diameter of the reservoir. Assume that the hole is at x=0, there is no acceleration in the x-direction, and there is no initial velocity in the y-direction.

Integrating the definition of acceleration in both the x and y directions twice yields the equations $x=v_0 t$ and $y=h_0-(g t^2)/2$. Solving Bernoulli's equation for v_0 and substituting into $v_0 t$, we get the parametric equations:

$$xt = t \sqrt{(2 g (2 - h_0)}$$
$$yt = h_0 - (g t^2) / 2$$

where t is the time in seconds, h_0 is the height of the hole in the reservoir in meters, and g is the TI-85 gravitational constant.

Procedure

1. Press [2nd] MODE. Select **Param**.

2. Press [GRAPH]. Select ⟨E(t)=⟩, select ⟨ALL–⟩ to turn off all functions.

3. To plot the equations with the hole at height **0.5** meters, enter the equations (**g** may be entered from the keyboard or from the CONS menu):

   xt3=t√(2g(2–0.5)
   yt3=0.5–(g*t²)/2

Procedure
(Continued)

4. Press [ENTER] to move to **xt4**. Press [2nd] [RCL] **xt3** to recall the contents of **xt3** into **xt4** and then change the height to **0.75** meters. Repeat for **yt4**.

5. Repeat step 3 to create three more pairs of equations using the heights **1.0**, **1.5**, and **1.75** meters.

6. Select ⟨RANGE⟩. Set the RANGE variables:

tMin = 0	**xMin = 0**	**yMin = 0**
tMax = √(4/g)	**xMax = 2**	**yMax = 2**
tStep = 0.01	**xScl = 0.5**	**yScl = 0.5**

7. Select ⟨FORMT⟩. Select **SimulG**.

8. Select ⟨GRAPH⟩ to graph the trajectory of the water jets from the 5 chosen heights. What height seems to provide the maximum distance for the water jet? (Use CLEAR to see the graph without the menu.)

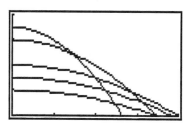

9. Use TRACE to determine the time elapsed before each water jet hits the ground.

Predator-Prey Model

Using the TI-85 differential equations plotting, you can explore models such as the well-known predator-prey model in biology. Determine the numbers of wolves and rabbits that maintain population equilibrium.

Problem

Explore a population of wolves and rabbits in a certain region using the TI-85 differential equations model. Let:

W = Density of the wolves in the region.
r_W = Instantaneous death rate of the wolves in the absence of rabbits.
k_W = Measure of skill of the wolves catching the rabbits.
R = Density of the rabbits in the region.
r_R = Innate capacity for increasing the rabbit population assuming plenty of population.
k_R = Measure of skill of rabbits in eluding the wolves.

And the equation for the rate of change of the wolf population is:

$dW/dt = (-r_W + k_W * R)W$

Then the equation for the rate of change of the rabbit population is:

$dR/dt = (r_R - k_R * W)R$

This is a coupled system of two first-order differential equations that can be translated into TI-85 syntax and plotted using several different initial conditions.

Procedure

1. Press ⟨2nd⟩ MODE. Select **DifEq**.

2. Press ⟨GRAPH⟩. Select ⟨Q't)=⟩, select ⟨ALL−⟩ to turn off all functions.

3. Enter the differential equations where **Q'1** is the rate of change of the wolf population, **Q'2** is the rate of change of the rabbit population, and r_W=0.5, k_W=0.02, r_R=1, and k_R=0.1.

   Q'1=(-0.5+0.02Q2)Q1
   Q'2=(1−0.1Q1)Q2

**Procedure
(Continued)**

4. Select ⟨RANGE⟩. Set the RANGE variables:

tMin = 0	xMin = 0	yMin = 0
tMax = 40	xMax = 40	yMax = 80
tStep = 0.2	xScl = 10	yScl = 10
tPlot = 0		difTol = 0.001

5. Select ⟨INITC⟩. Set the initial conditions to:

QI1 = 4	(number of wolves)
QI2 = 20	(number of rabbits)

6. Select ⟨AXES⟩. Set the axes to **x=t** (time) and **y=Q** (plots both rabbits and wolves) and select ⟨GRAPH⟩ to see the population of wolves and rabbits over time.

7. Select ⟨RANGE⟩. Set **tMax = 10**.

8. Select ⟨AXES⟩ and change the axes to **x=Q1** (wolves) and **y=Q2** (rabbits) and select ⟨GRAPH⟩ to see the Phase Plane of the system.

9. Select ⟨StPic⟩ and store the picture **PRED**.

10. Move the cursor to where you think the equilibrium point might be. Do not press ENTER.

11. Press 2nd [QUIT] to return to the Home screen, enter **x→QI1:y→QI2**, and press ENTER.

12. Press GRAPH and select ⟨GRAPH⟩ to plot with your new guess.

13. Select ⟨RcPic⟩ and recall the picture **PRED**. Select ⟨StPic⟩ and store the new picture **PRED** showing both graphs.

14. Position the cursor for a new guess, and repeat steps 11, 12, and 13 until you are pleased with the solution.

Program: Sierpinski Triangle

This program creates a drawing of a famous fractal, the Sierpinski Triangle, and stores the drawing in a picture variable, TRIANGLE.

Procedure

1. Enter the program.

```
PROGRAm:SIERPIN
:FnOff
:ClDrw
:0→K
:0→xMin                          Set viewing rectangle
:1→xMax
:0→yMin
:1→yMax
:rand→x
:rand→y
:While (K<3000)                  Control density of picture
:rand→N
:If N≤(1/3)
:Then
:.5x→x
:.5y→y
:PtOn(x,y)
:End                             End of Then group
:If N>(1/3) and N≤(2/
3)
:Then
:.5(.5+x)→x
:.5(1+y)→y
:PtOn(x,y)
:End                             End of Then group
:If N>(2/3)
:Then
:.5(1+x)→x
:.5y→y
:PtOn(x,y)
:End                             End of Then group
:K+1→K
:End                             End of While group
:StPic TRIANGLE
```

2. Return to Home screen, execute program **SIERPIN**.

Note: After executing this program, you can recall and display the picture **TRIANGLE**.

Chapter 18: Memory Management

This chapter describes how to manage memory on the TI–85. To increase the amount of memory available for use in new applications, occasionally you may want to delete from memory items that you are no longer using.

Chapter Contents

The MEM (Memory) Menu

[2nd] [MEM] **accesses memory management, where you display the amount of memory available and used, delete variables, clear memory, or reset the calculator.**

The MEM Menu   When you press [2nd] [MEM], the menu keys are labeled with the memory menu.

RAM   DELET   RESET

Item	Accesses
RAM	Displays the amount of RAM available and used, by type of named item (page 18–3).
DELET	Allows you to access named items by data type to delete (page 18–3).

ALL   REAL   CPLX   LIST   VECTR
MATRX STRNG   EQU   CONS   PRGM
GDB   PIC

Item	Accesses
RESET	Allows you to delete all named items, reset defaults, or both (page 18–5).

Managing Memory

The RAM menu item displays how much memory is available for you to use and how much is used by each data type and by each variable within a data type. The TI-85 has approximately 28 kilobytes of memory available for your use.

Checking Available Memory

To display the amount of memory used, by data type, and the amount available for use:

1. Press [2nd] [MEM] to display the memory management menu.

2. Select ⟨RAM⟩. The MEM screen temporarily replaces the screen on which you are working.

   The number of bytes of memory currently available for use is shown on the top line. For each data type, the number of bytes used is shown. (The values vary depending on your variables.)

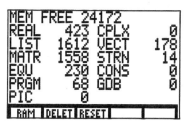

   Note: **xStat, yStat, Ans,** and Last Entry always occupy space in memory and cannot be deleted.

Checking Memory Used by Specific Variables

The DELET menu item (page 18–4) shows the bytes of memory used by individual items.

Deleting Items from Memory

Any item that you have created and named can be deleted from memory from the DELETE screen.

**Deleting
Individual
Named Items**

1. Press [2nd] [MEM] to display the memory management menu.

2. Select ⟨DELET⟩. The DELETE screen and menu temporarily replace the screen on which you are working.

ALL	REAL	CPLX	LIST	VECTR
MATRX	STRNG	EQU	CONS	PRGM
GDB	PIC			

3. Select the data type. The names of the variables in that data type are displayed in alphabetical order.

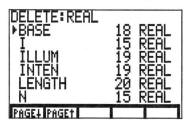

4. An arrow at the left of the name indicates the selection cursor. To move around the list:

   • Press a letter to move quickly to function names beginning with that letter. (The keyboard is set in ALPHA-lock.)

   • Use ⟨PAGE↓⟩ and ⟨PAGE↑⟩ to move to the next screen of names.

   • Use [▲] and [▼] to move up and down the list.

5. Select [ENTER] to delete the item that the cursor is on. **The item is deleted immediately.**

You may continue to select single items to delete.

Note: You cannot delete **xStat**, **yStat**, **PRegC**, or **RegEq**. To delete a parametric equation, delete the **xt**n component.

Resetting the TI-85

Resetting the TI-85 restores memory to the factory settings.
Because there are other operations that clear only selected
portions of memory, the TI-85 should need to be reset only
under special circumstances.

**Resetting the
Calculator**

To reset the TI-85:

1. Press [2nd] [MEM] to display the memory management
   menu.

2. Select ⟨RESET⟩. The menu keys are labeled with the
   RESET menu.

   ALL   MEM   DFLTS

3. Make the appropriate menu selection.

   • To reset both memory and defaults, select ⟨ALL⟩.

   • To clear only values stored in memory, including
     programs, graph databases, and pictures, but leave
     the defaults as you have them set, select ⟨MEM⟩.

   • To return the defaults to the factory settings, but
     leave values stored in memory, select ⟨DFLTS⟩.

4. The message **Are you sure?** is displayed.

   • If you do not want to reset, select ⟨NO⟩. You are
     returned to the Home screen.

   • If you want to reset, select ⟨YES⟩. The TI-85 is
     reset and the messages **Mem cleared** and/or
     Defaults set are displayed on the Home screen.

Leaving a Memory Management Screen

You can leave any memory management screen at any time.

Leaving a Memory Management Screen

To leave any memory management screen or menu:

- Press the appropriate keys to go to an application.

- Press [2nd] [QUIT] to return to the Home Screen.

Chapter 19: Communications Link

The TI–85 has a port to let you communicate with another TI–85 or with a PC or Macintosh®. This chapter describes how to communicate with another TI–85.

Chapter Contents

The TI-85 Link

The TI-85 communication capability lets you share variables and programs or entire memory contents with another TI-85. You also can share TI-85 variables, programs, or memory backup with a PC, and print TI-85 screens on a printer connected to a PC.

Linking Two TI-85s

The software to communicate between two TI-85s is built into the TI-85. The instructions are given in this chapter.

The cable to link two TI-85s comes with the TI-85.

Linking a TI-85 to a PC or Macintosh

An optional accessory, LINK-85, allows a TI-85 to communicate with a personal computer. To obtain the special cable, computer software (for either an PC-DOS compatible computer or a Macintosh® computer), and the instruction booklet, contact Texas Instruments Consumer Relations at 1–800–842–2737 (1–800–TI–CARES).

Connecting the TI-85 Link Cable

The TI-85 Link port is located at the center of the bottom edge of the calculator.

1. Insert either end of the cable into the port firmly.

2. Repeat with the other TI-85.

The LINK Menu

When you press [2nd] [LINK], the screen is cleared and the menu keys are labeled with the LINK menu.

SEND   RECV

Menu	Meaning
SEND	Accesses a menu of types of data to send.
RECV	Puts calculator in mode to receive.

Leaving a LINK Screen or Menu

- From SEND mode, press [EXIT] or [2nd] [QUIT].

- From RECV mode or while transmitting, press [ON] to interrupt and then ⟨EXIT⟩ to leave the ERROR screen.

- From an ERROR screen, select ⟨EXIT⟩ to leave the ERROR screen.

- After transmitting, press [EXIT] or [2nd] [QUIT].

Selecting Items to Send

You can send individual items (variables), all items, groups of items, or a memory backup from one TI-85 to another. To transmit from the TI-85, you first select what you want to send. The transmission does not begin until you select ⟨XMIT⟩ from the menu.

The SEND Menu

When you select ⟨SEND⟩, the menu keys are labeled with item types. Press MORE to move around the menu.

BCKUP	PRGM	MATRX	GDB	ALL
LIST	VECTR	REAL	CPLX	EQU
CONS	PIC	RANGE	STRNG	

- You can transmit individual items (variables).

- You can transmit all items.

- You can transmit groups of items.

- You can transmit an exact image of memory.

Selecting Items within a Type

When you select a variable type, the SEND selection screen is displayed. It lists the names of the variables in alphabetical order. (If there are no variables of the type selected, the message **NO VARS OF THIS TYPE** is displayed.)

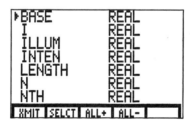

An arrow at the left of the name indicates the selection cursor. Use ▼ and ▲ to move the cursor.

- SELCT reverses the selection status of the name where the cursor is located. Selected names are marked with a square dot.

- ALL+ selects all variables of this type.

- ALL– unselects all variables of this type.

Selecting Items to Send (Continued)

The RANGE Items If you select <RANGE>, the selection screen is:

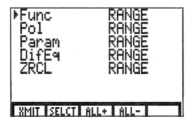

Use the menu keys to select the graphing mode(s) that you want to send. The variables that will be sent are:

- For Func, all variables on the **Func** RANGE screen, plus **lower** and **upper**, plus the FORMT settings.

- For Pol, all variables on the **Pol** RANGE screen, plus the FORMT settings.

- For Param, all variables on the **Param** RANGE screen, plus the FORMT settings.

- For DifEq, all variables on the **DifEq** RANGE screen, including **difTol**, and the AXES settings, plus the FORMT settings.

- For ZRCL, all user-zoom RANGE variables, regardless of the current graphing MODE, plus the FORMT settings.

Transmitting Items

Once you have selected what to send and the receiving unit is ready, you can begin transmitting. For easy distribution of items to several TI-85 units, items remain selected in both the sending and receiving unit and only three keystrokes are required to transmit the items again.

Transmitting Items

When you have selected what you want to transmit, select ⟨XMIT⟩. The receiving unit must be set to RECV before transmission can begin (page 19-6).

The name and type of each item is displayed, one per line, as the TI-85 tries to transmit it. After transmission is complete for all items, the message **Done** is displayed. Press ⬆ and ⬇ to scroll through the names.

After transmission is complete, the LINK menu is displayed on the bottom line.

Transmitting Items to an Additional TI-85

After sending or receiving data, you can repeat the same transmission to a different TI-85 without selecting what to send. The items selected on the sending unit or received on the receiving unit remain selected.

Before you make another selection, simply connect the unit to another TI-85, put the new unit in RECV mode, and select ⟨SEND⟩ ⟨ALL⟩ ⟨XMIT⟩.

Error Conditions

A transmission error will occur after one or two seconds if:

• There is not a cable attached to the port of the sending unit.

• There is not a receiving unit attached to the cable.

• The receiving unit is not in RECV mode.

If the ON key is pressed to interrupt transmission, an ERROR screen is displayed.

Select ⟨EXIT⟩ to leave the ERROR screen.

Receiving Items

Items are not transmitted until the receiving unit is ready.

The Receiving Unit

When you select ⟨RECV⟩ from the LINK menu, the message **Waiting** is displayed and the receiving unit is ready to receive transmitted items.

The receiving unit displays the name and type of each item as it is accepted. After transmission is complete for all items, the message **Done** is displayed. Press ▲ and ▼ to scroll through the names. The unit is not in RECV mode; select ⟨RECV⟩ to receive new items.

To leave RECV mode without receiving items, press ON . Select ⟨EXIT⟩ to leave the ERROR screen.

Duplicate Name

If an item of that name exists in the receiving unit, the receiving unit displays **ERROR 36 LINK DUPLICATE NAME** and the name and type of the item. The menu keys on the receiving unit are labeled:

RENAM   OVERW   SKIP   EXIT

- To store the item to a different name, select ⟨RENAM⟩. After **Name =** on the prompt line, enter a variable name that does not exist in the receiving unit (the keyboard is in ALPHA-lock). Press ENTER. Transmission resumes.

- To overwrite the existing item, select ⟨OVERW⟩. Transmission resumes.

- To skip this item (not copy it to the receiving unit), select ⟨SKIP⟩. Transmission resumes with the next item.

- To leave RECV mode, select ⟨EXIT⟩.

Insufficient Memory in Receiving Unit

If the receiving unit does not have sufficient memory to receive the item, the receiving unit displays **ERROR 34 LINK MEMORY FULL** and the name and type of the item. The menu keys on the receiving unit are labeled:

SKIP   EXIT

- To skip this item, select ⟨SKIP⟩. Transmission resumes with the next item.

- To leave RECV mode, select ⟨EXIT⟩.

Backing Up Memory

BCKUP transmits an image of memory to the receiving unit.

Memory Backup   To copy the exact contents of memory in the sending unit to the memory of the receiving unit, select ⟨BCKUP⟩.

When you select ⟨BCKUP⟩ from the LINK menu, the message **Memory Backup** is displayed.

Warning: BCKUP overwrites the memory in the receiving unit and all information in the memory of the receiving unit is lost. Press [EXIT] to leave LINK.

Select ⟨XMIT⟩ to begin transmission.

The Receiving Unit   As a safety check to prevent accidental loss of memory, when the receiving unit receives notice of a backup, the message **WARNING Memory Backup** is displayed. The menu keys are labeled:

CONT   EXIT

• To continue with the backup process, select ⟨CONT⟩. The transmission will begin.

• To prevent the backup, select ⟨EXIT⟩.

Note: If a transmission error occurs during a backup, the receiving unit is reset.

Example

Create and store a random matrix and a random complex number and then transfer them to another TI-85.

Example

1. From the Home screen, create and store the variables:

   randM(3,3)→RM
   (rand,rand)→RCN

2. Connect two TI-85s with the cable.

3. On the receiving unit:

   - Press [2nd] [LINK] to display the LINK menu.

   - Press [F2] to select ⟨RECV⟩.

4. On the sending unit:

   - Press [2nd] [LINK] to display the LINK menu.

   - Press [F1] to select ⟨SEND⟩.

   - Press [F5] to select ⟨ALL⟩.

   - Move the cursor to **RM**. Press [F2] to select **RM**. Repeat for **RCN**.

5. On the sending unit, press [F1] to select ⟨XMIT⟩. The items are transmitted and both units display:

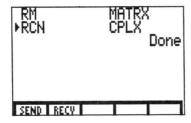

6. Press [EXIT] to leave LINK.

Appendix A: Tables

This appendix provides a list of all TI-85 command-line
instructions that you can use on the Home screen and in
programs and functions that you can use in expressions.

Table of Functions and Instructions

Functions (F) return a value, list, matrix, vector, or string and can be used in an expression; instructions (I) initiate an action. Some, but not all, have arguments. Menus/keys marked † are interactive except in the program editor, but can be typed on a command line or copied from the CATALOG. Except when indicated otherwise, list arguments return lists, evaluated on an element-by-element basis.

Operations and Arguments	Result	Menu/Keys	F/I Page
abs *arg1* • *arg1*: real/cplx num/list/matrx/vectr	Returns absolute value of real number or magnitude of complex number *arg1*; matrix of absolute values of *arg1* matrix elements; vector of absolute values of *arg1* vector elements	[2nd] [MATH] ⟨NUM⟩ ⟨abs⟩ [2nd] [CPLX] ⟨abs⟩ [2nd] [MATRX] ⟨CPLX⟩ ⟨abs⟩ [2nd] [VECTR] ⟨CPLX⟩ ⟨abs⟩	F 3–5 F 11–4 F 13–18 F 13–30

Addition: *arg1* **+** *arg2*
• *arg1*: real/cplx
  num/list/matrx/vectr
• *arg2*: real/cplx
  num/list/matrx/vectr
	Returns *arg1* plus *arg2*. Adds elements of list, matrix, or vector. If number and list, adds number to each list element. *See* concatenation	[+]	F
			3–2
			12–7
			13–10
			13–26

arg1 **and** *arg2* • *arg1*: real num • *arg2*: real num	Returns bit comparison of *arg1* and *arg2* (truncated to integers)	[2nd] [BASE] ⟨BOOL⟩ ⟨and⟩	F 10–7
angle *arg1* • *arg1*: real/cplx num/list/matrx/vectr	Returns polar angle of a number *arg1*, or of each element of a list, matrix, or vector *arg1*	[2nd] [CPLX] ⟨angle⟩ [2nd] [MATRX] ⟨CPLX⟩ ⟨angle⟩ [2nd] [VECTR] ⟨CPLX⟩ ⟨angle⟩	F 11–4 F 13–18 F 13–30
arc(*arg1*,*arg2*,*arg3*,*arg4*) • *arg1*: expression • *arg2*: var name • *arg3*: real num • *arg4*: real num	Returns length along function *arg1* in variable *arg2* from point *arg3* to point *arg4*	[2nd] [CALC] ⟨arc⟩	F 3–16
Assignment: *arg1* **=** *arg2* • *arg1*: var name • *arg2*: expression	Store *arg2* as variable *arg1* without evaluation	[ALPHA] [=]	I 2–9
aug(*arg1*,*arg2*) • *arg1*: real/cplx matrx • *arg2*: real/cplx matrx/vectr	Returns matrix *arg1* augmented by matrix *arg2* or vector *arg2*	[2nd] [MATRX] ⟨OPS⟩ ⟨aug⟩	F 13–14
Axes(*arg1*,*arg2*) • *arg1*: **x** axis variable • *arg2*: **y** axis variable	Define which variables are plotted for the axes in **DifEq** MODE	[GRAPH] ⟨Axes⟩†	I 7–4

AxesOff • no arguments	Set axis graphing format off	GRAPH 〈FORMT〉 〈AxesOff〉 †	I 4–7
AxesOn • no arguments	Set axis graphing format on	GRAPH 〈FORMT〉 〈AxesOn〉 †	I 4–7
arg1 **b** • real integer	Designates *arg1* as binary entry	2nd [BASE] 〈TYPE〉〈b〉	entry 10–4
Bin • no arguments	Set binary number base MODE	2nd [MODE] 〈Bin〉 †	I 1–26
arg1 ►**Bin** • *arg1*: real/cplx num/list/matrx/vectr	Display result *arg1* as binary	2nd [BASE] 〈CONV〉〈►Bin〉	I 10–6
Circl(*arg1*,*arg2*,*arg3*) • *arg1*: **x** value of center • *arg2*: **y** value of center • *arg3*: radius	Draw a circle with center (*arg1*,*arg2*) and radius *arg3*	GRAPH 〈DRAW〉 〈Circl〉 †	I 4–36
ClDrw • no arguments	Delete all drawn elements from a graph or drawing	GRAPH 〈DRAW〉 〈ClDrw〉 † STAT 〈DRAW〉 〈ClDrw〉 †	I 4–31 I 15–17
ClLCD • no arguments	Clear screen	PRGM 〈EDIT〉 〈I/O〉〈ClLCD〉	I 16–13
cnorm *arg1* • *arg1*: real/cplx matrx/vectr	Returns column norm of matrix or vector *arg1*	2nd [MATRX] 〈MATH〉〈cnorm〉	F 13–13
Concatenate: *arg1* + *arg2* • *arg1*: string • *arg2*: string	Returns a concatenated string	+	F 9–4
cond *arg1* • *arg1*: real/cplx matrx	Returns condition number of square matrix *arg1*	2nd [MATRX] 〈MATH〉〈cond〉	F 13–13
conj *arg1* • *arg1*: real/cplx num/list/matrx/vectr	Returns conjugate of number *arg1*, or of elements of list, matrix or vector *arg1*	2nd [CPLX] 〈conj〉 2nd [MATRX] 〈CPLX〉〈conj〉 2nd [VECTR] 〈CPLX〉〈conj〉	F 11–3 F 13–18 F 13–30
CoordOff • no arguments	Set coordinate graphing format off	GRAPH 〈FORMT〉 〈CoordOff〉 †	I 4–7
CoordOn • no arguments	Set coordinate graphing format on	GRAPH 〈FORMT〉 〈CoordOn〉 †	I 4–7

cos *arg1* • *arg1*: real/cplx num/list or square real matrix	Returns cosine of *arg1*	[COS]	F 3–2 13–11
cos⁻¹ *arg1* • *arg1*: real/cplx num/list	Returns arccos of *arg1*	[2nd] [COS⁻¹]	F 3–2
cosh *arg1* • *arg1*: real/cplx num/list	Returns hyperbolic cosine of *arg1*	[2nd] [MATH] ⟨HYP⟩ ⟨cosh⟩	F 3–8
cosh⁻¹ *arg1* • *arg1*: real/cplx num/list	Returns hyperbolic arccos of *arg1*	[2nd] [MATH] ⟨HYP⟩ ⟨cosh⁻¹⟩	F 3–8

cross(*arg1,arg2*)
• *arg1*: real/cplx
  2-D/3-D vectr
• *arg2*: real/cplx
  2-D/3-D vectr
	Returns cross product of
	vectors *arg1* and *arg2*
		[2nd] [VECTR]
		⟨MATH⟩ ⟨cross⟩
			F
			13–27

arg1▶**Cyl** • *arg1*: real 2-D/3-D vectr	Display result *arg1* as cylindrical coordinates	[2nd] [VECTR] ⟨OPS⟩ ⟨▶Cyl⟩	I 13–29
CylV • no arguments	Set cylindrical display MODE for vectors	[2nd] [MODE] ⟨CylV⟩ †	I 1–27
*arg1***d** • real number	Designates *arg1* as decimal entry	[2nd] [BASE] ⟨TYPE⟩ ⟨d⟩	entry 10–4
Dec • no arguments	Set decimal number base MODE	[2nd] [MODE] ⟨Dec⟩ †	I 1–26
arg1▶**Dec** • *arg1*: real/cplx num/list/matrx/vectr	Display result *arg1* as decimal	[2nd] [BASE] ⟨CONV⟩ ⟨▶Dec⟩	I 10–6
Degree: *arg1*° • *arg1*: real/cplx num/list	Interprets *arg1* as degrees	[2nd] [MATH] ⟨ANGLE⟩ ⟨°⟩	F 3–7
Degree • no arguments	Set degree MODE	[2nd] [MODE] ⟨Degree⟩ †	I 1–25
der1(*arg1,arg2,arg3*) • *arg1*: expression • *arg2*: var name • *arg3*: real/cplx num/list (opt)	Returns first derivative value of function *arg1* with respect to variable *arg2* at value *arg3*	[2nd] [CALC] ⟨der1⟩	F 3–14
der2(*arg1,arg2,arg3*) • *arg1*: expression • *arg2*: var name • *arg3*: real/cplx num/list (opt)	Returns second derivative value of function *arg1* with respect to variable *arg2* at value *arg3*	[2nd] [CALC] ⟨der2⟩	F 3–14

det *arg1* • *arg1*: real/cplx square matrx	Returns determinant of matrix *arg1*	2nd [MATRX] ⟨MATH⟩ ⟨det⟩	F 13–12
DifEq • no arguments	Set differential equation graphing MODE	2nd [MODE] ⟨DifEq⟩ †	I 1–26
dim *arg1* • *arg1*: real/cplx matrx/vectr	Returns dimensions of matrix *arg1* as a list or length of vector *arg1*	2nd [MATRX] ⟨OPS⟩ ⟨dim⟩ 2nd [VECTR] ⟨OPS⟩ ⟨dim⟩	F 13–15 F 13–28
arg1 ►**dim** *arg2* • *arg1*: real 2-element list • *arg2*: matrx name	Creates (if necessary) or redimensions matrix *arg2* to dimension *arg1*	2nd [MATRX] ⟨OPS⟩ ⟨dim⟩	F 13–15
arg1 ►**dim** *arg2* • *arg1*: real integer ≥ 0 • *arg2*: vectr name	Creates (if necessary) or redimensions vector *arg2* to dimension *arg1*	2nd [VECTR] ⟨OPS⟩ ⟨dim⟩	F 13–28
dimL *arg1* • *arg1*: real/cplx list	Returns length of list *arg1*	2nd [LIST] ⟨OPS⟩ ⟨dimL⟩	F 12–10
arg1 ►**dimL** *arg2* • *arg1*: real integer ≥ 0 • *arg2*: list name	Creates (if necessary) or redimensions list *arg2* to length *arg1*	2nd [LIST] ⟨OPS⟩ ⟨dimL⟩	F 12–10
Disp • no arguments	Display Home screen	PRGM ⟨EDIT⟩ ⟨I/O⟩ ⟨Disp⟩	I 16–11
Disp *arg1,arg2,*... • arg: value or string	Display variable *arg1*, *arg 2*, ...	PRGM ⟨EDIT⟩ ⟨I/O⟩ ⟨Disp⟩	I 16–11
DispG • no arguments	Display graph	GRAPH ⟨DispG⟩ † PRGM ⟨EDIT⟩ ⟨I/O⟩ ⟨DispG⟩	I 4–43 16–12
Division: *arg1/arg2* • *arg1*: real/cplx num/list/vectr • *arg2*: real/cplx num/list≠0	Returns *arg1* divided by *arg2*	÷	F 3–2 12–7 13–26
arg1 ►**DMS** • *arg1*: real num	Display result *arg1* in DMS format	2nd [MATH] ⟨ANGLE⟩⟨►DMS⟩	I 3–7
DMS entry: *arg1'arg2'arg3'* • *arg1*: real integer • *arg2*: real integer • *arg3*: real num	Interpret entry as *arg1* degrees, *arg2* minutes, *arg3* seconds	2nd [MATH] ⟨ANGLE⟩⟨'⟩	entry 3–7
dot(*arg1,arg2*) • *arg1*: real/cplx vectr • *arg2*: real/cplx vectr	Returns dot product of vectors *arg1* and *arg2*	2nd [VECTR] ⟨MATH⟩ ⟨dot⟩	F 13–27

DrawDot	Set dot graphing format	GRAPH ⟨FORMT⟩	I
• no arguments		⟨DrawDot⟩ †	4–7
DrawF *arg1*	Draw function *arg1*	GRAPH ⟨DRAW⟩	I
• *arg1*: expression in **x**		⟨DrawF⟩	4–37
		STAT ⟨DRAW⟩	I
		⟨DrawF⟩	15–12
DrawLine	Set connected line	GRAPH ⟨FORMT⟩	I
• no arguments	graphing format	⟨DrawLine⟩ †	4–7
DrInv *arg1*	Draw inverse of	GRAPH ⟨DRAW⟩	I
• *arg1*: expression in **x**	function *arg1*	⟨DrInv⟩	4–37
DS<(*arg1***,***arg2***)**	Decrement variable *arg1*	PRGM ⟨EDIT⟩	I
• *arg1*: user var name	by 1, skip next command	⟨CTL⟩ ⟨DS⟩>	16–18
• *arg2*: real num	if *arg1*<*arg2*		
dxDer1	Set **der1** as	2nd [MODE]	I
• no arguments	differentiation type	⟨dxDer1⟩ †	1–27
dxNDer	Set **nDer** as	2nd [MODE]	I
• no arguments	differentiation type	⟨dxNDer⟩ †	1–27
e^*arg1*	Returns **e** raised to	2nd [e^x]	F
• *arg1*: real/cplx num/list	*arg1* power		3–2
or square real matrx			13–11
eigVc *arg1*	Returns matrix of	2nd [MATRX]	F
• *arg1*: real/cplx square	eigenvectors of	⟨MATH⟩ ⟨eigVc⟩	13–12
matrx	matrix *arg1*		
eigVl *arg1*	Returns list of	2nd [MATRX]	F
• *arg1*: real/cplx square	eigenvalues of matrix	⟨MATH⟩ ⟨eigVl⟩	13–12
matrx	*arg1*		
Else:			
If *arg1***:Then:**commands...	Execute **Then** commands	PRGM ⟨EDIT⟩	I
:Else:commands...**:End**	if *arg1* is true, **Else**	⟨CTL⟩ ⟨Else⟩	16–15
• *arg1*: condition	commands if *arg1* is false		
End	Identifies end of **While**,	PRGM ⟨EDIT⟩	I
• no arguments	**For**, **Repeat**, or	⟨CTL⟩ ⟨End⟩	16–15
	If–Then–Else loop		
Eng	Set engineering display	2nd [MODE]	I
• no arguments	MODE	⟨Eng⟩ †	1–25
Eq►St(*arg1***,***arg2***)**	Convert equation *arg1*	2nd [STRNG]	I
• *arg1*: equation var name	to a string and store	⟨Eq►St⟩	9–5
• *arg2*: string var name	in string *arg2*		

Equal to: *arg1* **= =** *arg2*
• *arg1*: real/cplx num/list/
  matrx/vectr/string
• *arg2*: real/cplx num/list/
  matrx/vectr/string
	Returns 1 if *arg1* = *arg2*
	Returns 0 if *arg1* ≠ *arg2*
	If *arg1* and *arg2* are
	lists, returns list for
	element-by-element
	comparison
		2nd [TEST]
		⟨==⟩
			F
			3–18
			13–11
			13–26

Equal: *arg1* **=** *arg2* • *arg1*: expression • *arg2*: expression	Returns *arg1* − (*arg2* if *arg1* is not a variable name at the beginning of a line. *See* assignment.	ALPHA [=]	F 1–8
eval *arg1* • *arg1*: real num	Returns list of values of graph functions at **x** = *arg1*	[MATH] ⟨MISC⟩ ⟨eval⟩	F 3–10
evalF(*arg1*,*arg2*,*arg3*) • *arg1*: expression • *arg2*: var name • *arg3*: real/cplx num/list	Returns value of function *arg1*, evaluated for variable *arg2* at value *arg3*	2nd [CALC] ⟨evalF⟩	F 3–12
Exponent: *arg1* E*arg2* • *arg1*: real/cplx num/list • *arg2*: −999<integer<999	Returns *arg1* raised to *arg2* power of 10.	EE	entry 2–3
ExpR *arg1*,*arg2* • *arg1*: x list (real) (opt) • *arg2*: y list (real) (opt)	Perform exponential model regression analysis using lists *arg1* and *arg2*	STAT ⟨CALC⟩ ⟨ExpR⟩ †	I 15–16
Factorial: *arg1***!** • *arg1*: 0 ≤ intgr/list ≤ 449	Returns factorial of *arg1*	2nd [MATH] ⟨PROB⟩ ⟨!⟩	F 3–6
fcstx *arg1* • *arg1*: real num	Returns forecasted **x** at **y** = *arg1* using current **RegEq**	STAT ⟨fcstx⟩ †	F 15–16
fcsty *arg1* • *arg1*: real num	Returns a forecasted **y** at **x** = *arg1* using current **RegEq**	STAT ⟨fcsty⟩ †	F 15–16
Fill(*arg1*,*arg2*) • *arg1*: real/cplx num • *arg2*: list/matrx/vectr name	Store value *arg1* to each element in list, matrix, or vector *arg2*	2nd [LIST] ⟨OPS⟩ ⟨Fill⟩ 2nd [MATRX] ⟨OPS⟩ ⟨Fill⟩ 2nd [VECTR] ⟨OPS⟩ ⟨Fill⟩	I 12–9 I 13–14 I 13–28
Fix *arg1* • *arg1*: 0 ≤ integer ≤ 11	Set fixed display MODE for *arg1* decimal places	2nd [MODE] ⟨Fix⟩ †	I 1–25
Float • no arguments	Set floating display MODE	2nd [MODE] ⟨Float⟩ †	I 1–25

fMax(*arg1,arg2,arg3,arg4***)** • *arg1*: expression • *arg2*: var name • *arg3*: real num • *arg4*: real num	Returns **x** value for maximum of function *arg1*, with respect to variable *arg2*, between lower value *arg3*, upper value *arg4*	2nd [CALC] ⟨fMax⟩	F 3–16
fMin(*arg1,arg2,arg3,arg4***)** • *arg1*: expression • *arg2*: var name • *arg3*: real num • *arg4*: real num	Returns **x** value for minimum of function *arg1*, with respect to variable *arg2*, between lower value *arg3*, upper value *arg4*	2nd [CALC] ⟨fMin⟩	F 3–16
fnInt(*arg1,arg2,arg3,arg4***)** • *arg1*: expression • *arg2*: var name • *arg3*: real num • *arg4*: real num	Returns function integral of *arg1*, with respect to variable *arg2*, between lower limit *arg3*, upper limit *arg4*	2nd [CALC] ⟨fnInt⟩	F 3–15
FnOff • no arguments	Unselect all functions	⟨GRAPH⟩ ⟨FnOff⟩ †	I 4–11
FnOff *arg1,arg2,arg3,...* • arg: 1 ≤ integer ≤ 99	Unselect *arg1*, *arg2*, *arg3*... functions	⟨GRAPH⟩ ⟨FnOff⟩ †	I 4–11
FnOn • no arguments	Select all functions	⟨GRAPH⟩ ⟨FnOn⟩ †	I 4–11
FnOn *arg1,arg2,arg3,...* • arg: 1 ≤ integer ≤ 99	Select *arg1*, *arg2*, *arg3*... functions	⟨GRAPH⟩ ⟨FnOn⟩ †	I 4–11
For(*arg1,arg2,arg3,arg4***)** :commands...:**End** • *arg1*: var name • *arg2*: real num • *arg3*: real num • *arg4*: real num (opt)	Execute loop, incrementing variable *arg1*, beginning at *arg2*, by increment *arg4*, until *arg1>arg3*	PRGM ⟨EDIT⟩ ⟨CTL⟩ ⟨For⟩	I 16–16
fPart *arg1* • *arg1*: real/cplx num/list/matrx/vectr	Returns fractional part of *arg1* or of each element of *arg1*	2nd [MATH] ⟨NUM⟩ ⟨fPart⟩	F 3–4 13–11 13–26
arg1▶**Frac** • *arg1*: real/cplx num/list/matrx/vectr	Display result *arg1* as most simplified fraction	2nd [MATH] ⟨MISC⟩ ⟨▶Frac⟩	I 3–10
Func • no arguments	Set function graphing MODE	2nd [MODE] ⟨Func⟩ †	I 1–26
gcd(*arg1,arg2***)** • *arg1*: 0 ≤ integer<1E12 • *arg2*: 0 ≤ integer<1E12	Returns greatest common divisor of *arg1* and *arg2*	2nd [MATH] ⟨MISC⟩ ⟨gcd⟩	F 3–10

getKy	Return value of last	PRGM ⟨EDIT⟩	F
• no arguments	keystroke	⟨I/O⟩ ⟨getKy⟩	16–13
Goto *arg1*	Transfer control to	PRGM ⟨EDIT⟩	I
• *arg1*: label name	label *arg1*	⟨CTL⟩ ⟨Goto⟩	16–17
Greater than: *arg1*>*arg2*	Returns 1 if *arg1*>*arg2*	2nd [TEST]	F
• *arg1*: real num/list	Returns 0 if *arg1* ≤ *arg2*	⟨>⟩	3–18
• *arg2*: real num/list	If *arg1* and *arg2* are lists, returns list		
Greater than or equal to: *arg1* ≥ *arg2*	Returns 1 if *arg1* ≥ *arg2* Returns 0 if *arg1*<*arg2*	2nd [TEST] ⟨≥⟩	F 3–18
• *arg1*: real num/list	If *arg1* and *arg2* are		
• *arg2*: real num/list	lists, returns list		
GridOff	Set grid graphing	GRAPH ⟨FORMT⟩	I
• no arguments	format off	⟨GridOff⟩ †	4–7
GridOn	Set grid graphing	GRAPH ⟨FORMT⟩	I
• no arguments	format on	⟨GridOn⟩ †	4–7
*arg1***h**	Designates *arg1* as	2nd [BASE]	entry
• real integer	hexadecimal entry	⟨TYPE⟩ ⟨h⟩	10–4
Hex	Set hexadecimal number	2nd [MODE]	I
• no arguments	base MODE	⟨Hex⟩ †	1–26
arg1▶**Hex**	Display result *arg1*	2nd [BASE]	I
• *arg1*: real/cplx num/list/matrx/vectr	as hexadecimal	⟨CONV⟩ ⟨▶Hex⟩	10–6
Hist *arg1*,*arg2*	Draw a histogram of	STAT ⟨DRAW⟩	I
• *arg1*: x list (real) (opt)	stat data using lists	⟨Hist⟩ †	15–17
• *arg2*: freq list (integers ≥ 0) (opt)	*arg1* and *arg2* or **xStat** and frequencies of 1		
ident *arg1*	Returns identity matrix	2nd [MATRX]	F
• *arg1*: integer>0	of dimension *arg1* × *arg1*	⟨OPS⟩ ⟨ident⟩	13–14
If *arg1*:command1		PRGM ⟨EDIT⟩	I
:command2	If *arg1* = 0 (false), skip	⟨CTL⟩ ⟨If⟩	16–15
• *arg1*: condition	command1		
If *arg1***:Then:**commands...	Execute command after	PRGM ⟨EDIT⟩	I
:End	**Then** if *arg1* is true	⟨CTL⟩ ⟨Then⟩	16–15
• *arg1*: condition			
If *arg1***:Then:**commands...	Execute **Then** commands	PRGM ⟨EDIT⟩	I
:Else:commands...**:End**	if *arg1* is true, **Else**	⟨CTL⟩ ⟨Else⟩	16–15
• *arg1*: condition	commands if *arg1* is false		

imag *arg1*	Returns nonreal part of	[2nd] [CPLX]	F
• *arg1*: real/cplx num/list	*arg1*	⟨imag⟩	11–3
imag *arg1*	Returns matrix of nonreal	[2nd] [MATRX]	F
• *arg1*: real/cplx matrx	part of matrix *arg1*	⟨CPLX⟩ ⟨imag⟩	13–18
imag *arg1*	Returns vector of nonreal	[2nd] [VECTR]	F
• *arg1*: real/cplx vectr	part of vector *arg1*	⟨CPLX⟩ ⟨imag⟩	13–30
InpSt *arg1*	Prompt for string to	[PRGM] ⟨EDIT⟩	I
• *arg1*: var name	store to variable *arg1*	⟨I/O⟩ ⟨InpSt⟩	16–12
InpSt *arg1,arg2*	Display string *arg1*,	[PRGM] ⟨EDIT⟩	I
• *arg1*: string	store entered string	⟨I/O⟩ ⟨InpSt⟩	16–12
• *arg2*: var name	to *arg2*		
Input	Display graph	[PRGM] ⟨EDIT⟩	I
• no arguments		⟨I/O⟩ ⟨Input⟩	16–10
Input *arg1*	Prompt for value to	[PRGM] ⟨EDIT⟩	I
• *arg1*: var name	store to variable *arg1*	⟨I/O⟩ ⟨Input⟩	16–10
Input *arg1,arg2*	Display string *arg1*,	[PRGM] ⟨EDIT⟩	I
• *arg1*: string	store entered value	⟨I/O⟩ ⟨Input⟩	16–10
• *arg2*: var name	to *arg2*		
int *arg1*	Returns integer	[2nd] [MATH]	F
• *arg1*: real/cplx	≥ *arg1* or each	⟨NUM⟩ ⟨int⟩	3–4
num/list/matrx/vectr	element of *arg1*		13–11
			13–26
inter(*arg1,arg2,arg3, arg4,arg5***)**			
• *arg1*: real num	Returns interpolated or	[2nd] [MATH]	F
• *arg2*: real num	extrapolated **y** value,	⟨inter⟩ †	3–11
• *arg3*: real num	at **x** = *arg5*,		
• *arg4*: real num	given (*arg1*,*arg2*)		
• *arg5*: real num	and (*arg3*,*arg4*)		
Inverse: *arg1*⁻¹	Returns 1 divided by *arg1*	[2nd] [**x**⁻¹]	F
• *arg1*: real/cplx num/list	or inverted matrix		3–2
or square matrx (det≠0)			13–10
iPart *arg1*	Returns integer part of	[2nd] [MATH]	F
• *arg1*: real/cplx	*arg1* or of each element	⟨NUM⟩ ⟨iPart⟩	3–4
num/list/matrx/vectr	of *arg1*		13–11
			13–26
IS>(*arg1,arg2***)**	Increment variable *arg1*	[PRGM] ⟨EDIT⟩	I
• *arg1*: user var name	by 1, skip next command	⟨CTL⟩ ⟨IS>⟩	16–18
• *arg2*: real num	if *arg1* > *arg2*		

LabelOff • no arguments	Set axis label graphing format off	(GRAPH) ⟨FORMT⟩ ⟨LabelOff⟩ †	I 4–7
LabelOn • no arguments	Set axis label graphing format on	(GRAPH) ⟨FORMT⟩ ⟨LabelOn⟩ †	I 4–7
Lbl *arg1* • *arg1*: label name	Assign label *arg1* to the command	(PRGM) ⟨EDIT⟩ ⟨CTL⟩ ⟨Lbl⟩	I 16–17
lcm(*arg1***,***arg2***)** • *arg1*: $0 \leq$ integer$<$1E12 • *arg2*: $0 \leq$ integer$<$1E12	Returns least common multiple of *arg1* and *arg2*	(2nd) [MATH] ⟨MISC⟩ ⟨lcm⟩	F 3–9
Less than: *arg1*$<$*arg2* • *arg1*: real num/list • *arg2*: real num/list	Returns 1 if *arg1*$<$*arg2* Returns 0 if *arg1* $\geq$ *arg2* If *arg1* and *arg2* are lists, returns list	(2nd) [TEST] ⟨<⟩	F 3–18
Less than or equal to: *arg1* $\leq$ *arg2* • *arg1*: real num/list • *arg2*: real num/list	Returns 1 if *arg1* $\leq$ *arg2* Returns 0 if *arg1*$>$*arg2* If *arg1* and *arg2* are lists, returns list	(2nd) [TEST] ⟨ $\leq$ ⟩	F 3–18
Line(*arg1***,***arg2***,***arg3***,***arg4***)** • *arg1*: 1st **x** value • *arg2*: 1st **y** value • *arg3*: 2nd **x** value • *arg4*: 2nd **y** value	Draw a line from (*arg1*,*arg2*) to (*arg3*,*arg4*)	(GRAPH) ⟨DRAW⟩ ⟨Line⟩ †	I 4–34
LinR *arg1***,***arg2* • *arg1*: x list (real) (opt) • *arg2*: y list (real) (opt)	Perform linear model regression analysis using lists *arg1* and *arg2*	(STAT) ⟨CALC⟩ ⟨LinR⟩ †	I 15–16
li►vc *arg1* • *arg1*: real/cplx list	Returns list *arg1* converted to a vector	(2nd) [LIST] ⟨OPS⟩ ⟨li►vc⟩ (2nd) [VECTR] ⟨OPS⟩ ⟨li►vc⟩	F 12–9 F 13–29
ln *arg1* • *arg1*: real/cplx num/list	Returns natural logarithm of *arg1*	(LN)	F 3–2
lngth *arg1* • *arg1*: string	Returns length of string *arg1*	(2nd) [STRNG] ⟨lngth⟩	F 9–4
LnR *arg1***,***arg2* • *arg1*: x list (real) (opt) • *arg2*: y list (real) (opt)	Perform logarithmic model regression analysis using lists *arg1* and *arg2*	(STAT) ⟨CALC⟩ ⟨LnR⟩ †	I 15–16
log *arg1* • *arg1*: real/cplx num/list	Returns logarithm of *arg1*	(LOG)	F 3–2

LU(*arg1*,*arg2*,*arg3*,*arg4***)** • *arg1*: real/cplx square matrx • *arg2*: matrix name • *arg3*: matrix name • *arg4*: matrix name	Calculate LU decomposition of matrix *arg1*, store lower triangular matrix in *arg2*, upper in *arg3*, permutation matrix in *arg4*	2nd [MATRX] ⟨MATH⟩⟨LU⟩	I 13–12
max(*arg1*,*arg2***)** • *arg1*: real/cplx num/list • *arg2*: real/cplx num/list	Returns the larger of *arg1* and *arg2*	2nd [MATH] ⟨NUM⟩⟨max⟩	F 3–5
max(*arg1***)** • *arg1*: real/cplx list	Returns largest value in list *arg1*	2nd [LIST] ⟨OPS⟩⟨max⟩	F 12–8
Menu(*arg1*,*arg2*,*arg3*,...**)** • *arg1*: 1, 2, 3, 4, or 5 • *arg2*: string • *arg3*: label	Sets up branches based on menu items	PRGM ⟨EDIT⟩ ⟨CTL⟩⟨Menu⟩	I 16–17
min(*arg1*,*arg2***)** • *arg1*: real/cplx num/list • *arg2*: real/cplx num/list	Returns the smaller of *arg1* and *arg2*	2nd [MATH] ⟨NUM⟩⟨min⟩	F 3–5
min(*arg1***)** • *arg1*: real/cplx list	Returns smallest value in list *arg1*	2nd [LIST] ⟨OPS⟩⟨min⟩	F 12–8
mod(*arg1*,*arg2***)** • *arg1*: real num • *arg2*: real num	Returns the modulus of *arg1* with respect to *arg2*	2nd [MATH] ⟨NUM⟩⟨mod⟩	F 3–5
mRAdd(*arg1*,*arg2*,*arg3*,*arg4***)** • *arg1*: real/cplx num • *arg2*: real/cplx matrix • *arg3*: 0<integer ≤ 255 • *arg4*: 0<integer ≤ 255	Returns matrix with row *arg3* of matrix *arg2* multiplied by *arg1*, added to row *arg4*, and stored in row *arg4*	2nd [MATRX] ⟨OPS⟩⟨mRAdd⟩	F 13–16

Multiplication: *arg1* ∗ *arg2*
• *arg1*: real/cplx
  num/list/matrx/vectr
• *arg2*: real/cplx
  num/list/matrx/vectr
	Returns *arg1* multiplied
	by *arg2*
		☒	F
			3–2
			12–7
			13–10
			13–26

multR(*arg1*,*arg2*,*arg3***)** • *arg1*: real/cplx num • *arg2*: real/cplx matrx • *arg3*: 0<integer ≤ 255	Returns matrix with row *arg3* of matrix *arg2* multiplied by *arg1*, and stored in row *arg3*	2nd [MATRX] ⟨OPS⟩⟨multR⟩	F 13–16
arg1 **nCr** *arg2* • *arg1*: 0<integer • *arg2*: 0<integer	Returns number of combinations of *arg1* items taken *arg2* at a time	2nd [MATH] ⟨PROB⟩⟨nCr⟩	F 3–6

nDer(arg1**,**arg2**,**arg3**)** • arg1: expression • arg2: var name • arg3: real/cplx num/list (opt)	Returns approximate numerical derivative of function arg1 with respect to arg2 at value arg3	2nd [CALC] ⟨nDer⟩	F 3–13
Negation: **-**arg1 • arg1: real/cplx num/list/matrx/vectr	Returns negative of arg1 Negates elements of list, matrix, or vector	(–)	F 3–2 13–10 13–26
norm arg1 • arg1: real/cplx num/list/matrx/vectr	Returns norm of matrix or vector arg1. Returns absolute value of number or list arg1	2nd [MATRX] ⟨MATH⟩ ⟨norm⟩ 2nd [VECTR] ⟨MATH⟩ ⟨norm⟩	F 13–12 13–27
Normal • no arguments	Set normal display MODE	2nd [MODE] ⟨Normal⟩ †	I 1–25
not arg1 • arg1: real num	Returns one's complement of arg1	2nd [BASE] ⟨BOOL⟩ ⟨not⟩	F 10–7
Not equal: arg1≠arg2 • arg1: real/cplx num/list/ matrx/vectr/string • arg2: real/cplx num/list/ matrx/vectr/string	Returns 1 if arg1≠arg2 Returns 0 if arg1 = arg2 If arg1 and arg2 are lists, returns list for element-by-element comparison	2nd [TEST] ⟨≠⟩	F 3–18 13–11 13–26
arg1 **nPr** arg2 • arg1: integer>0 arg2: integer>0	Returns number of permutations of arg1 items taken arg2 at a time	2nd [MATH] ⟨PROB⟩ ⟨nPr⟩	F 3–6
arg1**o** • real integer	Designates arg1 as octal entry	2nd [BASE] ⟨TYPE⟩ ⟨o⟩	entry 10–4
Oct • no arguments	Set octal number base MODE	2nd [MODE] ⟨Oct⟩ †	I 1–26
arg1▶**Oct** • arg1: real/cplx num/list/matrx/vectr	Display result arg1 as octal	2nd [BASE] ⟨CONV⟩ ⟨▶Oct⟩	I 10–6
OneVar arg1**,**arg2 • arg1: x list (real) (opt) • arg2: freq list (integers ≥ 0) (opt)	Perform one-variable statistical analysis using lists arg1 and arg2	STAT ⟨CALC⟩ ⟨OneVa⟩ †	I 15–16
arg1 **or** arg2 • arg1: real num • arg2: real num	Returns bit comparison of arg1 and arg2 (truncated to integer)	2nd [BASE] ⟨BOOL⟩ ⟨or⟩	F 10–7

Outpt(arg1,arg2,arg3**)** • arg1: 1 ≤ integer ≤ 8 • arg2: 1 ≤ integer ≤ 21 • arg3: value/string	Display arg3, beginning at line arg1, column arg2	PRGM ⟨EDIT⟩ ⟨I/O⟩ ⟨Outpt⟩	I 16–12
P2Reg arg1,arg2 • arg1: x list (real) (opt) • arg2: y list (real) (opt)	Perform second order polynomial regression using lists arg1 and arg2	STAT ⟨CALC⟩ ⟨P2Reg⟩ †	I 15–16
P3Reg arg1,arg2 • arg1: x list (real) (opt) • arg2: y list (real) (opt)	Perform third order polynomial regression using lists arg1 and arg2	STAT ⟨CALC⟩ ⟨P3Reg⟩ †	I 15–16
P4Reg arg1,arg2 • arg1: x list (real) (opt) • arg2: y list (real) (opt)	Perform fourth order polynomial regression using lists arg1 and arg2	STAT ⟨CALC⟩ ⟨P4Reg⟩ †	I 15–16
Param • no arguments	Set parametric graphing MODE	2nd [MODE] ⟨Func⟩ †	I 1–26
Pause • no arguments	Suspend execution until ENTER is pressed	PRGM ⟨EDIT⟩ ⟨CTL⟩ ⟨Pause⟩	I 16–18
Pause arg1 • arg1: real/cplx num/list/ matrx/vectr/string	Display arg1, suspend execution until ENTER is pressed	PRGM ⟨EDIT⟩ ⟨CTL⟩ ⟨Pause⟩	I 16–18
Percent: arg1% • arg1: real num	Returns arg1 divided by 100	2nd [MATH] ⟨MISC⟩ ⟨%⟩	F 3–10
pEval(arg1,arg2**)** • arg1: real/cplx list • arg2: real/cplx value	Returns value of polynomial with arg1 coefficients at **x** = arg2	2nd [MATH] ⟨MISC⟩ ⟨pEval⟩	F 3–10
Pol • no arguments	Set polar graphing MODE	2nd [MODE] ⟨Pol⟩ †	I 1–26
arg1▶**Pol** • arg1: cplx num/list/matrx/vectr	Display result arg1 as polar coordinates	2nd [CPLX] ⟨▶Pol⟩	I 11–4
arg1▶**Pol** • arg1: real 2-D vectr	Display result arg1 as polar coordinates	2nd [VECTR] ⟨OPS⟩ ⟨▶Pol⟩	I 13–29

PolarC • no arguments	Set polar display for complex numbers	[2nd] [MODE] ⟨PolarC⟩ †	I 1–26
Polar complex: **(**_arg1_<_arg2_**)** • _arg1_: real num • _arg2_: real num	Interpret _arg1_ as magnitude, _arg2_ as angle	[2nd] [∠]	entry 11–2
PolarGC • no arguments	Set polar graphing coordinate format	[GRAPH] ⟨FORMT⟩ ⟨PolarGC⟩ †	I 4–7
poly _arg1_ • _arg1_: real/cplx list	Returns list of roots of polynomial with _arg1_ coefficients	[2nd] [POLY] †	F 14–9
Power of ten: **10**^_arg1_ • _arg1_: real/cplx num/list	Returns 10 raised to _arg1_ power	[2nd] [10ˣ]	F 3–2
Powers: _arg1_^_arg2_ • _arg1_: real/cplx num/list or square matrx • _arg2_: real/cplx num/list	Returns _arg1_ raised to _arg2_ power. _arg2_ must be real integer ≤255 if _arg1_ is matrix	[^]	F 3–2 13–10
prod _arg1_ • _arg1_: real/cplx list	Returns product of list _arg1_	[2nd] [MATH] ⟨MISC⟩ ⟨prod⟩ [2nd] [LIST] ⟨OPS⟩ ⟨prod⟩	F 3–9 F 12–9
Prompt _arg1_,_arg2_,_arg3_... • arg_n: var name	Prompt for variable _arg1_, then variable _arg2_, etc.	[PRGM] ⟨EDIT⟩ ⟨I/O⟩ ⟨Promp⟩	I 16–10
PrtScrn • no arguments	Send current display to printer	⟨I/O⟩ ⟨PrtScrn⟩	I 16–13
PtChg(_arg1_,_arg2_**)** • _arg1_: **x** value • _arg2_: **y** value	Change point at (_arg1_,_arg2_)	[GRAPH] ⟨DRAW⟩ ⟨PtChg⟩ †	I 4–39
PtOff(_arg1_,_arg2_**)** • _arg1_: **x** value • _arg2_: **y** value	Erase point at (_arg1_,_arg2_)	[GRAPH] ⟨DRAW⟩ ⟨PtOff⟩ †	I 4–39
PtOn(_arg1_,_arg2_**)** • _arg1_: **x** value • _arg2_: **y** value	Draw point at (_arg1_,_arg2_)	[GRAPH] ⟨DRAW⟩ ⟨PtOn⟩ †	I 4–39
PwrR _arg1_,_arg2_ • _arg1_: **x** list (real) (opt) • _arg2_: **y** list (real) (opt)	Perform power model regression analysis using lists _arg1_ and _arg2_	[STAT] ⟨CALC⟩ ⟨PwrR⟩ †	I 15–16

rAdd(*arg1*,*arg2*,*arg3*) • *arg1*: real/cplx matrx • *arg2*: 0<integer ≤ 255 • *arg3*: 0<integer ≤ 255	Returns matrix with row *arg2* of matrix *arg1* added to row *arg3*, and stored in row *arg3*	2nd [MATRX] 〈OPS〉〈rAdd〉	F 13–16
Radian: *arg1*ʳ • *arg1*: real/cplx num/list	Interpret *arg1* as radians	2nd [MATH] 〈ANGLE〉〈ʳ〉	F 3–7
Radian • no arguments	Set radian MODE	2nd [MODE] 〈Radian〉 †	I 1–25
rand • no arguments	Returns 0<random number<1 seeded from value in **rand**	2nd [MATH] 〈PROB〉〈rand〉	F 3–6
randM(*arg1*,*arg2*) • *arg1*: 0<integer ≤ 255 • *arg2*: 0<integer ≤ 255	Returns an *arg1*x*arg2* matrix with random –9 ≤ integer ≤ 9 elements	2nd [MATRX] 〈OPS〉〈randM〉	F 13–14
RcGDB *arg1* • *arg1*: database name	Recalls graph database *arg1* as the current graph	GRAPH 〈RcGDB〉 †	I 4–40
RcPic *arg1* • *arg1*: picture name	Recalls picture *arg1* onto the current graph	GRAPH 〈RcPic〉 † 〈STAT〉〈DRAW〉 〈RcPic〉 †	I 4–41 I 15–17
real *arg1* • *arg1*: real/cplx num/list/matrx/vectr	Returns real part of number *arg1* or of each element of list, matrix, or vector *arg1*	2nd [CPLX] 〈real〉 2nd [MATRX] 〈CPLX〉〈real〉 2nd [VECTR] 〈CPLX〉〈real〉	F 11–3 F 13–18 F 13–30
arg1▶**Rec** • *arg1*: cplx num/list/matrx/vectr	Display result *arg1* as rectangular coordinates	2nd [CPLX] 〈▶Rec〉	I 11–4
arg1▶**Rec** • *arg1*: real 2-D vectr	Display result *arg1* as rectangular coordinates	2nd [VECTR] 〈OPS〉〈▶Rec〉	I 13–29
RectC • no arguments	Set rectangular display for complex numbers	2nd [MODE] 〈RectC〉 †	I 1–26
RectGC • no arguments	Set rectangular graphing coordinate format	GRAPH 〈FORMT〉 〈RectGC〉 †	I 4–7
RectV • no arguments	Set rectangular display MODE for vectors	2nd [MODE] 〈RectV〉 †	I 1–27
ref *arg1* • *arg1*: real/cplx matrx	Returns row echelon form of matrix *arg1*	2nd [MATRX] 〈OPS〉〈ref〉	F 13–16

Repeat *arg1*:commands...			
:End	Execute loop until	PRGM ⟨EDIT⟩	I
• *arg1*: condition	condition is true	⟨CTL⟩ ⟨Repea⟩	16–16
Return	Returns to calling	PRGM ⟨EDIT⟩	I
• no arguments	program	⟨CTL⟩ ⟨Retur⟩	16–18
rnorm *arg1*	Returns row norm of	2nd [MATRX]	F
• *arg1*: real/cplx	matrix *arg1*	⟨MATH⟩ ⟨rnorm⟩	13–13
matrx/vectr			
Root: *arg1*ˣ√*arg2*	Returns *arg1* root of	2nd [MATH]	F
• *arg1*: real/cplx num/list	*arg2*	⟨MISC⟩ ⟨ˣ√⟩	3–10
• *arg2*: real/cplx num/list			
rotL *arg1*	Returns *arg1* with	2nd [BASE]	F
• *arg1*: real integer	bits rotated to left	⟨BIT⟩ ⟨rotL⟩	10–8
rotR *arg1*	Returns *arg1* with	2nd [BASE]	F
• *arg1*: real integer	bits rotated to right	⟨BIT⟩ ⟨rotR⟩	10–8
round(*arg1*,*arg2***)**	Returns *arg1* rounded to	2nd [MATH]	F
• *arg1*: real/cplx	*arg2* decimal places	⟨NUM⟩ ⟨round⟩	3–4
num/list/matrx/vectr			13–11
• *arg2*: 0 ≤ integer ≤ 11 (opt)			13–26
rref *arg1*	Returns matrix *arg1* in	2nd [MATRX]	F
• *arg1*: real/cplx matrx	reduced row echelon form	⟨OPS⟩ ⟨rref⟩	13–16
rSwap(*arg1*,*arg2*,*arg3***)**	Returns matrix with	2nd [MATRX]	F
• *arg1*: real/cplx matrx	row *arg2* of matrix *arg1*	⟨OPS⟩ ⟨rSwap⟩	13–16
• *arg2*: 0<integer ≤ 255	swapped with row *arg3*		
• *arg3*: 0<integer ≤ 255			
Scatter *arg1*,*arg2*	Draw a scatter plot of	STAT ⟨DRAW⟩	I
• *arg1*: x list (real) (opt)	stat data using lists	⟨Scatte⟩ †	15–17
• *arg2*: y list (real) (opt)	*arg1* and *arg2* or **xStat**		
	and **yStat**		
Sci	Set scientific display	2nd [MODE]	I
• no arguments	MODE	⟨Sci⟩ †	1–25
seq(*arg1*,*arg2*,*arg3*,			
arg4,*arg5***)**	Returns list created by	2nd [MATH]	F
• *arg1*: expression	evaluating expression	⟨MISC⟩ ⟨seq⟩	3–9
• *arg2*: var name	*arg1*, for variable *arg2*,	2nd [LIST]	
• *arg3*: real num	beginning at *arg3*,	⟨OPS⟩ ⟨seq⟩	12–8
• *arg4*: real num	ending at *arg4*,		
• *arg5*: real num	with increment *arg5*		
SeqG	Set sequential graphing	GRAPH ⟨FORMT⟩	I
• no arguments	format	⟨SeqG⟩ †	4–7

Shade(*arg1*,*arg2*,*arg3*,*arg4*) • *arg1*: expression in **x** • *arg2*: expression in **x** • *arg3*: real num (opt) • *arg4*: real num (opt)	Shade area above *arg1*, below *arg2*, to right of **x** = *arg3* (default **lower**), to left of **x** = *arg4* (default **upper**)	GRAPH 〈DRAW〉 〈Shade〉	I 4–32
shftL *arg1* • *arg1*: real integer	Returns *arg1* with bits shifted to left	2nd [BASE] 〈BIT〉〈shftL〉	F 10–8
shftR *arg1* • *arg1*: real integer	Returns *arg1* with bits shifted to right	2nd [BASE] 〈BIT〉〈shftR〉	F 10–8
ShwSt • no argument	Display current stat results	STAT 〈CALC〉 〈ShwSt〉 †	I 15–16
sign *arg1* • *arg1*: real num/list	Returns –1 if *arg1*<0, 1 if *arg1*>0, 0 if *arg1* =0	2nd [MATH] 〈NUM〉〈sign〉	F 3–5
SimulG • no arguments	Set simultaneous graphing format	GRAPH 〈FORMT〉 〈SimulG〉 †	I 4–7
simult(*arg1*,*arg2*) • *arg1*: real/cplx matrx • *arg2*: real/cplx vectr	Returns a vector of the solution to a system of simultaneous equations	2nd [SIMULT] †	F 14–11
sin *arg1* • *arg1*: real/cplx num/list or square real matrx	Returns sine of *arg1*	SIN	F 3–2 13–11
sin⁻¹ *arg1* • *arg1*: real/cplx num/list	Returns arcsin of *arg1*	2nd [SIN⁻¹]	F 3–2
sinh *arg1* • *arg1*: real/cplx num/list	Returns hyperbolic sine of *arg1*	2nd [MATH] 〈HYP〉〈sinh〉	F 3–8
sinh⁻¹ *arg1* • *arg1*: real/cplx num/list	Returns hyperbolic arcsin of *arg1*	2nd [MATH] 〈HYP〉〈sinh⁻¹〉	F 3–8
Solver(*arg1*,*arg2*,*arg3*,*arg4*) • *arg1*: equation • *arg2*: var name • *arg3*: real num or 2-element real list • *arg4*: 2-element real list (opt)	Solve equation *arg1* for variable *arg2* using *arg3* guess(es) within bounds specified by *arg4*, result is stored in variable *arg2*	2nd [SOLVER] †	I 14–5

sortA *arg1* • *arg1*: real/cplx list	Returns list *arg1* with elements in ascending order	2nd [LIST] 〈OPS〉〈sortA〉	F 12–8
sortD *arg1* • *arg1*: real/cplx list	Returns list *arg1* with elements in descending order	2nd [LIST] 〈OPS〉〈sortD〉	F 12–8
Sortx *arg1*,*arg2* • *arg1*: x list (real) • *arg2*: y list (real)	Sort statistical data in order of x elements	STAT 〈Sortx〉†	I 15–17
Sorty *arg1*,*arg2* • *arg1*: x list (real) • *arg2*: y list (real)	Sort statistical data in order of y elements	STAT 〈Sorty〉†	I 15–17
arg1►**Sph** • *arg1*: 2-D/3-D real vectr	Display result *arg1* as spherical coordinates	2nd [VECTR] 〈OPS〉〈►Sph〉	I 13–29
SphereV • no arguments	Set spherical display MODE for vectors	2nd [MODE] 〈SphereV〉†	I 1–27
Square root: $\sqrt{arg1}$ • *arg1*: real/cplx num/list	Returns square root of *arg1*	2nd [√]	F 3–2
Squaring: *arg1* ^{2} • *arg1*: real/cplx num/list or square matrx	Returns *arg1* multiplied by itself	x^2	F 3–2 13–10
St►Eq(*arg1*,*arg2***)** • *arg1*: string var name • *arg2*: equation var name	Convert string *arg1* to an equation and store in equation *arg2*	2nd [STRNG] 〈St►Eq〉	I 9–5
StGDB *arg1* • *arg1*: database name	Store the current graph as database *arg1*	GRAPH 〈StGDB〉†I 	4–40
Stop • no arguments	End program execution, returns to Home screen	PRGM 〈EDIT〉 〈CTL〉〈Stop〉	I 16–18
Store a value: *arg1*►*arg2* • *arg1*: real/cplx num/list/ matrx/vectr/string • *arg2*: var name	Store value of *arg1* as variable *arg2*	STO►	I 2–5
StPic *arg1* • *arg1*: picture name	Store the current picture as picture *arg1*	GRAPH 〈StPic〉† I 〈STAT〉〈DRAW〉 〈StPic〉†	4–41 I 15–17

sub(*arg1*,*arg2*,*arg3*) • *arg1*: string • *arg2*: integer > 0 • *arg3*: integer > 0	Returns subset of string *arg1*, beginning at position *arg2*, length *arg3*	[2nd] [STRNG] ⟨sub⟩	F 9–4

Subtraction: *arg1* – *arg2*
• *arg1*: real/cplx
  num/list/matrx/vectr
• *arg2*: real/cplx
  num/list/matrx/vectr
	Returns *arg2* subtracted
	from *arg1*
	Subtracts elements of
	list, matrix, or vector
		[–]	F
			3–2
			12–7
			13–10
			13–26

sum *arg1* • *arg1*: real/cplx list	Returns sum of elements in list *arg1*	[2nd] [MATH] ⟨MISC⟩ ⟨sum⟩ [2nd] [LIST] ⟨OPS⟩ ⟨sum⟩	F 3–9 F 12–8
tan *arg1* • *arg1*: real/cplx num/list	Returns tangent of *arg1*	[TAN]	F 3–2
tan⁻¹ *arg1* • *arg1*: real/cplx num/list	Returns arctan of *arg1*	[2nd] [TAN⁻¹]	F 3–2
tanh *arg1* • *arg1*: real/cplx num/list	Returns hyperbolic tangent of *arg1*	[2nd] [MATH] ⟨HYP⟩ ⟨tanh⟩	F 3–8
tanh⁻¹ *arg1* • *arg1*: real/cplx num/list	Returns hyperbolic arctan of *arg1*	[2nd] [MATH] ⟨HYP⟩ ⟨tanh⁻¹⟩	F 3–8
TanLn(*arg1*,*arg2*) • *arg1*: expression in **x** • *arg2*: real num	Draw tangent of function *arg1* at **x** = *arg2*	[GRAPH] ⟨DRAW⟩ ⟨TanLn⟩	I 4–35
Then: **If** *arg1***:Then:**commands... **:End:**commands... • *arg1*: condition	Execute commands after **Then** if *arg1* is true, after **End** if false	[PRGM] ⟨EDIT⟩ ⟨CTL⟩ ⟨Then⟩	I 16–15
Trace • no arguments	Display graph and enter TRACE mode	[GRAPH] ⟨Trace⟩ †	I 4–42
Transpose: *arg1*ᵀ • *arg1*: real/cplx matrx	Returns matrix with elements transposed	[2nd] [MATRX] ⟨MATH⟩ ⟨ᵀ⟩	F 13–12
unitV *arg1* • *arg1*: real/cplx vectr	Returns unit vector of vector *arg1*	[2nd] [VECTR] ⟨MATH⟩ ⟨unitV⟩	F 13–27
vc►li *arg1* • *arg1*: real/cplx vectr	Returns vector *arg1* converted to a list	[2nd] [LIST] ⟨OPS⟩ ⟨vc►li⟩ [2nd] [VECTR] ⟨OPS⟩ ⟨vc►li⟩	F 12–9 F 13–29

Vert *arg1* • *arg1*: **x** value	Draw vertical line at **x** = *arg1*	GRAPH ⟨DRAW⟩ ⟨Vert⟩ †	I 4–35
While *arg1*:commands...**:End** • *arg1*: condition	Execute loop while condition is true	PRGM ⟨EDIT⟩ ⟨CTL⟩ ⟨While⟩	I 16–16
arg1 **xor** *arg2* • *arg1*: real num • *arg2*: real num	Returns bit comparison of *arg1* and *arg2* (truncated to integer)	2nd [BASE] ⟨BOOL⟩ ⟨xor⟩	F 10–7
xyline *arg1*,*arg2* • *arg1*: x list (real)(opt) • *arg2*: y list (real)(opt)	Draw a line plot of stat data using lists *arg1* and *arg2*	STAT ⟨DRAW⟩ ⟨xyline⟩ †	I 15–17
ZDecm • no arguments	Display graph in new viewing rectangle	GRAPH ⟨ZOOM⟩ ⟨ZDecm⟩ †	I 4–22
ZFit • no arguments	Display graph in new viewing rectangle	GRAPH ⟨ZOOM⟩ ⟨ZFit⟩ †	I 4–22
ZIn • no arguments	Display graph in new viewing rectangle	GRAPH ⟨ZOOM⟩ ⟨ZIn⟩ †	I 4–20
ZInt • no arguments	Display graph in new viewing rectangle	GRAPH ⟨ZOOM⟩ ⟨ZInt⟩ †	I 4–22
ZOut • no arguments	Display graph in new viewing rectangle	GRAPH ⟨ZOOM⟩ ⟨ZOut⟩ †	I 4–20
ZPrev • no arguments	Display graph in new viewing rectangle	GRAPH ⟨ZOOM⟩ ⟨ZPrev⟩ †	I 4–22
ZRcl • no arguments	Display graph in new viewing rectangle	GRAPH ⟨ZOOM⟩ ⟨ZRcl⟩ †	I 4–23
ZSqr • no arguments	Display graph in new viewing rectangle	GRAPH ⟨ZOOM⟩ ⟨ZSqr⟩ †	I 4–22
ZStd • no arguments	Display graph in new viewing rectangle	GRAPH ⟨ZOOM⟩ ⟨ZStd⟩ †	I 4–22
ZTrig • no arguments	Display graph in new viewing rectangle	GRAPH ⟨ZOOM⟩ ⟨ZTrig⟩ †	I 4–22

Table of System Variables

The variables listed below are used by the TI-85 in various ways and have certain restrictions on them.

Reserved-Name Variables

The TI-85 stores to reserved-name variables during calculations. You cannot store to reserved-name variables.

Ans	fnIntErr	n	a	b
$\bar{x}$	Sx	σx	Σx	Σx^2
$\bar{y}$	Sy	σy	Σy	Σy^2
Σxy	RegEq	corr	PRegC	

Variables Used by the TI-85

You can use the variable names listed below for user data of any type (except constants, programs, graph databases, or graph pictures). However, the TI-85 stores to them (during graphing, for example), so you may wish to avoid using the names.

x	y	t	r	θ
eqn	exp	QI1 ... QI9		Q1 ... Q9

Equation Variables

The variables below must be equations. You can store expressions or equations to them with an assignment instruction.

y1 ...y99	r1 ...r99
xt1 ...xt99	yt1 ...yt99
Q'1 ... Q'9	

STAT List Variables

The variables below must be real lists. You can store to them. The TI-85 stores to them during statistical calculations.

xStat   yStat

Real Variables

The variables below must be real numbers. You can store to them. The TI-85 may store to them during calculations.

xMin	xMax	xScl		
yMin	yMax	yScl		
tMin	tMax	tStep	tPlot	
θMin	θMax	θStep		
zxMin	zxMax	zxScl		
zyMin	zyMax	zyScl		
ztMin	ztMax	ztStep	ztPlot	
zθMin	zθMax	zθStep	Δx	Δy
xFact	yFact			
lower	upper	δ	tol	difTol

Appendix B: Reference Information

This appendix provides supplemental information that may be helpful as you use the TI-85. It includes procedures that may help you correct problems with the calculator, and it describes the service and warranty provided by Texas Instruments.

Appendix Contents

Battery Information

The TI-85 uses two types of batteries: four AAA alkaline batteries and a lithium battery as a back-up for retaining memory while you change the AAA batteries.

When to Replace the Batteries

As the batteries run down, the display begins to dim (especially during calculations), and you must adjust the contrast to a higher setting. If you find it necessary to set the contrast to a setting of 8 or 9, you will need to replace the batteries soon. You should change the lithium battery every three or four years.

Effects of Replacing the Batteries

If you do not remove both types of batteries at the same time or allow them to run down completely, you can change either type of battery without losing anything in memory.

Replacing the Batteries

1. Turn the calculator off and replace the slide cover over the keys to avoid inadvertently turning on the calculator. Turn the calculator so that the back is facing you.

2. Holding the calculator upright, push the latch on the battery cover down with your fingernail or a paper clip and pull the cover out.

3. Replace all four AAA alkaline batteries or the lithium battery. **To avoid loss of information stored in memory, the calculator must be off; do not remove the AAA batteries and the lithium battery at the same time.**

   - To replace the AAA alkaline batteries, remove all four discharged AAA batteries and install new ones as shown on the polarity diagram located in the battery compartment.

   - To replace the lithium battery, remove the screw and clip holding the lithium battery. Install the new battery, + side up. Then replace the screw and clip. Use a CR1616 or CR1620 (or equivalent) lithium battery.

   Dispose of used batteries properly. Do not incinerate or leave within reach of small children.

4. Replace the cover. When you turn the calculator on, the display shows the Home screen as it was when you last used it.

Accuracy Information

To maximize accuracy, the TI-85 carries more digits internally than it displays.

Computational Accuracy

Values in memory are stored using up to 14 digits with a 3-digit exponent.

You can store a value in the RANGE variables, **lower**, and **upper** using up to 12 digits (14 digits for **xScl**, **yScl**, **tStep**, and θ**Step**).

When a value is displayed, the displayed value is rounded as specified by the MODE setting (pages 1–24 through 1–27), with a maximum of 12 digits and a 3-digit exponent.

Information on calculations in hexadecimal, octal, and binary number bases is on page 7–2.

Error Conditions

When the TI–85 detects an error, it displays an error message ERROR *nn type* and the error menu. The general procedure for correcting errors is described on page 1-28. Each error type, including possible causes and suggestions for correction, are shown below.

01 OVERFLOW† You are attempting to enter, or have calculated, a number that is beyond the range of the calculator.

02 DIV BY ZERO† You are attempting to divide by zero.

You are attempting a linear regression with a vertical line.

03 SINGULAR MAT† A singular matrix (determinate = 0) is not valid as the argument for **-1**, **Simult**, or **LU**.

You are attempting a polynomial regression with lists that are not appropriate.

04 DOMAIN† The argument to a function or instruction is out of the valid range. See Appendix A and the appropriate chapter.

You are attempting a logarithmic or power regression with a -x or an exponential regression with a -y.

05 INCREMENT† The increment in **seq** is **0** or has the wrong sign. The increment for a loop is **0**.

06 BREAK You have pressed the ⌈ON⌉ key to break execution of a program, halt a DRAW instruction, or stop evaluaton of an expression.

07 SYNTAX The command contains a syntax error. Look for misplaced functions, arguments, parentheses, or commas. See Appendix A and the appropriate chapter.

Exponents cannot be more than three digits.

= is not valid in parentheses except where an expression is required.

Matrices, vectors, and list cannot be entered directly in an element of a matrix, vector, or list even if the expression evaluates to a real or complex number. Use a matrix, vector, or list variable in the expression instead.

Axes in **DifEq** must be **Q**, **t**, or **Q'**.

† Errors 1 through 5 do not occur during graphing. The TI–85 allows for undefined values on a graph.

08 NUMBER BASE You have entered an invalid digit in a number base; for example, **7b**.

You are attempting an operation that is not allowed in **Bin**, **Hex**, or **Oct** MODE.

09 MODE You are attempting to store to a RANGE variable in another graphing MODE or to perform an instruction while in the wrong MODE, such as **DrInv** in a graphing MODE other than **Func**.

10 DATA TYPE You have entered a value or variable that is the wrong data type.

A function (including implied multiplication) or an instruction has an argument that is an invalid data type; for example, a complex number where a real number is required. See Appendix A and the appropriate chapter.

In an editor, you have entered a type that is not allowed; for example, a complex number in the STAT editor. See the appropriate chapter.

You are attempting to store to a protected data type. You cannot store another type over a constant, program, picture, or graph database. In addition, some system variables are restricted by type; for example, **xStat** must be a real list. See Appendix A.

11 ARGUMENT A function or instruction does not have the correct number of arguments. See Appendix A and the appropriate chapter.

12 DIM MISMATCH You are attempting to perform an operation that has more than one list, matrix, or vector argument, but the dimensions do not match.

13 DIMENSION   The dimension of the argument is not appropriate for the operation.

Matrix element dimensions and vector element dimensions must be positive integers between 1 and 255. List dimensions must be integers ≥ 1.

A matrix must be square to invert it.

14 UNDEFINED   You are referencing a variable that is not currently defined.

15 MEMORY   There is insufficient memory in which to perform the desired command. You must delete item(s) from memory (Chapter 18) before executing this command.

Recursive problems, such as **A = A + 2:A**, display this error.

16 RESERVED   You are attempting to use a system variable inappropriately. See Appendix A.

17 INVALID   You are attempting to reference a variable or use a function in a place where it is not valid. For example, y(x) cannot reference **y**.

18 ILLEGAL NEST   You are attempting to use an invalid function in an argument to **seq** or a CALC function, for example, **der1(der1(x^3,x),x))**.

19 BOUND   You must define **lower < upper**. For **fMin** and **fMax**, the third argument must be less than the fourth argument.

20 GRAPH RANGE There is a problem with the RANGE variables.

You may have defined **xMax** $\leq$ **xMin**, **yMax** $\leq$ **yMin**, θ**Max** $\leq \theta$**Min** and θ**Step**>0 (or vice versa), **tStep = 0**, **tMax** $\leq$ **tMin** and **tStep**>0 (or vice versa), or **tPlot** not between **tMin** and **tMax**.

RANGE variables are too small or too large to graph correctly, which can occur if you attempt to zoom in or out so far that you are not within the numerical range of the calculator.

You cannot "go to" this error. Correct the RANGE variables.

21 ZOOM   A point or a line, rather than a box, is defined in ZBOX or a math error resulted from a ZOOM operation.

22 LABEL   The label in the **Goto** instruction is not defined with a **Lbl** instruction in the program.

23 STAT   You are attempting a stat calculation with lists that are not appropriate; for example, you are requesting a statistical analysis with fewer than two statistical data points. The frequency (y value) for a 1-VAR analysis must be an integer ≥ 0.

(xMax-xMin)/xScl must be ≤ 63 for a histogram.

24 CONVERSION   The "from" and "to" units are not in the same conversion type.

25 SOLVER   In the SOLVER editor, the equation does not contain a variable, or you are attempting to graph with the cursor positioned on **bound**.

26 SINGULARITY†   The SOLVER equation contains a singularity (a point at which the function is not defined).

27 NO SIGN CHNG†   The SOLVER did not detect a sign change.

28 ITERATIONS†   The SOLVER has exceeded the maximum number of iterations permitted.

29 BAD GUESS†   Initial guess must be within the bound.

The initial guess and several points around the guess are undefined.

† Errors 26 through 29 occur during the solving process. Examine a graph of the function in GRAPH or a graph of the variable vs. **left-rt** in the SOLVER. If the equation has a solution, change **bound** and/or the initial guess.

30 DIF EQ SETUP	Equations in the Q'(t) editor must be **Q'1 ... Q'**n and each must have an associated initial condition **QI1 ... QI**n.
31 DIF EQ MATH	The step size used by the fitting algorithm has gotten too small. Check the equations and initial values. Try a larger value for **difTol**. Try changing **tMin** or **tMax** to examine a different region of the solution.
32 POLY	All coefficients are **0**.
33 TOL NOT MET	The algorithm cannot return a result accurate to the requested tolerance.
34 LINK MEMORY FULL	Unable to transmit item because there is insufficient available memory in the receiving unit. You may skip the item or exit RECV mode.
35 LINK TRANSMISSION ERROR	Unable to transmit item. Check to see that the cable is firmly connected to both units and that the receiving unit is in RECV mode.
	ON was used to break during transmission.
36 LINK DUPLICATE NAME	Unable to transmit item because a variable with that name already exists in receiving unit.
37 LINK MEMORY FULL	Unable to transmit memory backup. The receiving unit does not have enough memory to receive all items in memory in the sending unit. A message indicates the number of bytes the sending unit must delete to do the memory backup. Delete items and try again.

In Case of Difficulty

If you have difficulty operating the calculator, the following suggestions may help you to correct the problem.

Handling a Difficulty

1. If an error occurs, follow the procedure on page 1–28. Refer to the more detailed explanations about specific errors beginning on page B–4, if necessary.

2. If you cannot see anything on the display, follow the instructions on page 1–3 to adjust the contrast.

3. If the cursor is a checker-board pattern, memory is full. Press [2nd] [MEM] <DELET> and delete some items from memory.

4. If the calculator does not appear to be working at all, be sure the batteries are installed properly and that they are fresh.

5. If the difficulty persists, see page B–10 for information on contacting Consumer Relations to discuss the problem or obtain service.

6. If the dotted bar busy indicator is displayed, a graph or program is paused and the TI–85 is waiting for input.

Service Information

If the solutions suggested by "In Case of Difficulty" do not correct a problem you may have with your calculator, please call or write Consumer Relations to discuss the problem.

For Service and General Information

If you have questions about service or the general use of your calculator, please call Consumer Relations toll-free at:

1–800–TI–CARES (1–800–842–2737)

You may also write to the following address:

Texas Instruments Incorporated
Consumer Relations
P.O. Box 53
Lubbock, Texas 79408–0053

Please contact Consumer Relations:

- Before returning the calculator for service.

- For general information about using the calculator.

For Technical Information

If you have technical questions about calculator operation or programming applications, write to Consumer Relations at the address given above, or call 1–806–741–2663. Please note that this is a toll number, and collect calls are not accepted.

Express Service

Texas Instruments offers an express service option for fast return delivery. Please call Consumer Relations for information.

Returning Your Calculator for Service

A defective calculator will be either repaired or replaced with the same or comparable reconditioned model (at TI's option) when it is returned, postage prepaid, to a Texas Instruments Service Facility.

Texas Instruments cannot assume responsibility for loss or damage during incoming shipment. For your protection, carefully package the calculator for shipment and insure it with the carrier. Be sure to enclose the following items with your calculator:

* Your full return address and daytime phone number
* Any accessories related to the problem
* A note describing the problem you experienced
* A copy of your sales receipt or other proof of purchase to determine warranty status

Please ship the calculator postage prepaid; COD shipments cannot be accepted.

In-Warranty Service

For a calculator covered under the warranty period, no charge is made for service.

Out-of-Warranty Service

A flat-rate charge by model is made for out-of-warranty service. To obtain the service charge for a particular model, contact Consumer Relations **before** returning the product for service. (We cannot hold products in the Service Facility while providing charge information.)

Texas Instruments Service Facilities

U.S. Residents (U.S. Postal Service)
Texas Instruments
P.O. Box 2500
Lubbock, TX 79408–2500

U.S. Residents (other carriers)
Texas Instruments
2305 N. University
Lubbock, TX 79408–3508

Canadian Residents Only
Texas Instruments
41 Shelley Road
Richmond Hill, Ontario L4C 5G4

One-Year Limited Warranty

This Texas Instruments electronic calculator warranty extends to the original consumer purchaser of the product.

Warranty Duration

This calculator is warranted to the original consumer purchaser for a period of one (1) year from the original purchase date.

Warranty Coverage

This calculator is warranted against defective materials or workmanship. **This warranty is void if the product has been damaged by accident, unreasonable use, neglect, improper service, or other causes not arising out of defects in material or workmanship.**

Warranty Disclaimers

Any implied warranties arising out of this sale, including but not limited to the implied warranties of merchantability and fitness for a particular purpose, are limited in duration to the above one-year period. Texas Instruments shall not be liable for loss of use of the calculator or other incidental or consequential costs, expenses, or damages incurred by the consumer or any other user.

Some states do not allow the exclusion or limitations of implied warranties or consequential damages, so the above limitations or exclusions may not apply to you.

Legal Remedies

This warranty gives you specific legal rights, and you may also have other rights that vary from state to state.

Warranty Performance

During the above one-year warranty period, a defective TI calculator will either be repaired or replaced with a reconditioned comparable model (at TI's option) when the product is returned, postage prepaid, to a Texas Instruments Service Facility.

The repaired or replacement calculator will be in warranty for the remainder of the original warranty period or for six months, whichever is longer. Other than the postage requirement, no charge will be made for such repair or replacement.

Texas Instruments strongly recommends that you insure the product for value prior to mailing.

Index

This index contains an alphabetical listing of major topics covered in this guidebook and their page references. (See also the Table of Commands in Appendix A.)

D (Continued)

dim function, 1–8, 13–15, 13–28, A–5
Dimension of a list, 12–10
Dimension of a matrix, 13–15
Dimension of a vector, 13–28
dimL function, 1–8, 12–10, A–5
Disp instruction, 16–9, 16–11, A–5
DispG instruction, 4–43, 16–9, 16–12, A–5
Display contrast, 1–3
Display MODE, 1–24 to 1–27
Displaying a graph, 4–14, 4–15, 16–12
Displaying text, 16–11
Displaying the Home screen, 16–11
Distance on a graph, 4–28
Division function (÷), 1–8, 3–2, 3–14, 12–7, 13–26, A–5
DMS entry, 3–7
▶DMS instruction, 3–7, A–5
dot function, 1–8, 13–27, A–6
Dot product, 13–27
DRAW menu, 4–30, 15–12
DrawDot FORMT instruction, 4–6, 4–7, A–6
DrawF instruction, 4–30, 4–37, 4–43, 15–12, A–6
Drawing, 4–30 to 4–38
    Functions, 4–37
    Inverse functions, 4–37
    Lines, 4–34, 4–35
    Points, 4–39
    Statistical data, 15–13
    Tangent lines, 4–35
DrawLine FORMT instruction, 4–6, 4–7, A–6
DrInv instruction, 4–30, 4–37, 4–43, A–6
DS< instruction, 16–14, 16–18, A–6
dxDer1 MODE instruction, 1–24, 1–27, 3–16, A–6
dxNDer MODE instruction, 1–24, 1–27, 3–16, A–6

E

$\varepsilon 0$ (permittivity of a vacuum) constant, 8–2
e (natural log) constant, 3–2
e^ function, 1–8, 3–2, 3–14, 13–11, A–6

E (Continued)

ec (electron charge) constant, 8–2
Editors, 1–20, 1–21
    constant, 8–4, 8–5
    E(t), 6–2
    list, 12–5, 12–6
    matrix, 13–6 to 13–9
    program, 16–6 to 16–8
    $Q'(t)$, 7–2
    $r(\theta)$, 5–2
    stat, 15–6, 15–7
    vector, 13–24, 13–25
    $y(x)$, 4–8, 4–42
Eigenvalues, 13–12
Eigenvectors, 13–12
eigVc function, 1–8, 13–12, A–6
eigVl function, 1–8, 13–12, A–6
Element of list, 1–9, 12–2, 12–3
Element of matrix, 1–9, 13–15, 13–19
Element of vector, 1–9, 13–21, 13–28
Else instruction, 16–14, 16–15, A–6
End instruction, 16–14, 16–15, A–6
Eng MODE instruction, 1–24, 1–25, A–6
Engineering display MODE, 1–25
Entering
    complex numbers, 11–2
    constants, 8–4, 8–5
    exponents, 2–3
    expressions, 1–12, 1–13
    graph functions, 4–8 to 4–10
    lists, 12–2 to 12–6
    matrices, 13–2 to 13–9
    negative numbers, 1–9
    program commands, 16–6 to 16–8
    statistics, 15–2 to 15–7
    vectors, 13–21 to 13–25
EOS^{TM}, 1–8, 1–9
Eq▶St instruction, 9–5, A–7
eqn variable, 3–12, 14–2, A–22
Equal sign (=), 1–8, 4,10, 14–2, A–7
Equal-to function (= =), 1–8, 3–18, 13–11, 13–26, A–7
Equation Operating System, 1–8, 1–9
Equation to string conversion, 9–5
Equation variables, xii, 2–9 to 2–11
Equations, parametric, 6–2 to 6–6
Equations, solving, 14–2 to 14–11
Erasing a program, 16–2, 16–3
Errors, 1–28, B–4 to B–8
E(t), 6–2, 6–3

M

$\mu 0$ (permeability of a vacuum) constant, 8-2
Magnitude of complex numbers, 1-26, 3-5, 11-2 to 11-4
Magnitude of vectors, 13-20
MATH menus, 3-3, 4-24, 13-12, 13-27
Mathematical functions, 1-8, 3-2
Matrices, xii, 13-2 to 13-19
  Condition, 13-13
  Determinant, 13-12
  Dimensions, 13-15
  Elements, 13-2 to 13-9
  Entering and editing, 13-2 to 13-9
  Inversion, 13-10
  Math operations, 13-10 to 13-13
  Menus, 13-5
  Negation, 13-10
  Rounding, 13-11
  Row operations, 13-16, 13-17
  Squaring, 13-10
  Transpose, 13-12
MATRX menu, 13-5
max function, 1-8, 3-5, 12-8, A-12
Maximum of a function, 3-16, 4-27
Maximum value, 3-5, 12-8
Me (electron mass) constant, 8-2
Mean, 15-10
MEM menu, 18-2
Memory, 1-2, 18-2 to 18-6
Menu instruction, 16-14, 16-17, A-12
Menus, xii, 1-16 to 1-20
  ANGLE, 3-7
  BASE, 10-3
  CALC, 3-12
  Cancelling, 1-19
  CHAR, 9-6
  CONS, 8-2
  CONV, 8-6
  CPLX, 11-3, 13-18, 13-30
  CTL, 16-14
  CUSTOM, 1-23
  DRAW, 4-30, 4-43, 15-12
  GRAPH, 4-4, 4-42, 4-43, 5-2, 6-2, 7-2
  HYP, 3-8
  I/O, 16-9
  LIST, 12-4

M (Continued)

Menus (continued)
  MATH, 3-3, 4-24, 4-43, 13-12, 13-27
  MATRX, 13-5
  MEM, 18-2
  MISC, 3-9
  NUM, 3-4
  OPS, 13-14, 13-28
  PRGM, 16-5
  PROB, 3-6
  STAT, 15-3
  STRNG, 9-4
  TEST, 3-18
  VARS, 2-7, 4-42
  VECTR, 13-23
  ZOOM, 4-18, 4-42
min function, 1-8, 3-5, 12-8, A-12
Minimum of a function, 3-16, 4-27
Minimum value, 3-5, 12-8
MISC (CHAR), 9-7
MISC (MATH), 3-3, 3-9
Miscellaneous characters, 9-7
Mn (neutron mass) constant, 8-2
mod function, 1-8, 3-5, A-12
MODE screen, 1-24
MODE settings, 1-24 to 1-27, 16-20
Modulus, 3-5
Modulus of complex numbers. See *Magnitude of complex numbers*
Mp (proton mass) constant, 8-2
mRAdd function, 1-8, 13-16, A-12
Multiargument functions, 1-8
Multiplication function (∗), 1-8, 3-2, 3-14, 12-7, 13-10, 13-26, A-12
multR function, 1-8, 13-16, A-12

N

n variable, 15-10, A-22
Na (Avagadro's number) constant, 8-2
Natural log and inverse log, 3-2
nCr function, 1-8, 3-6, A-12
nDer function, 1-8, 3-12 to 3-14, 3-16, A-13

N (Continued)

Negating a matrix, 13–10
Negation function (-), 1–8, 1–9,
    3–2, 13–10, 13–26, A–13
Nonreal numbers, 11–2 to 11–4
norm function, 1–8, 13–12, 13–27,
    A–13,
Normal display MODE, 1–25
Normal MODE instruction, 1–24, 1–25,
    A–13
not Boolean function, 1–8, 10–7,
    A–13
Not equal function (≠), 1–8, 3–18,
    13–11, 13–26, A–13
Notation display format, 1–25
nPr function, 1–8, 3–6, A–13
NUM menu, 3–3, 3–4
Number base MODE, 1–26
Number bases, 10–2 to 10–8
Numeric differentiation MODE, 1–27
Numerical derivative, 3–13, 4–26

O

o octal designator, 10–4
►Oct instruction, 10–6, A–13
Oct MODE instruction, 1–24, 1–26,
    A–13
Octal MODE, 1–26
Octal numbers, 10–3 to 10–6
Octal result display, 10–4, 10–6
OFF key, 1–2
ON key, 1–2
OneVar instruction, 15–16, A–13,
One-variable stat analysis, 15–2,
    15–16
OPS menu, 13–14, 13–28
or Boolean function, 1–8, 10–7, A–13
Outpt instruction, 16–9, 16–12, A–14

P

P2Reg, P3Reg, P4Reg instructions,
    15–16, A–15
Param MODE instruction, 1–24, 1–26,
    A–14
Parametric equations, 6–2 to 6–6
Parametric graphing MODE, 1–26, 6–2
    to 6–6
Parentheses, 1–8, 1–9
Pause instruction, 16–14, 16–18,
    A–14

P (Continued)

PEN feature, 4–38
Percent function (%), 1–8, 3–10,
    A–14
Permutations, 3–6
pEval function, 1–8, 3–10, A–14
Pi, 3–2
Pictures, 2–12, 4–41
Pixel, 4–13
Plotting statistical data, 15–12
Points, drawing, 4–39
►Pol instruction, 11–3, 11–4, 13–29,
    A–14
Pol MODE instruction, 1–24, 1–26,
    A–14
Polar complex number MODE, 1–26
Polar coordinate display, 4–7
Polar equations, 5–2 to 5–6
Polar graphing MODE, 1–26, 5–2 to
    5–6
Polar result display, 11–3, 11–4
Polar vector, 1–27, 13–20
PolarC MODE instruction, 1–24, 1–26,
    A–14
PolarGC FORMT instruction, 4–6, 4–7,
    A–14
POLY feature, 14–8
poly function, 1–8, 14–9, A–14
Polynomial evaluation, 3–10
Polynomial regression, 15–8, 15–11
Polynomial root finder, 14–8, 14–9
Power function (^), 1–8, 3–2, 3–14,
    13–10, 13–14, A–15
Power of ten function (10^), 1–8,
    3–2, 3–14, 13–14, A–15
Power regression, 15–8
PRegC variable, 15–11, A–22
PRGM menu, 16–5
PROB menu, 3–3, 3–6
Probability functions, 3–6
prod function, 1–8, 3–9, 12–8, 12–9,
    A–15
Programming commands, 16–9 to
    16–18
Programs, 2–12, 16–2 to 16–20
Prompt instruction, 16–9, 16–10,
    A–15
PrtScrn instruction, 16–9, 16–13,
    A–15
PtChg, PtOn, PtOff instructions,
    4–30, 4–39, 4–43, A–15
PwrR instruction, 15–16, A–15

S (Continued)

Shade instruction, 4–30, 4–32, 4–33, A–18

Shading a drawing, 4–32, 4–33

shftL, shftR functions, 1–8, 10–8, A–18

Shift bits, 10–8

ShwSt instruction, 15–16, A–18

sign function, 1–8, 3–5, 3–14, A–18

SimulG FORMT instruction, 4–6, 4–7, A–18

SIMULT feature, 14–10 to 14–12

simult function, 1–8, 14–11, A–18

Simultaneous equations, 14–10, 14–11

Simultaneous plotting FORMT, 4–6, 4–7

sin, sin⁻¹ functions, 1–8, 3–2, 3–14, 13–11, A–18

sinh, sinh⁻¹ functions, 1–8, 3–8, 3–14, A–18

Sines, 3–2

Smart Graph, 4–5, 4–14, 4–17, 4–31

SOLVER, 14–2

Solver instruction, 14–5, A–18

Solving equations, 14–2 to 14–12

sortA, sortD functions, 1–8, 12–8, A–19

Sortx, Sorty instructions, 15–15, 15–17, A–19

Sorting stat data, 15–7, 15–15, 15–17

Special characters, 9–7

▶Sph instruction, 13–29, A–19

SphereV MODE instruction, 1–24, 1–27, 13–20, 13–21, 13–29, A–19

Spherical vector MODE, 1–27

Square function (²), 1–8, 3–2, 3–14, 13–10, A–19

Square root function (√), 1–8, 3–2, 3–14, A–19

Standard deviation, 15–10

STAT menu, 15–3

Statistical analysis, 15–2 to 15–18

Statistical data, 15–2 to 15–7

Statistical result variables, 15–10, A–22

St▶Eq instruction, 9–5, A–19

StGDB instruction, 4–40, 4–43, 5–3, 6–2, 7–3, A–19

Stop instruction, 16–14, 16–18, A–19

S (Continued)

Storing

  Constants, 8–3, 8–4

  Equations, 2–9

  Expressions, 2–9

  Functions to graph, 4–8

  Graphs, 4–40, 4–41, 5–3, 6–2, 7–3

  Lists, 12–3 to 12–6

  Numbers, 2–5

  Pictures, 4–41, 5–3, 6–2, 7–3

  Values, 2–5

StPic instruction, 4–41, 4–43, 5–3, 6–2, 7–3, 15–17, A–19

Strings, 9–2 to 9–8

STRNG menu, 9–4

sub function, 1–8, 9–4, A–20

Subroutines, 16–19

Subset of a string, 9–4

Subtraction function (–), 1–8, 3–2, 3–14, 12–7, 13–10, 13–26, A–20

sum function, 1–8, 3–9, 12–8, A–20

Summation, 3–9, 12–8

System of equations, 14–10 to 14–12

System variables, A–22

T

θ variable, 3–12, 5–2, 5–3, A–22

θMin, θMax, θStep variables, 5–3, A–22

t variable, 3–12, 6–2, 7–2, A–22

ᵀ function, 1–8, 13–12, A–20

tan, tan⁻¹ functions, 1–8, 3–2, 3–14, A–20

Tangent line, 4–28, 4–35

Tangents, 3–2

tanh, tanh⁻¹ functions, 1–8, 3–8, 3–14, A–20

TanLn instruction, 4–30, 4–35, 4–43, A–20

TANLN operation, 4–28

TEST menu, 3–18

Tests, comparisions, 3–18

Then instruction, 16–14, 16–15, A–20

tMax, tMin variables, 6–3, 7–4, A–22

tol variable, 3–15 to 3–17, 4–26 to 4–28, A–22

TOLER editor, 3–17

Tolerances, 3–15 to 3–17, 4–26 to 4–28

tPlot variable, 7–4, A–22

T (Continued)

TRACE feature, 4–17
Trace instruction, 4–42, A–20
Tracing a graphed function, 4–17
Transposing a matrix, 13–12
Trigonometric functions, 3–2
tStep variable, 6–3, 7–4, A–22
Turning a function on and off, 4–11
Turning the TI–85 on and off, 1–2
Two–variable stat analysis, 15–2 to 15–17

U

u (atomic mass unit) constant, 8–2
unitV function, 1–8, 13–27, A–20
Unit vectors, 13–27
upper variable, 4–25, 14–3, 14–5, 14–7, A–22
Unselecting a function, 4–11
User–defined ZOOM, 4–23

V

Variables, xii, 2–4 to 2–12
VARS menu, 2–7
vc▶li function, 1–8, 12–8, 12–9, 13–28, 13–29, A–20
Vectors, xii, 13–20 to 13–30
   Coordinate display MODE, 1–27
Vert instruction, 4–30, 4–35, 4–43, A–21
Viewing rectangle, 4–12, 4–13, 5–3, 6–3, 7–4

W

While instruction, 16–14, 16–16, A–21

X

Δx variable, 4–13, 4–16, 4–22
x variable, 3–12, 4–9, 4–14 to 4–16, A–22
xFact variable, 4–21, A–22
xMax, xMin variables, 4–12, 4–13, 5–3, 6–3, 7–4, A–22
xor Boolean function, 10–7, A–21
xScl variable, 4–12, 4–13, 5–3, 6–3, 7–4, A–22
xStat list, 15–2, 15–4, 15–5, 15–15, 15–17, A–22
xt variables, 6–2, A–22
xyline instruction, 15–12, 15–17, A–21

Y

Δy variable, 4–13, 4–16, 4–22
y variable, 4–9, 4–14 to 4–16, A–22
y intercept, 4–26
y(x), 4–2 to 4–11
yFact variable, 4–21, A–22
yMax, yMin variables, 4–12, 4–13, 5–3, 6–3, 7–4, A–22
yScl variable, 4–12, 4–13, 5–3, 6–3, 7–4, A–22
yStat list, 15–2, 15–4, 15–5, 15–15, 15–17, A–22
yt variables, 6–2, A–22

Z

ZDecm instruction, 4–18, 4–22, 4–42, 5–5, 6–5, 7–6, A–21
ZFACT screen, 4–21
ZFit instruction, 4–18, 4–22, 4–42, 5–5, 6–5, 7–6, A–21
ZIn instruction, 4–18, 4–20, 4–42, 5–5, 6–5, 7–6, A–21
ZInt instruction, 4–18, 4–22, 4–42, 5–5, 6–5, 7–6, A–21
ZOOM BOX, 4–18, 4–19, 5–5, 6–5, 7–6
ZOOM factors, 4–18, 4–21, 5–5, 6–5, 7–6, A–22
ZOOM menu, 4–18
Zooming on a graph, 4–18 to 4–23
ZOOMX, ZOOMY operations, 4–18, 4–20, 5–5, 6–5, 7–6, A–21
ZOut instruction, 4–18, 4–20, 4–42, 5–5, 6–5, 7–6, A–21
ZPrev instruction, 4–18, 4–22, 4–42, 5–5, 6–5, 7–6, A–21
ZRcl instruction, 4–18, 4–23, 4–42, 5–5, 6–5, 7–6, A–21
ZSqr instruction, 4–18, 4–22, 4–42, 5–5, 6–5, 7–6, A–21
ZStd instruction, 4–18, 4–22, 4–42, 5–5, 6–5, 7–6, A–21
ZSTO operation, 4–23
ZTrig instruction, 4–18, 4–22, 4–42, 5–5, 6–5, 7–6, A–21
zxMax, zxMin, zxScl, zyMax, zyMin, zyScl variables, 4–23, A–22